John Nix
Farm Management
Pocketbook

FORTY SECOND EDITION (2012)
Published September 2011

Copies of this book may be obtained from:
The Pocketbook, 2 Nottingham Street,
Melton Mowbray, Leicestershire LE13 1NW.
(Tel: 01664 564 508 Fax: 01664 503 201)
www.thepocketbook.co.uk

PRICE £21.00 + £2.00 p&p
5 to 19 copies: £20.00
20 to 100 copies: £18.50
Over 100 copies: *p.o.a*
*Postage & Packaging free for 5 or more copies
in single deliveries*

ISBN 978-0-9514588-8-4

*The John Nix Farm Management Pocketbook
published by Agro Business Consultants Ltd*

*We take all reasonable steps to ensure that the information in the Pocketbook is correct.
However, we do not guarantee the correctness or completeness of material within it. We
shall not be liable or responsible for any kind of loss or damage that may result to you or a
third party as a result of your or their use of this book.*

FOREWORD TO THE FIRST EDITION

This booklet is intended for farmers, advisers, students and everyone else who, frequently or infrequently, find themselves hunting for data relating to farm management - whether it is for blunt pencil calculations on the back of an envelope or for feeding into a computer. The material contained is based upon the sort of information which the author finds himself frequently having to look up in his twin roles as adviser and teacher in farm management. There are several excellent handbooks already in existence, but this pocketbook endeavours to cover a wider field and thus to be substantially more comprehensive. It is intended that most of the data herein contained will have a national application, although there is inevitably some bias towards conditions in the south-eastern half of the country.

The development of farm planning techniques in recent years has outstripped the quality and quantity of data available. It is hoped that this booklet will go a little further in supplying the type of information required. It cannot, however, claim to be the ultimate in this respect. For example, there are many variations in labour requirements according to farm conditions and sizes and types of machine used and there are many more variations in sheep and beef systems than are dealt with here. More detailed data on these lines are gradually becoming available from various sources. It is hoped further to refine the material in this booklet and to keep it up to date in subsequent editions, as the information becomes available. As a help towards this end, any comments or criticisms will be gratefully received.

The author wishes to thank his many friends and colleagues who have given him so much time and help in compiling this information.

John Nix
October, 1966

First published October 1966

Forty-second Edition   September 2011

FOREWORD TO THE FORTY SECOND EDITION

Such extremes in farm economics as seen over the last twelve months make the need to budget and understand costs of production ever greater. We should remind ourselves that such dramatic change can occur in either direction, equally fast. We note that commodities are the most volatile of all asset groups and those whose business output is based on them are exposed to more uncertainty than most. Let's not allow recent price rises to lead to any complacency because more change awaits us; big spenders beware. The information in this book is designed to support the farmer to understand his costs and outputs and manage them accordingly.

This Edition is written for budgeting purposes for 2012, a year that will mark 50 years of the Common Agricultural Policy (CAP). It was initially a simple policy designed to ensure sufficient food supply across all (six) Member States (it was not even 'efficient food supply'). Since then the policy has become highly complex with multiple objectives including the environment, food security, production efficiency and rural development. Multiple objectives mean multiple stakeholders making negotiating reform more challenging without considerable compromise. From this, the CAP will be renegotiated throughout 2012, with yet more objectives being introduced such as climate change. Implications of CAP reform to the farming sector are discussed in chapter 3.

In this Edition, as ever, the figures have been comprehensively revised, with amended notes where changes have occurred. The book continues to progress, with sections having revisions to their layout and information provision where appropriate, all of which are explained.

Figures in this book are estimated for 2012. Thus the crops data relate to the 2012 harvest. The livestock data relate either to the 2012 calendar year (e.g. for milk production) or to 2012/13 (e.g. for winter finished beef). The yields and prices assume a 'normal' or average season, based on trends. Looking 6-18 months ahead to 2012/13, no one can predict what the actual average yield and price for that particular year will be. *The figures should be adjusted as appropriate according to circumstances and price and cost differences.* Assumptions are set out to enable this to be done.

As always I would like to thank all those who have contributed to the editing of this Edition.

John Nix
August 2011

CONTENTS

I. GENERAL

1. THE USE OF GROSS MARGINS

DEFINITION

The data on the crop and livestock enterprises in the Pocketbook are based on gross margins. The gross margin of an enterprise is its output less its variable costs. Enterprise output includes the market value of production retained on the farm. The variable costs must (a) be specific to the enterprise and (b) vary in proportion to the size of the enterprise, i.e. number of hectares or head of stock. The main items of variable costs are: Crops: fertiliser, seed, sprays, casual labour and contract work specific to the crop. Non-Grazing Livestock: concentrate feed, vet. and med., marketing expenses. Grazing Livestock is as for non-grazing livestock, plus forage crop variable costs.

POINTS TO NOTE

1. The gross margin is in no sense a profit figure. The so-called 'fixed costs' (rent, labour, machinery, general overheads), have to be covered by the total farm gross margin before arriving at a profit.

2. The gross margin of an enterprise will differ from season to season, partly because of yield and price differences affecting output and partly because variable costs may vary, e.g. the number and type of sprays required. Different soils and other natural factors, as well as level of management, will also cause differences between farms.

3. Items of variable cost may vary from farm to farm, e.g. some farmers have greater weed control costs than others; some farmers employ a contractor to combine their cereals (a variable cost), others employ their own equipment (a fixed cost); some employ a contractor to deliver their sugar beet to the factory (a variable cost), others have their own lorry (a fixed cost). These differences must be borne in mind in making inter-farm comparisons.

4. Provided points 2 and 3 are borne in mind, comparison of gross margins (particularly averages over several seasons) with standards can be a useful check on technical performance.

5. The other main usefulness of gross margins lies in farm planning. This is not simply a matter of substituting high gross margin enterprises in place of low gross margin enterprises. The gross margin is only one feature of an enterprise, albeit an important one. It says nothing about the call the enterprise makes on the basic farm resources - labour at different times of the year, machinery, buildings, working capital requirements, etc. All these factors and more have to be taken into account in the planning process.

6. This is not to argue that these other costs should be allocated. Complete allocation of many farm expenses is only possible on an arbitrary basis, since they are shared by two or more, possibly all farm enterprises. Allocation can therefore be completely misleading when making planning decisions. The same is true even when regular labour and machinery are employed specifically on certain enterprises, if such costs are calculated on a per hectare or per head basis. This is because when enterprises are substituted, expanded, contracted or deleted the variable costs for each enterprise will vary roughly in proportion to the size of that enterprise, but other costs will not, except possibly for fuel and some repair costs. Most 'fixed' costs may stay the same, others will change - but not smoothly in small amounts at a time. Either the same regular labour force will cope with a revised plan or a smaller or larger number of men will be needed. The same is true of tractors, other machines and buildings. Such cost changes

must of course be taken into account, but allocating these costs on a per hectare or per head basis will not aid, and may positively confuse, planning decisions. The only point of making such calculations is for efficiency comparisons, e.g. labour costs per cow.

7. Allocating fixed costs at a flat rate (e.g. per hectare) for all enterprises, deducting this from the gross margin and hence calculating a 'net profit' from each enterprise can also be misleading. It ignores the whole problem of enterprise inter-relationships, differences between enterprises in total and seasonal requirements for labour, machinery and capital, and other factors such as different quality land on the same farm.

8. Changes in the scale of an enterprise may well affect its gross margin per unit, e.g. increasing the area of winter wheat from 30% to 55% on a farm will mean more second and third crop wheats being grown and a smaller proportion of the crop being drilled under the best conditions; hence yields may fall. Even if yields remain the same, variable costs (e.g. fertiliser) may be higher.

9. Gross margins used for planning future changes should also take account of possible changes in price, and the effect of changes in production techniques.

LOW, AVERAGE AND HIGH LEVELS

The three levels of production given for most crop and livestock enterprises are meant to indicate differences in managerial skill or natural factors, soil productivity, etc., given the level of variable costs. They refer, to an average for each level over several years taking trends into account. Higher variable costs do not necessarily mean greater output, but depends on other factors too such as timing of applications.

2.   COMPLETE ENTERPRISE COSTINGS

Requests are occasionally made for this book to include 'complete' enterprise costings, by which is meant the allocation of all costs to each individual enterprise, not only the variable costs as in the calculation of gross margins.

The main reasons for not developing full net margins are given in item 6 of the previous section explaining gross margins. Much meaningless and arbitrary allocation of 'joint costs' is required, (attempting 'to allocate the unallocatable'), and the results are often misleading in making farm decisions.

Another problem in 'complete enterprise costing' is where to stop. For example should interest on capital be included, whether borrowed or not? Further problems of asset valuation and allocation are involved if so. Variations between farms in their financial situations are considerable as, ranging from the farmer who owns all his land without any mortgage and has no other borrowings to the one with both a rent to pay for all his land and heavy borrowings in addition.

The above problems arise when 'costs per tonne' or 'costs per litre' are calculated. Wheat can be calculated to cost anything between £90 and £165 a tonne according to just what costs are included, how they are allocated and their yield.

It is natural to want to know 'unit costs' to compare for example with prices received. Sometimes these calculations clarify particular costs and therefore efficiency gains that could be made. For these reasons costs per litre of milk are included, although the calculation of some of the 'fixed cost' items is difficult. If a farm has only one enterprise such calculations on that farm are obviously straightforward. However, even on solely dairy farms followers are usually reared or forage grown, which are separate enterprises to milk production.

If required, a cost per tonne of combinable crops can be calculated by adding the fixed costs per hectare of mainly cereals farms (according to size range, given on page 199) to the variable costs per hectare given in the enterprise gross margin data and dividing by the selected yield. Such calculations need to be interpreted with caution because the allocation of fixed costs per hectare is inevitably crude.

The allocation of specific labour (e.g. a full-time cowman), machinery (e.g. a potato harvester) and buildings (e.g. a grain store) is relatively simple and can provide useful information both for purposes of efficiency comparisons and partial budgeting. For some enterprises on many mixed farms, there are few such specific items and the question of the other so-called fixed cost items remains if a full costing is attempted.

A modern method of calculating total costs of production is to allocate machinery and labour according to fuel use. This is not a perfect science but attributes the various costs more accurately than per hectare or per unit of yield.

3.   TOTAL FARM GROSS MARGINS

No attempt is made in this book to compile whole farm gross margins, based on the forecasts made for individual enterprises for 2011. Nor has it ever been the intention in The Pocketbook to include 'historical data', except for some of the material in the Agristats section. Hence total farm survey results, which are inevitably a year or two old by the time they are published, are not included. Their usefulness for any particular farm is limited. This data is readily available from surveys of farm businesses.

4.   FARM BUSINESS SURVEY DATA

ENGLAND

The Farm Business Survey (FBS) is a key source of farm business data in England. It is carried out on behalf of DEFRA by a consortium of Universities. Its site; www.farmbusinesssurvey.co.uk holds a number of sets of FBS data and publications on specialist enterprises:

WALES

The Farm Business Survey in Wales is undertaken on behalf of the Welsh Assembly Government by the University of Aberystwyth.   The results are published at - www.aber.ac.uk/en/ibers/enterprise-kt/fbs/

SCOTLAND

In Scotland the data for the Farm Accounts Survey is collected by the Scottish Agricultural College. It is available in the publication 'Farm Incomes in Scotland'. See www.scotland.gov.uk/Topics/Statistics/15631/8884

NORTHERN IRELAND

The Department of Agriculture and Rural Development for Northern Ireland undertakes the Farm Business Survey in the province.   Results can be found at www.dardni.gov.uk/index/dard-statistics/statistical-reports/agricultural-statistics-farm-business-survey.htm

5.   MAIN ASSUMPTIONS

Budgeting future prices, by necessity requires making several assumptions about how they are likely to move in the future from current levels (August 2011). This 42nd Edition of the Pocketbook uses the following key assumptions:

- The pound: euro exchange rate throughout the book is 88pence per euro, equivalent to 1.136 euro per pound.

- Fertiliser prices for nitrogen (N), phosphate (P) and potash (K) are the same throughout. A full schedule of fertiliser valuations can be found on page 250. For calculating the gross margins, the following are used:

    o   N: 99 p/kg   (£340/t 34.5% N)   (UK Ammonium Nitrate)

    o P_2O_5:   95 p/kg   (£435/t 46% P_2O_5) (Triple Super Phosphate)

    o K_2O: 58 p/kg   (£350/t 60% K_2O) (Muriate of Potash)

- Farm machinery fuel price (red diesel) is taken to be 66ppl.

- Feed wheat price (from which many other commodity prices are benchmarked), is £140/tonne. This is an ex-farm price for November 2012 delivery.

II. ENTERPRISE DATA

1. CROPS

WINTER WHEAT

Feed Wheat

Production level	Low	Average	High
Yield: tonnes per ha (tons per acre)	6.75 (2.7)	8.35 (3.4)	9.75 (3.9)
	£	£	£
Output	945 (383)	1169 (473)	1365 (553)
Variable Costs:			
Seed...		59 (24)	
Fertiliser..................................		276 (112)	
Sprays......................................		161 (65)	
Total Variable Costs		496 (201)	
Gross Margin per ha (acre)	449 (182)	673 (273)	869 (352)

Milling Wheat

Production level	Low	Average	High
Yield: tonnes per ha (tons per acre)	6.15 (2.5)	7.70 (3.1)	9.00 (3.6)
	£	£	£
Output	953 (386)	1194 (484)	1395 (565)
Variable Costs:			
Seed...		64 (26)	
Fertiliser..................................		328 (133)	
Sprays......................................		166 (67)	
Total Variable Costs		558 (226)	
Gross Margin per ha (acre)	395 (160)	636 (258)	837 (339)

1. Prices. The average feed wheat price for the 2012 harvest crop (i.e. 2012/13 marketing year) is £140 per tonne.

   The average milling price is £155/tonne. This is based on a 'full specification' premium of £25 over feed wheat, a 'biscuit' grade milling specification of £12 and a 20% failure rate of achieving the specification. The average premium achieved varies widely according to quality and season: see note 3. Full specification is defined as NABIM Group 1 wheat with a minimum Hagberg of 250, 13% Protein and a bushel weight of at least 76Kg/hl.

2. *Yields.* The average yield for all winter wheat, i.e. all varieties, is calculated as 8.1 tonnes per hectare, the trend yield (3.3 tons/acre) based on the above yields and their proportional weighting by area.

3. *Milling v. Feed.* The yield of bread and biscuit wheat (generically known as milling) averages about 8% below that of feed wheat (greater reduction on more fertile land, less on poorer land and also tends to be greater on second than first wheats). Slightly higher seed, fertiliser and spray costs are normal for milling wheats. The price premium varies each season according to quality and scarcity. Also, not all deliveries achieve full specification. Grade 2 varieties normally achieve a premium of a few pounds a tonne (£12 used here) but their yields are higher than Grade 1 varieties. Full

specification breadmaking premium averaged £16.70/tonne from 2006 to 2009 and nearly £30 for the last two years, with a range of nothing to £62.00 per tonne. The 2010/2011 bread-wheat premium averaged £28.70/tonne. NABIM wheat group 1 varieties account for about 16% of wheat area, comparable with Group 2 area. The proportion of Group 4 wheats has been rising steadily to c57% in 2011 from 18% in 2005 at the expense of Group 3 varieties.

4. *First v. Second (Feed) Wheat.* The effect of different types and lengths of rotational breaks on subsequent wheat yields varies given the differences between seasons (weather), soils, varieties etc. The table below assumes a yield reduction of 10% for second wheats compared with first and higher input costs as shown (the later the sowing date the less the yield gap tends to be). Only average and high levels are shown. Third wheats could yield 10-15% below second wheats; variable costs are likely to be similar. This varies according to management, soil type and varietal choice. Heavy, well-structured, well-drained clay soils appear to be best suited to second wheats; lighter, silty soils usually have a greater risk of Take-all; a firm seedbed is needed.

Comparison between First and Second Feed Wheat Crops

Production level	Average		High	
Year (after break)	First	Second	First	Second
Yield: tonnes per ha (tons/acre)	8.35 (3.4)	7.50 (3.0)	9.75 (3.9)	8.80 (3.6)
	£	£	£	£
Output	1,169 (473)	1,050 (425)	1,365 (553)	1,232 (499)
Variable Costs	496 (201)	512 (207)	496 (201)	512 (207)
Gross Margin per ha (acre)	673 (273)	538 (218)	869 (352)	720 (292)

5. *Straw* is costed as being incorporated. Average yield is approx. 3·5 tonnes per hectare (range 2½ to 5); value £50 to £60 per tonne (£5 less in big bales); variable costs (string) approx. £3.00 per tonne. Unbaled straw (sold for baling): anything from no value to £170/ha (£70/acre), national average around £30/ha (£12/acre).

6. *Seed.* rates vary according to soil, season, variety, drilling date etc. Seed: main range £370-450 per tonne (C2) with a single purpose dressing (£380 and £390 used for feed and milling respectively); 175kg/ha in good conditions; Farm-saved included at 35% (feed) 25% (milling) including grain value, cleaning, dressing, testing and BSPB levy of £36.10/tonne (£5.88 per hectare) for autumn 2010.

7. *Fertiliser* costs are based on P and K replacement cost for an average yield crop, with straw incorporated. RB209 suggests Phosphate and Potash is replaced at 7.8kg/t and 5.6kg/t of grain weight harvested respectively (65 and 47kg/ha respectively in this gross margin). Nitrogen is 190kg/ha for feed wheat and 250kg/ha for milling.

8. *Sprays.* Amounts vary according to season, variety, etc. Typical breakdown: herbicides 39%, fungicides 44%, insecticides 2%, growth regulators 6%, other 9%.

9. For *Contractor's Charges*, see page 180.

10. *Fuel and Repairs* (per hectare). Grain £125, straw £45.

11. *Specialised Equipment Prices.* see p.174.

12. *Labour:* see p. 157.

SPRING WHEAT

Production level	Low	Average	High
Yield: tonnes per ha (tons per acre)	4.75 (1.9)	5.75 (2.3)	6.75 (2.7)
	£	£	£
Output	725.6 (294)	878.31 (356)	1031 (418)
Variable Costs:			
Seed..		78 (32)	
Fertiliser.....................................		209 (85)	
Sprays...		100 (41)	
Total Variable Costs		387 (157)	
Gross Margin per ha (acre)	**338.6** (137)	**491** (199)	**644.1** (261)

1. *Price:* In general, see Winter Wheat (previous pages). A far higher proportion of spring wheat is sold for milling compared with winter wheat. Here we assume 85% making the average price £152.75/tonne for 2012 harvest.

2. *Straw:* See Winter Wheat but yields are considerably lower.

3. *Seed:* £410/tonne at 200kg/ha used. Home saved included at 15% including grain value, cleaning, dressing, testing and BSPB levy (refer to p 256).

4. *Fertiliser:* 150kg/ha N used, and P and K replacing off-take at 45kg/ha and 32kg/ha respectively.

4. For *Contractor's Charges*, see page 180.

5. *Fuel and repairs* (per hectare): grain £125, straw £45.

6. *Specialised Equipment Prices:* see page. 174.

7. *Labour:* see p. 157.

Normally, only about 1% of the UK wheat area is spring sown although survey data is hard to come by. It is popular after root crops. The percentage is naturally higher after a particularly wet autumn such as 2008/09. The percentage is even lower in Scotland (1% or less) than in England or Wales. The area has risen in recent years by about 7,000 hectares because of new very hard 'Red Wheat' varieties grown to contract.

WINTER BARLEY

Feed Barley

Production level	Low	Average	High
Yield: tonnes per ha (tons per acre)	5.5 (2.2)	6.9 (2.8)	7.9 (3.2)
	£	£	£
Output	742.5 (301)	932 (377)	1067 (432)
Variable Costs:			
Seed..		63 (26)	
Fertiliser..		222 (90)	
Sprays..		115 (47)	
Total Variable Costs		400 (162)	
Gross Margin per ha (acre)	**343** (139)	**532** (215)	**667** (270)

Malting Barley

Production level	Low	Average	High
Yield: tonnes per ha (tons per acre)	5.0 (2.0)	6.0 (2.4)	6.9 (2.8)
	£	£	£
Output	750 (304)	900 (365)	1035 (419)
Variable Costs:			
Seed..		63 (26)	
Fertiliser..		163 (66)	
Sprays..		127 (51)	
Total Variable Costs		353 (143)	
Gross Margin per ha (acre)	**397** (161)	**547** (222)	**682** (276)

1. *Prices.* The feed barley price for 2012 harvest (i.e. 2011/12 marketing year) is taken to be £135/tonne, a £5 discount to feed wheat (the average over 5 and 20 years is about £4.60, but was substantially higher in 2010/11). The winter malting price (£150/tonne) assumes an average premium over feed of £15/tonne. This accounts for some that don't meet malting standards. For the best malting barleys the premium in the past has been £25 and in some years higher.

2. *Straw* is costed as being incorporated. Average yield is approx. 2·75 tonnes per hectare, value £60 to £90 per tonne, rising to £100 per tonne in the West, baled ex-field (£10 less in big bales); variable cost (string) approximately £3.00 per tonne. Prices rise in years of forage shortage so prices in 2012 could be high.

3. *Seed.* Winter barley seed averages £395 for feed and malting at 175kg/ha. Seed includes 25% farm-saved including grain, dressing, testing and BSPB levy (see p 256).

4. Fertiliser costs are based on N at 160kg/ha for feed, 100kg/ha for malting crops. P and K replacement cost, with straw incorporated making 53:38kg/ha for feed and 45:32kg/ha for malting crops.

5. *Sprays.* Amounts variable according to season, variety, policy, etc. Typical breakdown: herbicides 43%, fungicides 44%, growth regulators 6%, other 7%.

6. If *Contractor* employed, extra variable costs as shown for Winter Wheat (note 9).

7. *Fuel and Repairs* (per hectare): grain £125, straw £45.

8. *Specialised Equipment Prices*: see p. 174.

9. *Labour:* see p. 157.

SPRING (MALTING) BARLEY

Production level	Low	Average	High
Yield: tonnes per ha (tons per acre)	4.6 (1.9)	5.45 (2.2)	6.3 (2.6)
	£	£	£
Output	713 (289)	845 (342)	976.5 (395)
Variable Costs:			
Seed...		68 (28)	
Fertiliser....................................		138 (56)	
Sprays.......................................		91 (37)	
Total Variable Costs		297 (120)	
Gross Margin per ha (acre)	**416** (168)	**548** (222)	**680** (275)

1. *Prices.* Virtually all spring barley grown is malting varieties, grown for a premium. Spring malting premiums usually exceed those for winter varieties. Here the premium over feed barley is £20/tonne. Again, this allows for failed samples making £155/t.

2. *Seed.* Spring barley seed used is £445/tonne at a seed rate of 175Kg/ha. 35% is home saved (refer to p 256).

3. *Fertiliser* costs are based on N at 80kg/ha. P and K replacement cost, with straw incorporated making 43:31kg/ha.

3. *Sprays* consist typically of: herbicides 47%, fungicides 38%, PGRs 6%, other 9%.

OATS

Winter Oats

Production level	Low	Average	High
Yield: tonnes per ha (tons per acre)	5.3 (2.1)	6.3 (2.6)	7.7 (3.1)
	£	£	£
Output	682.5 (276)	819 (332)	994.5 (403)
Variable Costs:			
Seed…………………………………....		63 (26)	
Fertiliser…………………………….....		155 (63)	
Sprays………………………………….		81 (33)	
Total Variable Costs		299 (121)	
Gross Margin per ha (acre)	**384** (155)	**520** (211)	**696** (282)

Spring Oats

Production level	Low	Average	High
Yield: tonnes per ha (tons per acre)	4.5 (1.8)	5.5 (2.2)	6.5 (2.6)
	£	£	£
Output Feed	585 (237)	715 (290)	845 (342)
Variable Costs:			
Seed………………………………….....		67 (27)	
Fertiliser…………………………….....		128 (52)	
Sprays………………………………….		68 (28)	
Total Variable Costs		263 (107)	
Gross Margin per ha (acre)	**322** (130)	**452** (183)	**582** (236)

1. Price used is £130/tonne for the 2012 harvest crop, i.e. the 2012/13 marketing year for milling oats. Milling specification requires a minimum bushel weight of 50Kg/Hl. Conservation grade milling oats may obtain a premium of £10-20/tonne.

2. Seed: priced here at £425/tonne, at 175kg/ha and 185kg/ha for winter and spring respectively, both with 40% home saved (refer to p 256).

3. *Fertiliser;* winter costs are based on N at 90kg/ha winter and 70kg/ha spring. P and K replacement cost, with straw incorporated making 50:36kg/ha for winter and 43:31kg/ha for spring.

4. Straw is not included above. Average yield is 3.5 tonnes per hectare; value £55 to £85 per tonne according to region and season; variable costs (string) £3.00 per tonne.

5. If a contractor is employed, extra variable costs will be as shown for Winter Wheat (note 9).

6. For Naked Oats refer to page 21

7. *Fuel and Repairs* (per hectare): grain £125, straw £45.

8. *Specialised Equipment Prices*: see p. 174.

9. *Labour:* see p 157.

10. The high majority of GB oats are winter crops; the proportion increases from north to south; (over 90% in England/Wales but less in Scotland).

OILSEED RAPE

Winter Rape

Production level	Low	Average	High
Yield: tonnes per ha (tons per acre)	2.40 (1.0)	3.40 (1.4)	4.40 (1.8)
	£	£	£
Output	816 (330)	1156 (468)	1496 (606)
Variable Costs:			
Seed..		52 (21)	
Fertiliser...................................		254 (103)	
Sprays......................................		136 (55)	
Total Variable Costs		442 (179)	
Gross Margin per ha (acre)	**374** (152)	**714** (289)	**1054** (427)

Spring Rape

Production level	Low	Average	High
Yield: tonnes per ha (tons per acre)	1.5 (0.6)	2.00 (0.8)	2.75 (1.1)
	£	£	£
Output	510 (207)	680 (275)	935 (379)
Variable Costs:			
Seed..		56 (23)	
Fertiliser...................................		118 (48)	
Sprays......................................		83 (34)	
Total Variable Costs		257 (104)	
Gross Margin per ha (acre)	**253** (102)	**423** (171)	**678** (275)

1. *Prices*. The price assumed for the 2012 crop is £340/tonne, including oil bonuses.

2. *Varieties*. Inputs are lower with spring-sown crops, pigeons are less trouble and the late summer/autumn workload is eased. Spring yields average only 60% of those of winter rape; hence normally less than 5% of the total oilseed rape crop is spring-sown. The proportion of the total area sown with hybrid winter rape is about a quarter.

3. *Seed* price is a blend of 42% conventional merchant's seed (£52/ha), 25% hybrid (£70/ha) and 33% home saved conventional (refer to p 256 For Home Saving costs).

4. *Fertiliser* costs are based on N at 190kg/ha for winter, 80kg/ha for spring. P and K replacement cost, with straw incorporated making 45:35kg/ha for winter and 28:22kg/ha for spring crops.

5. *Sprays*. Typically: herbicides 53%, fungicides 26%, insecticides 5%.

6. *Labour:* see p157.

LINSEED

Spring Linseed

Production level	Low	Average	High
Yield: tonnes per ha (tons per acre)	1.25 (0.5)	1.75 (0.7)	2.75 (1.1)
	£	£	£
Output	468.8 (190)	656 (266)	1031 (418)
Variable Costs:			
Seed..		80 (32)	
Fertiliser....................................		114 (46)	
Sprays.......................................		56 (23)	
Total Variable Costs		250 (101)	
Gross Margin per ha (acre)	**219** (89)	**406** (165)	**781** (316)

Winter Linseed

Production level	Low	Average	High
Yield: tonnes per ha (tons per acre)	1.50 (0.6)	2.50 (1.0)	3.00 (1.2)
	£	£	£
Output	562.5 (228)	938 (380)	1125 (456)
Variable Costs:			
Seed..		150 (61)	
Fertiliser....................................		191 (77)	
Sprays.......................................		68 (28)	
Total Variable Costs		409 (166)	
Gross Margin per ha (acre)	**154** (62)	**529** (214)	**716** (290)

1. The price for the 2012 crop is £375/tonne (OSR price plus 10%). Contract prices are normally tied to a standard 38% oil and 9% moisture. Some specialist contracts for specific varieties such as Yellow Linseed can be worth more.

2. Most linseed is spring-sown (about 27,000 of 32,000ha total), drilling mid-March to mid-April (best mid-March to end March). It should not be grown more than 1 year in 5. Too much nitrogen (over 130 kg/ha) can cause lodging, delayed maturity and excessive weed growth and hence difficult harvesting, poor quality and lower yields; it should be applied early. Harvesting: spring normally end Aug-early Sept. Moisture content most likely 12-16%: must be dried to 9% for storage.

3. Inputs: seed, 50kg/ha (sold in hectare bags) minimal home saved, Fertiliser N/P/K of spring 80/25/19 and winter 90:75:50.

Winter Linseed area has been rising with approximately 5,000ha grown in the UK because of easier establishment and earlier harvest (late July). Yield is affected by frost heave, disease and thrips (thunder-bugs), most varieties susceptible to lodging; pigeons and rabbits can also be troublesome. Early sowing (early to mid-September) is best.

Linola is also known by the *misnomer;* 'edible linseed' (all linseed is edible). The oil contains more linolaeic and less linolenic acid than conventional linseed, like sunflower oil so does not dry like linseed oil. It is difficult to see much future for the crop, because its gross margin is very low. It is grown on contract, with the price based on the oilseed rape price. Spring-sown: agronomy and yield similar to conventional linseed; good weed control is essential.

FIELD PEAS

Blue Peas

Production level	Low	Average	High
Yield: tonnes per ha (tons per acre)	3.0 (1.2)	3.75 (1.5)	5.0 (2.0)
	£	£	£
Output	570 (231)	713 (289)	950 (385)
Variable Costs:			
Seed...		87 (35)	
Fertiliser....................................		54 (22)	
Sprays..		140 (57)	
Total Variable Costs		281 (114)	
Gross Margin per ha (acre)	**289** (117)	**432** (175)	**669** (271)

Marofats

Production level	Low	Average	High
Yield: tonnes per ha (tons per acre)	2.7 (1.1)	3.40 (1.4)	4.5 (1.8)
	£	£	£
Output	580.5 (235)	731 (296)	967.5 (392)
Variable Costs:			
Seed...		105 (43)	
Fertiliser....................................		49 (20)	
Sprays..		163 (66)	
Total Variable Costs		317 (128)	
Gross Margin per ha (acre)	**263.5** (107)	**414** (168)	**650.5** (263)

1. *Price*. All peas are now grown for a premium market. Only a small proportion (5-10%) are compounded as second grade peas or go for pet food. The high premium for food consumption justifies pea cleaning to remove discoloured and damaged peas. Feed value is therefore not relevant as a base price but a discount. The price forecast for the Blue Peas here is £190/tonne, taking account of some very high premiums (achieving up to £350/tonne) and a failure rate. Most peas are Blues, used for micronising and exports.

   Marofats, the other main group of peas can achieve even higher prices. They are no longer priced with a premium over wheat, as the markets bear little relationship. They are used for canning, packets and export trade. About a third is grown on a forward contract. They command a higher price than blues but yield about 10% less. The average price in this gross margin is £215/tonne accounting for all samples including those that miss the premium grade and those that have to be cleaned. Sometimes the crop is desiccated before direct combining.

2. EU Protein Supplement has now ended (not Wales) (See Winter Beans Note 2).

3. *Seed:* Blues, £425/tonne planted at 210 to 250kg/ha (230kg here), Marofats £500/tonne at 230kg/ha. About 50% farm-saved (refer to p 256).

4. *Fertiliser*: based on 9kg phosphate and 10kg potash per tonne of pea harvested per hectare. No nitrogen is applied making 0:34:38kg/ha Blues and 0:30:34 Marofats.

5. *Labour:* see p. 157.

FIELD BEANS

Winter Beans

Production level	Low	Average	High
Yield: tonnes per ha (tons per acre)	3.0 (1.2)	4.0 (1.6)	5.0 (2.0)
	£	£	£
Output	561 (227)	748 (303)	935 (379)
Variable Costs:			
Seed..		71 (29)	
Fertiliser...................................		57 (23)	
Sprays......................................		117 (47)	
Total Variable Costs		245 (99)	
Gross Margin per ha (acre)	**316** (128)	**503** (204)	**690** (279)

Spring Beans

Production level	Low	Average	High
Yield: tonnes per ha (tons per acre)	2.8 (1.1)	3.7 (1.5)	4.6 (1.9)
	£	£	£
Output	560 (227)	740 (300)	920 (373)
Variable Costs:			
Seed..		78 (32)	
Fertiliser...................................		53 (21)	
Sprays......................................		87 (35)	
Total Variable Costs		218 (88)	
Gross Margin per ha (acre)	**342** (139)	**522** (211)	**702** (284)

Winter Bean Notes

1. *Price*. The 2012 harvest price for winter feed beans is budgeted at £175 per tonne, a premium over feed wheat of £35/tonne. White Hylum varieties carry a premium of another £20/tonne with no yield penalty, thus these are almost exclusively grown. The gross margin builds this into the calculation (60% hitting specification) making the average price £187/tonne. The higher price is achievable subject to meeting minimum quality criteria.

2. *EU Protein Supplement*. The protein supplement under the Single Payment of €55.57/ha (£39/ha) is removed in England and Scotland (refer to page 140)

3. *Seed:* 185-220 kg per hectare (200kg used here) @ £330-400/tonne (£390). About 60% is farm-saved as in this gross margin (refer to p 256).

4. *Fertiliser:* 9kg phosphate and 10kg potash/t bean harvested/ha. No nitrogen is applied making 0:36:40kg/ha.

5. *Sprays*. Typically: herbicides 47%, fungicides 35%, insecticides 8%.

6. *Labour:* see p 157.

Spring Bean Notes

6. *Price*. Spring beans are all grown for the human consumption market. It is only the poor quality beans (predominantly Bruchid beetle damaged) that are rejected and redirected to feed compounders. Damaged samples can be cleaned if the premium justifies it. A large proportion of the crop is exported (to North Africa). Spring bean

price is budgeted here at £200/tonne. In a 'normal' year, about 30-40% of spring beans will not make the export (human consumption) grade. This is accounted for in the price.

7. *Seed:* 185-220 kg per hectare (200kg/ha here) at £425/tonne. About 40% is farm-saved. Sprays: as for winter beans.

8. *Fertiliser:* 9kg phosphate and 10kg potash/t bean harvested/ha. No nitrogen is applied making 0:33:37kg/ha.

9. *Winter versus Spring Beans.* The key determinant between which to crop is soil type. Winter beans are more suited to heavy soils and springs on lighter land. As the schedules illustrate, there is little real difference between the gross margins.

Peas or Beans?
In 2010 the area of peas was 18% of the UK pulse area having fallen from 40% 10 years earlier. High quality and good yields can return high gross margins and offer wider benefits to the farming system although they can be difficult to grow.

LUPINS

The following table refers to spring sown *white lupins*. Differences in yield and price for yellow and blue lupins are given in the accompanying notes:

Production level	Low	Average	High
Yield: tonnes per ha (tons per acre)	2.25 (0.9)	3.00 (1.2)	3.75 (1.5)
	£	£	£
Output	630 (255)	840 (340)	1,050 (425)
Variable Costs:			
Seed		126 (51)	
Fertiliser..............................		81 (33)	
Sprays		90 (36)	
Total Variable Costs	297 (120)	297 (120)	297 (120)
Gross Margin per ha (acre)	**333** (135)	**543** (220)	**753** (305)

The price used here is £280 per tonne. Few lupins are traded on the open market, but the value tends to fall between that of feed beans and soya. The previous area-based Protein Supplement is no longer available for the 2012 harvest onwards.

A leguminous crop traditionally associated with light land. Their protein content is about 40 to 50% higher than peas and beans, making lupins a good substitute for soya bean meal in livestock feed compounds. They are a non-GM source of high quality digestible protein. The crop can be cut whole for silage, crimped or milled and fed directly to stock or the grain traded as a cash crop.

The area grown in the UK has stabilised in the last few years at around 5,000 hectares (*12,500 acres*). Varieties are virtually all spring lupins. Around 75% of the total area is likely to be whole-cropped. Determinate varieties (single stem, uniform ripening) can be harvested easily; non-determinate varieties (with multiple heads at various stages of ripening) are more difficult.

Lupins can be grown on all but the heaviest land but are not tolerant of alkaline soils. They need a good cereal seedbed and pre-emergence weed control. Sowing is from mid-March to early April and harvest from mid-August onwards (and can be late September). If the crop is for silage, sowing can be as late as mid-May using an appropriate variety. No nitrogen fertiliser is necessary although 15-25kg per ha is often used to accelerate early stage growth. Replacement P and K at 30-50kg per ha is assumed. There are no serious crop pests. Anthracnose is a potentially serious threat but plant health measures have so far kept it under control. Other diseases are not a problem. Determinant varieties do not generally need pre-harvest desiccants if weed-free, non-determinant ones do.

Appropriate species and variety choice is important depending on area of the country, soil pH, intended end use and growth habit required. There are three distinct species of spring lupins, white (lupinus albus), blue (lupinus angustifolus) and yellow (lupinus luteus). All are suitable for grain or livestock feed. White lupins have higher protein and potentially greater yield than blue lupins but require a longer growing season. Yellow lupins fall between blue and white on both counts.

About 70% of the national lupin area is white, 25% blue and 5% yellow. In the South-East and East Anglia 90%+ of lupins are white. In the North of England and Scotland 50% are blue, 25% white and 25% yellow, with the blue grown for combining or crimping and white & yellows being used for whole crop.

Lupin characteristics

	White *Lupinus Albus*	**Yellow** *Lupinus Luteus*	**Blue** *Lupinus Angustifolius*
Flower Colour	white or blue	yellow	white or blue
Growth habit	semi-determinate	semi-determinate	fully or semi-determinate
pH tolerance	5 to 7.6	4.6 to 6.8	5 to 6.8
Protein	36-40%	38-42%	31-35%
Oil content	10%	5%	6%
Main use	Combining in Southern England on acidic land. Forage in all areas	Mainly used for forage in the North.	Combining in the North (determinate) Forage in the very North (semi-determinate)
Yield	3.0-3.5 t/ha	2.5-3.0 t/ha	3.0-3.5 t/ha

Acknowledgement: Thanks to - Soya UK, Tel: 02380 696922. Premium Crops, Tel: 02392 632 883.

HERBAGE SEEDS

	Italian Ryegrass		Early Perennial Ryegrass	
	Average	High	Average	High
	£	£	£	£
Yield (tonnes per ha)	1,3	1.7	1.20	1.50
Price per 50 kg (£)	45		45	
Output	1170	1530	1080	1350
Variable Costs:				
Seed	95		85	
Fertiliser	334		334	
Sprays	105		105	
Cleaning / Certification.............	221	281	206	251
Total Variable Costs	755	815	730	775
Gross Margin per ha	**415**	**715**	**350**	**575**
Gross Margin per acre	168	289	142	233

	Intermediate Perennial Ryegrass		Late Perennial Ryegrass	
	Average	High	Average	High
	£	£	£	£
Yield (tonnes per ha)	1.2	1.5	1.00	1.50
Price per 50 kg (£)	55		60	
Output	1320	1650	1200	1800
Variable Costs:				
Seed	95		85	
Fertiliser	334		334	
Sprays	110		110	
Cleaning / Certification.............	206	251	176	251
Total Variable Costs	745	790	705	780
Gross Margin per ha	**575**	**860**	**495**	**1020**
Gross Margin per acre	233	348	200	413

	Hybrid Ryegrass		Kent Wild White Clover & Kent Indig. Peren. R'grass	
	Average	High	Average	High
	£	£	£	£
Yield (tonnes per ha)	1.2	1.6	0.09 (Clover)	0.11 (C)
			0.6 (R'grass)	0.8 (R)
Price per 50 kg (£)	65		350 (C)	60 (R)
Output	1560	2015	1350	1730
Variable Costs:				
Seed	95		65	
Fertiliser	317		134	
Sprays	110		110	
Cleaning / Certification.............	206	259	143	179
Total Variable Costs	728	781	452	488
Gross Margin per ha	**832**	**1234**	**898**	**1242**
Gross Margin per acre	337	500	364	503

1. The following were the number of hectares entered for certified seed production for the main grasses and clovers in the UK for the 2010 harvest;

Italian / Westerwold Ryegrass....	181	Cocksfoot................................	184
Early Perennial Ryegrass............	27	Timothy	69
Inter. Perennial Ryegrass............	1,346	Red Fescue..............................	361
Late Perennial Ryegrass	1,620	White Clover	33
Amenity Perennial Ryegrass	884	Red Clover..............................	78
Hybrid Ryegrass	547	Common Vetch.......................	107

The ryegrasses total 4,605 ha (*11,378 acres*).

All herbage seeds total 5,437 ha (*13,435 acres*).

2. The *yields* shown are averages for cleaned certified seed. The crop is risky, i.e. yields are highly variable, depending especially on the weather at, and precise timeliness of, harvesting. However, the use of growth regulators and stripper headers has reduced the risk. A considerable amount of skill is necessary to average the 'high' levels over a number of years. Most grasses give their highest yield in their first harvest year, assuming good establishment. Yields can be increased by up to 30% with a combination of higher Nitrogen applications along with a growth regulator (e.g. Moddus). The cost of the growth regulator is likely to add £25 per ha (*£10 per acre*) to the chemical figure in the margins above, with a similar cost increase for the extra Nitrogen.

3. Prices in the table are estimated prices for certified seed for the 2012 year. The figures relate to Diploid varieties. Very little early Diploid is now grown. Tetraploid prices are slightly lower, but yields should be higher (intermediate and late varieties achieving 1,300-2,200kg per ha). High sugar varieties should command a small premium over the values seen in the tables. Amenity ryegrasses and fescues also command a premium for high quality sports use, and some yield nearly as much as agricultural varieties.

4. No allowance has been made above for by-products. Some crops produce 4 to 5 tonnes of threshed hay, which is, however, of low feeding value. This could be worth £300 or more per hectare. Some grasses, especially spring-sown ryegrass, also provide substantial quantities of autumn and winter grazing. Clovers can be either grazed or cut for hay or silage and do not have to be 'shut up' until mid or late May, or, in some cases and seasons, even early June. More grazing (until end of May) and better quality threshed hay is provided with a combination of ryegrass and white clover than with the specialist herbage seed grasses.

5. The seed rate is around 10kg per ha for autumn sowing, less for spring. If the seed crop is to be undersown, specialist growers often reduce the seed rate for the cover crop by up to half and restrict nitrogen dressing: the cereal yield may thus be reduced by up to 0.6 tonnes per ha. If this is not done the grass seed yield is usually lower in the first year compared with direct drilling, except for ryegrass.

6. Chemical costs will vary depending on the prevalence of grass weeds. Autumn sown crops will have higher costs than spring sown ones, although yields for autumn crops should be higher in the first year. The margin assumes an autumn-sown crop.

7. Labour: see page 157.

Acknowledgement: Thanks to - British Seed Houses, Tel: 01522 868 714; Herbage Seed Services, Tel: 01962 774 432; NIAB, Tel: 01223 342 238.

RYE

Production level	Low	Average	High
Yield: tonnes per ha (tons per acre)	4.90 (2.0)	6.20 (2.5)	7.50 (3.0)
	£	£	£
Output	784 (318)	992 (402)	1200 (486)
Variable Costs:			
Seed		98 (39)	
Fertiliser..		218 (88)	
Sprays		105 (43)	
Total Variable Costs	421 (170)	421 (170)	421 (170)
Gross Margin per ha (acre)	**363** (147)	**571** (231)	**779** (316)

1. The price assumed is £170 per tonne for 2012 harvest. This is based on the 2011 contract which was made up of 50% at a fixed price (here assumed to be £170 per tonne) and the remaining 50% being at a £10 per tonne premium to the prevailing feed wheat price at the point of movement, based on Oct-Dec delivery. The price assumes the milling specification is achieved. Deductions are made for low quality, and if it is feed grade, price then falls between feed wheat and feed barley. Only a small percentage of the crop is grown for the free market.

Largely grown on light, low fertility, sandy or stony soils, not suited to other cereals. Yields would clearly be higher on better soils, but then rye has difficulty in competing with wheat and barley; it could never do so on good wheat land. The average yield in the UK in the five years 2006 to 2010 was 6.16 tonnes per ha.

The area grown in the UK has ranged between 5,000-6,000 ha for several years. Rye crispbread is the major outlet. It is also milled into flour, used in mixed-grain bread and muesli. About two-thirds of UK requirements are imported, mainly from Canada (which produces the highest quality), Denmark, Germany and Spain. Demand for UK-grown rye has been falling in recent years, owing to increased competition in the crispbread market.

Rye, which is autumn-sown, is drought tolerant and very hardy, can withstand low temperatures and starts growing early in the spring. It has all-round resistance to wheat and barley diseases, e.g. eyespot, and suffers less from take-all than wheat – hence it is a possible replacement for third or fourth wheat. Its vigour keeps weeds down. Its herbicide, fungicide and fertiliser requirements are lower than for other cereals, except for growth regulators. Rye is harvested earlier than winter wheat (useful for following with oilseed rape).

Drawbacks: it sprouts in a wet harvest: must therefore harvest early, at relatively high moisture content. It grows very tall and lodges easily: hence high levels of nitrogen are not possible; but growth regulators help. Its heavy straw crop means very slow combining (takes about twice as long per hectare as wheat and barley), and difficult straw incorporation. New hybrid varieties, with shorter, stiffer straw, are being developed; these would improve the comparative profitability of rye on better soils.

Drilling: 2nd and 3rd weeks September. Harvesting: by mid-August at relatively high moisture content, then dry to 14-15% (no drying costs included in margin).

TRITICALE

Production level	Low	Average	High
Yield: tonnes per ha (tons per acre)	4.00 (1.6)	5.00 (2.0)	7.20 (2.9)
	£	£	£
Output	540 (219)	675 (273)	972 (394)
Variable Costs:			
Seed		52 (21)	
Fertiliser...............................		205 (83)	
Sprays		65 (26)	
Total Variable Costs	322 (130)	322 (130)	322 (130)
Gross Margin per ha (acre)	**218** (88)	**353** (143)	**650** (263)

A 'man-made' cross between rye and hard wheat. It combines the hardiness of rye and the marketability of feed wheat. It is used in livestock feed, particularly pig and poultry rations, having high levels of lysine. However it is not widely used by feed compounders. The area grown in the UK has risen over recent years to over 18,000ha. A large proportion of this rise is likely to be in the newer spring varieties (see below).

The price is usually £4 or £6 per tonne below the price for feed wheat, but this tends to vary from season to season; £155 per tonne is assumed above for the 2012 harvest crop.

The average yield in the UK in the five years 2006 to 2010 was only 4.14 tonnes/ha,. But in the five years 1996-2000 the average had been over 5.90 tonnes per ha – showing that the potential of the crop is not always fully realised. The low yields are a result of it mainly being grown on light land, especially thin, drought-prone, poorish, marginal cereal-growing soils. In these circumstances, it can frequently out-yield wheat or barley, especially the former, and it has lower input requirements. Its yields tend to be more consistent on such soil than those of barley. Triticale tends to do well compared with second and subsequent wheats owing to its resistance to drought and fungal diseases.

Lower levels of fungicide are needed because of its good disease resistance, except for ergot, but including take-all (making it a possible replacement for a third or fourth wheat, as indicated above). It is a tall crop, which helps to suppress weeds, but it is susceptible to lodging; growth regulators are beneficial. New semi-dwarf varieties are being developed, to overcome straw strength weakness and susceptibility to rust infections.

The crop is best drilled early (September) on very light, drought-prone soils; otherwise October is satisfactory. Harvesting is at approximately the same time as wheat. There is more straw, which slows combining, and incorporation is difficult; this is less of a problem on poor soils as there is less straw.

Spring Triticale

New spring varieties of this crop have been introduced in the last few years. These have been taken up strongly in livestock areas – the north and west of England, as well as western Scotland, Wales and N. Ireland. Being a spring crop means that winter water logging is not an issue, and it can be grown on a wider range of soils. In total over 5,000 ha of spring triticale may well now be grown in the UK: either on its own or as part of a mixture.

It has lower yields than winter triticale if it is harvested for grain in the conventional way. However, most is whole-cropped to produce an 'arable forage'. Often it is grown in a mixture with a proteins crop – peas or lupins for example. Inputs for spring triticale will be lower than those for winter varieties.

NAKED OATS

Production level	Low	Average	High
Yield: tonnes per ha (tons per acre)	4.50 (1.8)	5.50 (2.2)	6.50 (2.6)
	£	£	£
Output	846 (343)	1034 (419)	1222 (495)
Variable Costs:			
Seed		65 (26)	
Fertiliser....................................		175 (71)	
Sprays		100 (41)	
Total Variable Costs	340 (138)	340 (138)	340 (138)
Gross Margin per ha (acre)	**506** (205)	**694** (281)	**882** (357)

Naked oats have a higher protein, energy and oil content than 'traditional' oats, but the fibre content is lower – as the husk is removed during harvesting. Contracts require a maximum moisture content of 14%, which is also recommended for long-term storage.

The area being grown continues to increase steadily. Naked oats now account for in excess of 10% of the traded tonnage of UK oats (i.e. excluding those grown for on-farm use). The traditional markets such as racehorse feed, dog food, and bird feed markets are all increasing. Over recent years the human consumption market has developed so that at least half the crop is now sold for health foods, fancy breads and breakfast cereals. In future, a further growth area is likely to be from demand for inclusion of the crop in monogastric animal feeds. The poultry industry in particular is setting up supply chains.

The 2012 harvest crop price assumed is £215 per tonne, based on contracts offering premiums 35% above the average feed wheat price. The premium can be reduced according to husk content.

In a normal cropping year, over 90% of the crop is winter sown, although the proportion of spring cropping rises after a wet autumn. The margin above assumes winter cropping. NIAB survey results have suggested that yields average 20%-25% less than conventional oats. New spring varieties have become available that offer yields much closer to winter crops. The actual difference in yield will depend on the particular season, but are likely to be in the range 15%-20%.

The agronomy of naked oats is similar to that of husked oat varieties. Variable inputs are lower than for wheat or barley. Traditionally, high nitrogen use has not been possible due to the risk of lodging, however, new semi-dwarf varieties with stiff straw have been introduced. As well as increasing the scope for higher fertiliser applications, this means the crop is also suited to more fertile soils, and growth regulators may be avoided. Oats provide a break in the take-all cycle.

Harvest is early (coming just after winter barley). New varieties are less susceptible to shedding than in the past, however care needs to be taken with both the timing of harvest, and the set-up of the combine, to ensure a clean, saleable, sample.

Naked Barley

Naked barley, suitable for roasting, flaking or milling as pearl barley, is now rarely heard of. It is grown like normal barley, but yields are reckoned to be some 15% lower. It could be either autumn or spring sown.

DURUM WHEAT

Production level	Low	Average	High
Yield: tonnes per ha (tons per acre)	5.20 (2.1)	6.20 (2.5)	7.50 (3.0)
	£	£	£
Output	988 (400)	1178 (477)	1425 (577)
Variable Costs:			
Seed		90 (36)	
Fertiliser...............................		234 (95)	
Sprays		125 (51)	
Total Variable Costs	449 (182)	449 (182)	449 (182)
Gross Margin per ha (acre)	**539** (218)	**729** (295)	**976** (395)

Extra drying costs estimated at £12 per tonne not shown in the margin.

A Mediterranean crop. As well as pasta, it is used to produce ethnic foods, semolina, biscuits, etc. Must be grown under contract as there are a very limited number of end users. Domestic demand is relatively small; UK consumption per head is approx. 4% that of Italy and 10% that of France but total UK use nevertheless amounts to about 60,000 tonnes a year.

The crop started to be grown in England in the late 1970s and reached a high-point of 11,000 ha (*27,000 acres*) in 1984. The area has fluctuated since then, but is currently below 1,000 hectares (*2,500 acres*).

On average the crop should yield 75%-80% of conventional feed wheat in the same situation. These levels are assumed in the margins above.

Contracts are based on a premium over the feed wheat price. For the 2012 harvest this is assumed to be £60 per tonne delivered, resulting in an assumed ex-farm premium for 'Grade A' durum of £50 per tonne. This gives an estimated price of £210 per tonne. The price will be reduced if the crop does not fully meet quality specifications.

As with milling wheat, there is a risk of rejection if contaminated with excess foreign seeds, especially self-set cereals from previous crop; thus safer as a first cereal crop. A poor price is obtained if quality is too poor for pasta and thus has to go for feed.

The crop is likely to be grown only in the driest parts of the east/south east, where it can best compete with second and third wheats. It may be either autumn or spring sown; around two-thirds is currently autumn sown and this is assumed in the table above. The crop is very sensitive to stress and frost-kill in severe winters; the spring-sown crop is more reliable, and cheaper to grow, but the yield is usually 15-20% lower. Spring crops also allow more opportunities for black grass control. The crop has a higher disease resistance than other wheats, except for eyespot and ergot.

Harvesting is a critical operation; it needs to be done as soon as the crop reaches 20% moisture content, or at most 18%: it is very prone to sprouting and the quality for semolina is reduced if harvest is delayed. Durum must be dried (slowly) to 15%. It is easier and quicker to dry than normal wheat. The straw is of poorer quality and lesser quantity than conventional wheat straw and is therefore rarely baled.

MINORITY CROPS

Borage

Borage is indigenous to Britain (or at least here since Roman times); it has both grown in the wild, and been cultivated for centuries. It is produced principally for use as a dietary supplement, but it may also be used in cosmetics and pharmaceuticals. The oil has a high gamma linolenic acid (GLA) content. It was first grown as a field crop in the UK in the early 1980's. The last few years have usually seen around 5,000 hectares planted per year. However, due to a world-wide surplus of GLA, few, if any, contracts were offered for 2009 or 2010 crops, and limited amounts for 2011. For 2012 a slightly larger area is likely to be grown. As the market tends to be volatile, it is essential for a grower to have a buy-back contract with a reputable company. The crop should not be grown speculatively.

The crop is spring sown (March-April) into a good seedbed. Its aggressive growth gives good weed control with a high plant density. There are no significant pests and diseases, except for powdery mildew. Low rainfall areas are preferred owing to harvesting difficulties in wet conditions. It is combined in late July/early August, after swathing and drying, which takes a minimum of two weeks. Harvesting can be difficult and seed shedding at maturity is a problem. Seed should be promptly dried to 10% for safe storage. Cleaning may be necessary.

Borage should only be considered by those prepared to invest sufficient time in the crop's husbandry, harvest and storage. Borage is a low yield / high risk crop – yields are from virtually nothing to 0.75 tonnes per ha (*6 cwt per acre*); average 0.4 (3.2).

Contract prices are likely to be around £2,500 per tonne. Growing costs are likely to be in the range £275-£325 per ha.

Camelina Sativa

Camelina, Gold of Pleasure, or False Flax is a fast growing spring (or occasionally winter) sown crop. It is easily grown and harvested and is drought tolerant. The oil contains a range of essential fatty acids. It can be used as a food supplement or in industry as a drying oil. There is currently no commercial scale production in the UK that the authors are aware of. It is thought that current domestic usage requirements could support around 1,000 ha of the crop in the UK. Yields are in the 2.5tonne per ha range. Price is uncertain due to the absence of a domestic market but an indicative price is likely to be around £250-£300 per tonne.

Crambe - Abyssinian Mustard

Crambe is an industrial oilseed that contains high levels of erucic acid. Converted into erucamide it is used as a slip agent in plastics and is a constituent of heat sensitive dyes. The area of crambe in the UK had grown to around 5,000 ha. However, the major promoter/buyer of the crop went into receivership and little is being currently grown.

Crambe is a cruciferous spring crop managed in a similar way to spring oilseed rape. It has a short growing season, requiring only 100-120 days to reach maturity after emergence. As with oilseed rape, timely harvesting is important. Crambe can be combined direct, desiccated and combined or swathed. The crop should be stored and marketed at a moisture content of 9% or less. Yields are in the 2.5tonne per ha range. Contract prices offered in the past were £180 per tonne. Growing costs are likely to be around £300 per tonne.

Echium

Echium is a relatively new commercial plant to the UK. It has been cultivated on contract for less than a decade. It is a member of the Boraginacea family and is rich in stearidonic acid, which is used in cosmetic creams to reduce skin wrinkling and the effects of sunburn.

In past years there has been somewhat less than 1,000 ha or so grown in the UK. Similar to borage, a glut of the active ingredient led to no contracts being offered in 2009 or 2010, and restricted amounts in 2011. Availability of contracts should be greater for the 2012 crop. It is essential for a grower to have a buy-back contract with a reputable company, and the crop should not be grown speculatively. In the past prices have collapsed to almost nothing due to over-supply in the market.

The crop can be grown as far north as Yorkshire. It has a husbandry programme similar to that of borage but does not shed its seed as readily as borage. The seed is relatively small in size. Echium is suitable for light to medium land whereas borage performs better on a wider range of soil types.

The crop is sown in April and should come to harvest in July/August. There appear to be no significant pests of the crop. Harvesting is carried out with the use of a swather. Yields are approximately 250kg per ha (100kg per acre). Contract prices are likely to be around £3,500 per tonne of clean seed.

Evening Primrose

This crop is an important source of gamma linolenic acid (GLA), but it is no longer grown in the UK and very little is cultivated elsewhere in Western Europe – it has been largely superseded by borage, which is easier to grow. The crop is still widely grown in China where the climate is more suitable, and labour costs are lower. Previous editions have given details of the crop and possible gross margin data.

Flax (cut flax for industrial fibre)

Flax was re-introduced into the UK during the 1990s, not as the traditional, pulled, long fibre variety used for linen textiles but as a cut, combinable crop producing shorter fibres for industrial uses – 'short-fibre flax'. As a natural, biodegradable fibre and a renewable resource it was promoted as a 'green' alternative to synthetic fibres and plastics. New markets were developed and several processing plants set up – the area of flax expanded to 20,200 ha in 1996. Following low prices and reform of the subsidy regime, the area fell to less than 2,000 ha by 2003, and the one remaining processing facility in Wales was closed. Little, if any, is currently grown.

The agronomy of flax is similar to that of linseed but it is harvested earlier. It is spring sown, suitable for most soil types although lighter soil is preferred. It is a low input crop but weed control is essential. It grows best in areas of high rainfall such as Wales and the South-west. There are several harvesting options (described in earlier editions). Currently the preferred option is desiccation followed by combining. The straw is left to rett in the field and then baled. Retting takes 10-21 days, depending on weather conditions. The price paid for straw will reflect quality. The fibre content of a reasonable crop is 20-30%.

Hemp

The traditional use for hemp was in canvas and rope manufacture. New markets have recently been opened up, with the main uses of the fibre from the crop being in building insulation, and producing internal panels for the automotive industry. The core or pith of the plant is used for horse or poultry bedding. Although there is still a strong and growing demand from this market, it is also now being mixed with lime and used as a thermally efficient, environmentally friendly material in the construction industry.

The UK's main processor of the crop opened a new factory with the capacity to process the crop from 4,000 ha was opened in 2008. However, the severe downturn in the automotive sector sharply reduced demand for hemp fibre and the company entered into administration in 2009. The factory was purchased by one of its customers as a going-concern and is now called Hemp Technology Ltd. Contracts for around 1,000 ha were placed in 20010 and 2011 with the company looking to expand the area further.

Hemp is drilled in late April/May and the fibre crop grows 3 to 3.5m (10-12 feet) tall. Hemp Technology suggests a minimum area of 10 ha. A well-grown crop should have no weed or pest problems. Improved technology in the new factory means fibres do not have to be left to rett in the field for as long. Instead of a retting period of 4-6 weeks, the crop is mowed, and then baled when it is dry, bleached, and partially retted after 2-3 weeks. This increases saleable yields as the crop is allowed to grow for longer (cutting mid to late August), and there is less field-losses from the rows. Average yields should be around 7.5 tonne per ha (*3.0t per acre*), with target yields at 9.5 tonnes per ha (*3.8t per acre*). The margin below assumes that the grower will undertake the cutting and baling operations. If contractors are used then the variable costs will obviously be higher.

The crop must be stored under cover, and is delivered to the factory throughout the year. Due to the bulkiness of the crop, the majority of hemp is grown in the eastern counties, near to the processing facility. An average delivered price of £160 per tonne is assumed in the table below. The 2011 contract operated on a base price of £155 per tonne delivered to the factory in October, with £1.50 per tonne monthly increments. The 2012 contract is likely to offer similar terms. Transport costs need to taken into consideration. A figure of £15 per tonne is used in the table below. This should be applicable up to 50 miles from the factory (less if closer).

Hemp Gross Margin Schedule

Yield 7.5t/ha (3.0t/acre), Price £160/t delivered	£/ha	(£/ac)
Output	1200	(486)
Variable Costs:		
Seed	135	(55)
Fertiliser	235	(95)
Sprays	10	(4)
Haulage to factory (£15/tonne)	113	(46)
Total Variable Costs	493	(200)
Gross Margin per ha (acre).................................	**707**	(286)

Dual Hemp

Hemp may also be grown as a dual-purpose crop. In recent years, up to 10-15% of the national hemp crop has been of this type. The crop is left to mature longer, and then the top can be combined for the seed before the straw is mown and retted. A yield of 1.0-1.2 tonne per ha (*0.4-0.5t per ac*) of seed is possible, with a contract price estimated to be £510 per tonne. However, the yield of straw is lower at 5-6 tonnes per ha (*2.0-2.4t per ac*), with the price being the same as 'conventional' hemp. The seed is cold-pressed to produce high-value cooking oil, and is also used for bird feed, fishing bait and in nutritional supplements and cosmetics. Agronomy and costs are likely to be similar to a fibre crop. Because of the time needed to let the seed heads mature, an earlier-maturing variety is used. The later harvest also means that this crop is more suitable for early land in the East and South.

Grain Maize

Maize is one of the major global grains – with world output being higher than that for wheat. However, the climate of the UK has made it difficult to ripen the crop and most maize is grown for forage rather than grain. A combination of earlier varieties, the development of machinery that copes with wet conditions, and even possibly the effects of warmer summers has improved the prospects of this crop.

There is market potential, as well over a million tonnes of grain maize are imported annually. It is used in animal rations, human foods, and in industrial processes. Marketing the UK crop is a problem at present as consignments are generally not big enough to interest the major buyers. The animal feed market is the likeliest outlet for domestic production - a specialised or local market can be developed, for example feed for pigeons or corn-fed chickens. The basis of pricing in the margin is a £20-£30 per tonne premium over feed wheat.

There is no fundamental difference between forage and grain maize – the same varieties are simply left in the field for 3-6 weeks longer to let the cobs mature. It is difficult to know how much of the total UK maize area is taken for grain but it could be around 3,000 ha. The crop can be grown south of a line from Bristol to East Anglia, excluding the far south-west. Fields should be below 500ft in elevation and south-facing. To maximise heat units, the crop should be drilled as soon as soil temperatures are above 8°c – usually late April/May. Harvest by conventional combine with an adapted header in October/November. In UK conditions grain maize seldom drops below 30% moisture. The crop needs to be dried to 15% for storage which can be expensive and time-consuming. On good land the crop can yield 8-10 tonnes per ha but the average is not likely to be so high.

Grain Maize Gross Margin Schedule

	£/ha	(£/ac)
Yield 7.5t/ha (3.0t/acre), Price £165/t ex-farm		
Output	1238	(501)
Variable Costs:		
Seed	170	(69)
Fertiliser	204	(83)
Sprays	42	(17)
Total Variable Costs	416	(169)
Gross Margin per ha (acre).................................	**821**	(333)
But note high drying costs:		
£15-25/t on-farm; £20-30/t off-farm	113-225	(46-91)

The majority of grain maize is currently stored as a crimped product. This sees the crop cut at 30-35% moisture from mid October to early November with the 'wet' grain being processed, and an additive added (usually an organic acid). The overall cost of crimping and preservative is around £12-£15 per tonne. The grain is clamped or put into large bales or bags. It provides a very digestible dairy feed of high nutrition content. Yields can be 11-13 tonnes per ha and it sells for £150-£200 per tonne ex-farm.

Acknowledgement: Thanks to - Maize Growers Association, Tel: 01363 775040.

Millet

Millet describes a range of small-seeded grain plants covering a number of different species. The most commonly grown type in the UK is proso (also called white or common) millet. Millet has been cultivated since prehistoric times. It is a major food source in arid and semi-arid parts of the world; predominantly India, China, and parts of Africa. The crop has been grown in the UK for game cover for many years, but it has recently been commercialised to supply grain to the bird seed market.

Millet Gross Margin Schedule

Yield 3.0t/ha (1.2t/acre), Price £300/t ex-farm	£/ha	(£/ac)
Output	900	(365)
Variable Costs:		
Seed	100	(41)
Fertiliser	147	(60)
Sprays	55	(22)
Total Variable Costs	302	(122)
Gross Margin per ha (acre)......	**598**	(242)

The UK currently imports approximately 25,000 tonnes of millet for bird and pet feed each year. Domestic plantings in 2009 were in the region of 2,000-2,500 ha. There is the potential to raise this to around 6,000 ha. Full import substitution is unlikely to be possible as UK seed cannot match the quality of the best imported millet.

The crop can be grown on a range of soil types, but as it is drought tolerant, it is often planted on lighter land. It does not grow well in heavy or very chalky soils. The crop requires warm temperatures to ripen and is therefore best suited to the South of England.

The crop is late drilled, usually in May once the soil has warmed up sufficiently. It can be planted as late as June. It requires a fine seedbed. The crop grows to about a metre high and is ready to harvest after 4½ months in mid to late September. The crop is usually desiccated before harvesting with a conventional combine harvester.

Yields are in the range 2.5-4.0 tonnes per ha. The contract price for 2012 is not known at the time of writing, although contract values of around £300 per tonne were on offer for the 2011 harvest.

Acknowledgement: Thanks to - Premium Crops, Tel: 02392 632 883. Soya UK, Tel: 02380 696922.

Navy Beans

Navy beans are the basis for the familiar canned 'baked beans'. Over 100,000t of these are consumed annually in the UK – with the vast majority of these being imported from North America. A few years ago there was some interest in the crop, as varieties adapted to the soil types and climate of the UK were introduced. However, disappointing prices, variable yields, and the lack of area aid discouraged growers. Even following the change to the Single Payment, the economics of navy bean production in the UK looks marginal. Few, if any, contracts are currently available.

The crop requires good fertile land and some care in growing. Sowing is in mid-May when there is no further frost risk. Harvesting is late August/early September. The target yield is 3.0 tonnes per ha but the average is likely to be substantially less. When budgeting, an average of around 2.0 tonnes per ha (*0.8t per acre*) could be assumed. There is very little market information available on price, but it is likely to be in the region of £250-£300 per tonne. Variable costs are likely to be in the range £300-£350 per ha.

Poppies

The growing of this crop in the UK is a relatively recent development. The poppy heads are processed to produce morphine for pharmaceutical purposes. The seeds are sold into the culinary market. A bit less than 3,000 ha of the crop are currently grown – all on contract to the sole UK processor.

The crop needs free-draining alkaline soils; it is planted in the second half of March, and is harvested in early to mid August. The processor undertakes the harvesting operation with a specialised machine. Seed is included as part of the contract, as is agronomy advice (the processor specifies the pesticides to be used). The grower needs to be able to offer on-floor drying facilities.

Growing costs (excluding seed) will be in the range £300-£350 per ha. The contract for the 2012 harvest has not yet been finalised. In previous years a basic fee of £200 per ha was paid by the processor, which was then topped-up by a bonus based on the yield of the alkaloid from the crop. Total returns are likely to have been in the range £800-£1,000 per ha. Prices may be different under the 2012 contract – contact the processor for more details.

Acknowledgement: Thanks to – Macfarlan Smith, Tel: 01225 793 679.

Soya Beans

Soya is a sub-tropical crop in origin, grown mainly in North and South America, but also to a small extent in southern Europe. The UK imports three quarters of a million tonnes each year as beans and almost a further 2 million tonnes as meal, all for animal feed, so there would appear to be a ready market for the home grown product.

Various attempts have been made to commercialise the crop in the UK. In the late 1990's new varieties were introduced and by the early 2000's the area expanded to 1,700 ha. But after several difficult years the planted area declined. In recent years, less than 100 ha were being grown. However, the plant breeding process has continued and further varietal improvements yield and earliness have been made. Importantly, the soya price has also improved making the economics more attractive. An expansion in area is expected with additional contracts being offered for the 2012 harvest.

Soya Bean Gross Margin Schedule

	£/ha	(£/ac)
Yield 2.5t/ha (1.0t/acre), Price £375/t ex-farm		
Output	938	(380)
Variable Costs:		
Seed	140	(57)
Fertiliser	73	(30)
Sprays	70	(28)
Total Variable Costs	283	(115)
Gross Margin per ha (acre)................................	**654**	(265)

The crop is sown in late April or early May, depending on soil temperature, into a fine moist seedbed. The crop has a requirement for high temperatures and cumulative day-degrees of heat (similar to maize). This effectively restricts the crop to the southern half of England. The crop is combine harvested in September, usually after desiccation. The crop should be cleaned and dried to 14% moisture and 2% admixture.

As a legume, soya is a good alternative break crop, largely fixing its own nitrogen. Maintenance P and K is required plus 10-20kg of N to get the crop started. Spray costs also tend to be low.

Target yield is 3.0 tonnes per ha but the average is likely to be less; an average of 2.5 tonnes per ha (*1.0t per acre*) can be assumed. The price is largely determined by the price of imported crop. The UK crop is GM free, for which a premium is paid. A further premium may be paid for Identity Preserved UK crop which goes into human consumption or for organically grown soya. For 2012 harvest the price is estimated to be £375 per tonne.

Sunflower

The UK imports the equivalent of about 400,000 tonnes of sunflower seed each year, mainly as sunflower oil. Currently none is commercially crushed in the UK. There has been continued interest in sunflower, but late harvests and low yields have restricted the development of the crop. Currently only about 500 ha are grown, producing some 1,000 tonnes of seed. Almost all UK production goes into the pet-food or bird seed market; with good demand, but only in localised areas. Producers should satisfy themselves of the end-market before planting the crop. The birdseed market takes 20,000 tonnes of sunflower seed annually, so there is scope for import substitution. Some attempts have been made to cold-press sunflowers to produce a UK-sunflower oil, but this market is still in its infancy.

Extra-early maturing semi-dwarf hybrid varieties are the most suitable to conditions in the UK. The crop needs a relatively mild climate and is best grown south-east of a line from the Wash to east Dorset.

Sowing is from April to early May when the soil temperature is 7-8°C. Although sunflower will grow on a broad range of soil types its capacity to do well in dry and sandy soils and areas of low rainfall is a recommendation. Pre-emergence weed control may be necessary; at the right plant density weeds should not subsequently be a problem. As it is a broad row crop, chemical or mechanical weed control is possible. Sclerotina and botrytis, in a wet season, may affect the crop; on areas of less than 6 ha bird damage can be serious. Sunflower has a low nitrogen requirement.

Harvesting is from mid-September by combine harvester. Yields of up to 2.5 tonnes per ha with oil content of 44% are possible. The crop is dried to 8-9% for safe storage, which can be expensive. The price is usually based on a premium over the price of oilseed rape (around £50 per tonne), but other pricing mechanisms may be used in specialist markets. Growing costs will be in the region of £325-£375 per ha.

Others

Other crops that have been in the news in recent years as possible new crops for the future (or present crops capable of substantial development) include the following: chickpeas and lentils, fenugreek, meadowfoam, cuphea, peppermint, quinoa, buckwheat, honesty and herbs for their essential oils. At present there are no reliable data for these crops on average yield expectations and little on prices or variable costs, when grown on a commercial scale in this country. A number of them are either for the health food market or are sources of oil for industry as replacements for whale oil and light mineral oil. Research continues on many of them. More details may be available from the contact listed below;

Contact: National Non-Food Crops Centre (NNFCC): www.nnfcc.co.uk

VINING PEAS

Production level	Low	Average	High
	£	£	£
Output	1200 (486)	1425 (577)	1700 (689)
Variable Costs:			
Seed..		225 (91)	
Fertiliser....................................		118 (48)	
Sprays.......................................		120 (49)	
Total Variable Costs		463 (188)	
Gross Margin per ha (acre)	**737** (298)	**962** (390)	**1237** (501)

1. The table above relates to vining peas grown on contract where harvesting (approx. £70/tonne) and haulage (approx. £40/tonne) are paid for separately; the average price in this situation ranges from £280 to £350/tonne depending primarily on quality. The average yield is taken as 4.75 tonnes/ha; the national average (fresh weight) for the last five years has ranged between 3.8 and 4.9 although growers are paid on frozen weight. Top quality ('150 minute') peas have to be grown within 40 miles of the factory. More distant 'long haul' peas will be in the lower price range. A pea viner costs £315,000 - £360,000.

    The average yield of petit pois is lower but the price averages 12 to 15% more.

2. *Fertiliser.* Many growers use no fertiliser; but RB209 suggests P&K. Here $P_2O_5:K_2O = 85:65$kg/ha respectively.

3. *Sprays.* both herbicide and aphicide are commonly used with fungicides being used dependant on seasonal requirements.

4. *Labour:* see p.157.

5. *Total Area:* Around 36,000 ha are grown in the UK annually with a view to vining a 165,000-tonne crop.

MAINCROP POTATOES

Production level	Low	Average	High
Yield: tonnes per ha (tons per acre)	37.0 (15)	45.0 (18.2)	53.0 (21.5)
	£	£	£
Output	5698 (2308)	6930 (2807)	8162 (3306)
Variable Costs:			
Seed...		678 (275)	
Fertiliser.....................................		502 (203)	
Sprays.......................................		580 (235)	
Casual lab. (harvest & grading)............	666 (270)	810 (328)	954 (386)
Sundries (levy, sacks, etc.)...............	399 (161)	453 (184)	513 (208)
Total Variable Costs	2825 (1144)	3024 (1225)	3228 (1307)
Gross Margin per ha (acre)	**2873** (1164)	**3906** (1582)	**4934** (1998)

1. *Prices.* The price assumed above is £165 per tonne for ware and £20 for stock feed (assumed to be 7½ per cent), which is £154 per tonne for the whole crop. The actual price in any one season depends largely on the national crop size but also international trade. Variations according to quality and market (as well as season) are considerable. The eight-year average GB price for wares between 2003 and 2010 was £124/tonne.

2. *Physical Inputs.* Seed: 60% planted with certified seed: 2.8 tonnes per hectare at £250-300 per tonne (the price varies widely from season to season); 40% with once-grown seed: 2.6 tonnes per hectare at £200 per tonne. Sprays: herbicide, blight control, and haulm destruction.

3. *Casual Labour.* The figure in the table above is for assistance during (machine) harvesting and for grading/riddling (approx. £18.00/tonne); it is assumed that most of the labour for the latter is supplied by casuals.

4. *Contract* mechanical harvesting: approximately £640/hectare (excl. pickers, carting, etc.), £1070 inc. carting. Other contract work see page 180.

5. *British Potato Council (AHDB) levy:* £41.38/ha (£16.75/acre) for growers in 2011; exempt from levy if less than 3ha grown. 2012 rates as yet unpublished.

6. *Sprays.* Typically: herbicides 22%, fungicides 45%, insecticides 12%, PGRs 8%.

7. *Potato Land Rentals* range depending on the year, location, soil and water from over £550/ha (£225/acre) to as much as £950/ha (£380/acre). Potato rents are the product of potato profitability and also cereals as they are the alternative. In addition late harvested potatoes depress yield of following crop. As a result some have tried to increase potato rents on back of increased cereal prices.

8. *Sacks.* Approx. £8.30 per tonne.

9. *Fuel and Repairs* (per hectare): £290.

10. *Specialised Equipment Prices:* see page 174.

11. *Potato Store Costs:* see page 208.

12. *Labour:* see p. 157.

EARLY POTATOES

Production level	Low	Average	High
Yield: tonnes per ha (tons per acre)	18.0 (7)	23.0 (9.3)	28.0 (11.3)
	£	£	£
Output	3780 (1531)	4830 (1956)	5880 (2381)
Variable Costs:			
Seed………………………………….....		886 (359)	
Fertiliser………………………….....		363 (147)	
Sprays…………………………….....		290 (117)	
Casual labour……………………....		374 (152)	
Sundries (levy, sacks, etc.)……..........		290 (117)	
Total Variable Costs		2203 (892)	
Gross Margin per ha (acre)	**1577** (639)	**2627** (1064)	**3677** (1489)

1. *Prices and Yields.* The price assumed above is an average of £210 per tonne for a 23 tonne/ha yield. However, yields increase and prices fall as the season progresses. Thus both depend on the date of lifting, e.g. late May to early June, 7 to 12t/ha; July, 20 to 30 t/ha. Prices in late May to mid June are typically three times those in July; the very earliest crops (early May) can even fetch more than £1,000 per tonne, but the price could be down to £500 by mid May and to £250 or even £200 by the end of May (although in 2010 they remained far higher). Thus the average output of £4,830 given above could be obtained from 10 tonnes at £483 per tonne, 15 at £322, 20 at £241 or 30 at £161.

2. *Casual labour for planting*: £135 per hectare, plus help with harvesting/grading (£10.40/tonne).

3. *British Potato Council (AHDB) levy*: £41.38/ha (£16.75/acre) for growers in 2011; exempt from levy if less than 3ha grown. 2012 rates as yet unpublished.

4. *Fuel and Repairs* (£ per hectare): £260.

5. *Labour:* see p. 157.

   The percentages of the total potato area in Great Britain planted in early, second early and main crop, respectively are approximately 5, 31 and 63 in England, 20, 52 and 28 in Wales, 3, 38 and 59 in Scotland and 5, 33 and 62 of the total GB potato area.

SUGAR BEET

Production level	Low	Average	High
Yield: tonnes per ha (tons per acre)*	52.0 (21)	67.0 (27.1)	75.0 (30.4)
	£	£	£
Output	1649 (668)	2124 (860)	2378 (963)
Variable Costs:			
Seed..		171 (69)	
Fertiliser.................................		257 (104)	
Sprays.....................................		180 (73)	
Transport (Contract).................	260 (105)	335 (136)	375 (152)
Total Variable Costs	868 (352)	943 (382)	983 (398)
Gross Margin per ha (acre)	**781** (316)	**1181** (478)	**1395** (565)

* *'Adjusted tonnes' at standard 16% sugar content*

1. *Prices.* The 'all-in' delivered price for the 2012 crop is expected to be £31.70 per adjusted tonne. This is based on 90% sold 'in contract' 5% industrial contract entitlement (ICE) and 5% non contract. The 'in-contract' beet price is 27.53 plus average transport and delivery allowances of £5.00/tonne, ICE tonnage at £26.50 plus bonuses and the rest at £17/tonne.

   Late delivery bonus. 26 December - 7 January: 0.8% of price; thereafter, the rate rises by 0.2% per day.

   The sugar beet pricing formula is run in May/June for the following year. It takes into account four elements:

   a)   the direct costs of producing beet

   b)   a fixed uplift over this figure to cover overheads and a margin

   c)   a profit related adjustment linked to changes in currency

   d)   a wheat price related bonus linked to the LIFFE wheat futures price.

2. *Effect of Harvesting Date.* As the season progresses, changes occur in the crop before lifting, approximately as follows:

	from early Sept to early Oct.	from early Oct to early Nov.	from early Nov to early Dec.	from early Dec to early Jan.
Yield (t of washed beet /ha)	up 3.75	up 1.9	up 1.25	up 1.25
Sugar Content (%)	up 1%	up ¼%	down ¼%	down ¾%
Yield of Sugar (kg / ha)	up 1000	up 375	up 190	down 60

3. *Sprays.* Herbicides normally comprise 70% of the total spray cost.

4. *Contract.* Contract mechanical harvesting costs £250 per hectare excluding carting or £355-£365 per hectare including carting.

5. *Transport.* Contract haulage charges vary according to distance to factory. The figure assumed above is £5.00 per (unadjusted) tonne of unwashed beet including loading and cleaning (dirt and top tare assumed at 14% in total).

6. *Fuel and Repairs* (per hectare): £285

7. *Specialised Equipment Prices*: see page 174

8. *Labour*: see page 157

TOP FRUIT

The figures indicate a range within which the performance of most (established) orchards falls. The gross margin is calculated as lower yields less lower costs/higher yields less higher costs. In practice yields are not necessarily so directly linked to costs.

	Dessert Apples	*Culinary Apples*	*Pears*
Yield: tonnes/ha	15 - 55	25 - 50	15 - 30
Price (£/tonne)	500 - 850	250 - 500	450 - 650
	£	£	£
Output	7500 - 46750	6250 - 25000	6750 - 19500
Variable Costs*			
Orchard Depreciation	250 - 1600	150 - 1200	100 - 300
Fertilisers/Sprays	900 - 1500	700 - 1300	700 - 1150
Crop Sundries	150 - 600	200 - 500	150 - 400
Harvesting	855 - 3135	1175 - 2350	855 - 1710
Grading/Packing	1950 - 7150	3250 - 6500	1950 - 3900
Packaging	750 - 8250	750 - 3500	600 - 3600
Transport	900 - 4950	750 - 3500	675 - 2100
Commission/Levies	675 - 4200	560 - 2250	600 - 1750
Total Variable Costs*	6430 - 31385	7535 - 21100	6080 - 14910
Gross Margin	1070 - 15365	(1285) - 3900	670 - 4590

* Excludes Storage

1. *Price:* Average of all grades. Price is not only influenced by grade-out, but also by variety, customer and pack format (which in turn may affect packing, packaging costs).

2. *Orchard Depreciation:* Establishment costs written off over lifetime of orchard. Establishment includes trees and stakes and, in newer plantings, support structures and irrigation. Total establishment costs of £6,000 - £30,000 per hectare at planting densities of 750 – 4000 trees per hectare.

3. *Orchard Duration:* Traditional dessert apples around 20 years, with culinary and pears frequently 30 years plus. More recently planted denser apple systems likely to be nearer 15 years, with full cropping reached in years 3-5 (6-9 for traditional systems).

4. *Crop Sundries:* Including tree ties, stake replacement, tree replacement, bee hire, picking hods, bin depreciation etc.

5. *Harvesting:* Based on £57 per tonne average (to include supervision, Employer's NI & holiday allowance) for dessert apples and pears and £47 per tonne for bramley. In practice can vary significantly with variety, yield, fruit size and quality, etc.

6. *Grading and Packing:* Based on £130 per tonne. Can vary considerably, particularly with crop quality.

7. *Packaging:* Typical average of between £50 and £150 per tonne, although may be higher with specialist formats (e.g. overwrapped packs). Considerable variations arise from both crop quality (i.e. grade-out), customer and pack format.

8. *Transport:* Includes allowance for farm to packer, as well as delivery to final customer.

9. *Commission/Levies:* Including both marketeer's and retailer's commission, as well as levies (e.g. English Apples and Pears, AHDB). A total figure of 9% has been used, although it should be emphasised that charges can vary considerably. N.B. This category does not include levy payments under the Producer Organisation regime.

SOFT FRUIT

The figures – for soil-grown crops - indicate a range within which the performance of many, but not all crops is likely to fall. The gross margins are lower yields less lower costs/higher yields less higher costs. In practice, yields are not necessarily linked to costs.

	Strawberries Raised Bed June bearers	Strawberries Ever bearers	Raspberries
Yield: tonnes/ha	18-23	20-30	8-15
Price (£/tonne)	2400 - 3200	2500 - 3300	5000 - 6750
	£	£	£
Output	43200 -73600	50000 - 99000	40000 - 101250
Variable Costs			
Plants/planting/Sterilisation/Wirewrk	2850 - 3650	9500 -15000	1400 - 1700
Structures (average annual cost)	5000 - 8000	5000 - 8000	5000 - 8000
Fertilisers/Sprays/Predators	1000 - 1400	1000 - 1800	900 - 1200
Fieldwork	1500 - 3000	1800 - 3500	3000 - 4750
Harvesting	13000 - 17000	11000 - 19500	14000 - 26250
Grading/Packing	4500 - 5750	5000 - 7500	3600 - 7500
Packaging	6300 - 8050	7000 -10500	5600 10500
Transport	3060 - 3910	3400 - 5100	1760 - 3300
Commission	3890 - 6620	4500 - 8910	3600 - 9110
Total Variable Costs	41100 - 57380	48200 - 79810	38860 - 71560
Gross Margin	2100 - 16220	1800 - 20990	1140 - 29690

1. *Strawberries – June bearers:* Plants – assumes 35,000 per hectare with 60 day cropping in year 1 followed by 2 further years. Plants/planting/sterilisation written off over crop life of 3 years. Bed making not included as a variable cost.

   Structures – annual cost of poly-tunnels including both metalwork (w/o 10 years) and plastic (w/o 3 years). Costs also included for erection, dismantling and venting.

   Fieldwork – weeding, runner removal, leaf thinning etc.

   Harvesting- including supervision, Employer's NI & holiday allowance.

   Grading/Packing at £250/t. Packaging at £350/t, Transport at £170/t.

   Commission/Levies: Including both marketeer's and retailer's commission, as well as levies (e.g. AHDB). A total figure of 9% has been used, although it should be emphasised that charges can vary considerably. N.B. This category does not include levy payments under the Producer Organisation regime.

2. *Strawberries – Ever bearers:* Plants – assumes 25,000 per hectare. Plants/planting written off over crop life of one year. Sterilisation cost w/o over 3 years. Bed making not included as a variable cost.

   Structures/ Fieldwork/ Harvesting / Grading, Packing / Packaging / Transport / Commission - as for June bearers.

3. *Raspberries:* Plants – 8000/ha at 40p per plant. Planting at 12p per plant.

   • Structures – as for strawberries.

   • Wirework – to include material and labour.

- Plants/planting/wirework written off over crop life of 5 say years (crop life typically 4 to 7 years).

- Harvesting (including supervision, employer's NI & holiday allowance) – at £1750 per tonne (£1.75 per kilo).

- Grading/Packing – at £450 per tonne (45 pence per kilo).

- Packaging – at £700 per tonne (70 pence per kilo).

- Transport – at £220 per tonne (22 pence per kilo).

- *Commission/Levies:* Including both marketeer's and retailer's commission, as well as levies (e.g. AHDB). A total figure of 9% has been used, although it should be emphasised that charges can vary considerably. N.B. This category **does not** include levy payments under the Producer Organisation regime.

Blackcurrants

Although a soft fruit, this crop is much more of a field crop grown on arable farms with machine harvesting. The majority of the UK blackcurrant crop is grown for processing into cordial drink. Typical output is 6-7 tonnes/ha sold at £650-£700 per tonne = £3,900-£4,900/ha, with annual variable costs of say £1,400/ ha (principally share of crop establishment, fertilisers and sprays) leaving a gross margin of £2,400-£3,500/ha. Establishment costs approximately £7,000/ha for bushes with full production in year 2 followed by up to 10 years cropping.

Acknowledgement (Top & Soft Fruit): Thanks to - Andersons Midlands

FIELD-SCALE VEGETABLES

The enterprises shown are grown by farmers with suitable land, and the figures shown are on the basis that these output levels and variable costs represent 'typical' levels for the farmer with other major costs such as harvesting, packing and marketing expenses borne by the produce company taking the crop.

Per Hectare (acre)	Dry Bulb Onions	Cauliflower	Calabrese
Yield: tonnes/ha (tons/acre)	41 (16.6)		
Net Price (£/tonne)	120		
	£	£	£
Output	4,920 (1993)	2,275 (921)	2,062 (835)
Variable Costs:			
Seed	700 (284)	910 (369)	792 (321)
Fertiliser	416 (169)	516 (209)	457 (185)
Sprays	556 (225)	189 (77)	218 (88)
Total Variable Costs	1,672 (677)	1, 615 (654)	1,467 (594)
Gross Margin	2,428 (983)	660 (267)	595 (241)

Field scale vegetables have a high entry cost relative to other cropping alternatives, and bear significant risk. It is therefore necessary to research carefully the potential end market in terms of its expectations and cost structure. Fresh produce crops such as carrots, parsnips, leeks, lettuce, rhubarb, and brassicas, are now grown predominantly by a few highly specialised growers or produce companies. These growers supply the multiple retailers with high volumes and work to exacting specifications. The other key market for fresh produce is the local market with growers usually on a small scale and often tied into a local food chain such as a farm shop.

HOPS

Output Data

Yield: 2010; 30.06 zentners per ha (1 zentner = 50 kg), 2009; 26.73z/ha 2008, 26.31 z/ha 2004-2010 average: 28.1z/ha; range 26.0 (2006) to 31.6 (2004).

Average Price (£ per zentner)	Contract	Spot	Overall
2003	160	104	155
2004	164	67	134
2005	191	136	186
2006	199	-	198
2007	241	419	254
2008	241	394	265
2009	284	356	305
2010	334	237	283

Main Varieties			prices (£ per zentner)					
	2010		2010			2009		
	Ha	(z./ha)	contract	spot	overall	contract	spot	overall
Target	111	32.5	242	132	213	136	157	183
Challenger	81	30.0	292	150	254	250	320	259
Goldings	199	26.8	320	200	284	250	370	297
Fuggles	103	33.2	326	180	284	285	345	300
First Gold	162	15.2	302	302	302	300	300	300
Phoenix	9	35.5	266	191	244	195	-	195
Admiral	46	39.7	292	280	132	230	357	238
Others	352	26.4	320	150	240	260	350	325
Organic	19	13.0	650	550	500	650	-	650

Total area of hops (ha): 2010; 1067, 2009; 1080.7, 1997: 3,067; 1984: 5,091.

Variable Costs per mature hectare (acre) (materials only)	£/ha	(£/ac)
Fertilisers and Manure	236	(96)
Insecticide / Fungicide	650	(263)
Herbicide	140	(57)
String	198	(80)
Pockets / Bales	63	(26)
Drying Fuel	498	(202)
Total	1,785	(723)

Average Direct Labour Costs per mature hectare (acre)	£/ha	(£/ac)
Growing	1,220	(494)
Picking	2,187	(886)
Drying	513	(208)
Total	3,920	(1,588)

A new hop garden (erecting the poles, wiring and planting) could cost in the order of £20,000 per hectare (£8,000 per acre).

Acknowledgement: Thanks to - Chris Daws, English Hops and Herbs.

VINEYARDS

As at August 2010 the total area under vines in England and Wales was 1,324 hectares, although the actual area in production was 1,095 ha. This was the highest recorded area since the 'revival' of English wine industry in the 1980s. Total plantings have increased markedly in the last few years, after hitting a low point of 773 ha in 2004. Industry observers estimate that these official figures underestimate the area planted and that today (2011) the area under vines is nearer 1,500 ha.

There were 404 registered commercial vineyards as at August 2010; any vineyard over 0.1 ha must be registered with the Wine Standards Branch of the Food Standards Agency (FSA), though many of the smaller vineyards are run purely as a hobby. Although the average size of vineyards in the UK is only 3.3 ha, there are several vineyards of over 100 ha and around 60 vineyards account for 70% of the planted area.

In 2010 3,034,600 litres (2,771 litres per productive hectare) were produced in the UK. This is the largest amount of wine ever produced in the UK and reflects the increase in the productive area. The five-year average yield is 2,154 litres per ha. The low level of these average figures is down to there being many young vineyards included, together with vineyards that are under-performing and poorly managed. Yields in well run, favourably sited vineyards would be several times these levels. Around 80% of production is white wine and 20% red or rosé. Since the very warm year of 2003, the plantings of Champagne varieties (Chardonnay, Pinot Noir and Meunier) have increased significantly, and almost all plantings in the last few years (2004-2011) have been for the production of sparkling wine. Pinot Noir is now the most widely planted variety (325 ha), followed by Chardonnay (300 ha). Although these varieties now account for around 50% of the total vine area, the amount of sparkling wine on the market is still small as bottle-fermented sparkling wines take between 2 and 5 years to mature after bottling.

There is no EU ban on planting vines in the UK, and in 2008 it was confirmed that there will not be one in the future, whatever level production reaches. Changes to the vine variety legislation also mean that from August 2009, almost any variety may be legally planted in the UK.

A Quality Wine Scheme for England and Wales was introduced in 1991 and a Regional Wine Scheme in 1997, but in 2010 this was replaced with a new system of wine classification based upon the terms Protected Designation of Origin (PDO) and Protected Geographical Indication (PGI). PDO wines are broadly the same as Quality Wines and PGI wines the same as Regional wines and the terms Quality English/Welsh Wine and Regional English/Welsh Wine will continue to be used. Wines outside these two classifications can be labelled with the name of the grape variety and vintage, but not vineyard name, and are known as 'Varietal Wines'. There is also a PDO for certain sparkling wines (something not available under the old Quality Wine Scheme) which allows the term 'Traditional Quality Sparkling Wine' to be used. It is restricted to wines made from Chardonnay, Pinot Noir, Pinot Noir Précoce, Pinot Meunier, Pinot Blanc and Pinot Gris.

Domestically-produced wine supplies only 0.3% of the home market. The UK Vineyards Association (UKVA) has set up a marketing arm, English Wine Producers, to promote all English wine. All wines sold in the UK bear the same VAT and duty, irrespective of origin (although the duty on sparkling wines is higher than that for still wines). A significant proportion of home-produced wine is sold at the farm gate but supermarkets and off-licences are increasingly stocking it.

The quality of any wine is dependent on the quality of the site, and vineyards ideally need south facing, well-drained and sheltered land, less than 100 metres (330 ft.) above sea level, in the southern half of England or Wales. A high level of management and marketing is essential, as is expert advice. There is no minimum area for profitable production. A small enterprise selling wine at the farm gate and to local hotels and restaurants may be more profitable than one with 10 hectares selling only grapes. Some vineyards have associated gift shops and restaurants and are involved with corporate entertaining, which provide extra income. It is now possible to grow grapes under contract for several successful vineyard-wineries that have run out of suitable land of their own. Contracts vary, but prices can be up to £1,000/tonne for grapes for still wine and £1,500/tonne for sparkling.

The main growing system used in modern UK vineyards is the intensive Double Guyot; also the most commonly found in France and Germany. Other systems such as the extensive Geneva Double Curtain (GDC) and the divided canopy Scott Henry system are occasionally found, but are not the first choice of today's growers. The Double Guyot system will yield little until year 3 and with good management should be in full production in year 4. Geneva Double Curtain will not have a full yield until year 5 or 6 but crops more heavily. The Scott-Henry system crops fully in year 4 or 5.

Investment capital (to include materials and labour for planting and the first two years establishment but not the cost of the land) of £20,000 to £25,000/ha is typically required for the vineyard. Equipment for a winery costs a minimum of £75,000-£100,000 (less for still wine, more for sparkling) and a suitable building is needed. Contract winemaking is, however, generally considered better for smaller vineyards of less than 4 ha as it gives them access to state-of-the-art equipment and techniques. Growers who produce their own wine will also have to budget for the picking, processing and bottling of at least two vintages (still wine) or three to five vintages (sparkling wine) before income from selling their wines starts making a meaningful contribution to the enterprise.

Yields and quality are very variable, according to the variety of grape, the year and the quality of management - in particular the quality of pest and disease control. In a reasonable year a well-sited, well-managed vineyard should yield 7.5-10.0 tonnes/ha (3-4 tonnes/acre), but higher annual yields are possible. An average yield over ten years could be around 8.65 tonnes/ha (3.5 tonnes/acre). For still wine production, around 950 75cl bottles will be produced from 1 tonne of grapes; for sparkling wine the production will be nearer 750-800 75cl bottles per tonne.

The following costs refer to a commercial enterprise on a suitable site with a broad variety range. Establishment costs could be more if the site has to be drained and provided with windbreaks and rabbit and deer fencing. Annual growing costs can also be significantly greater, depending on planting density, variety, yield and management.

	Double Guyot	
	per ha	per acre
Number of Vines	2,600 - 5,000	(1,050 - 2,020)
	£ per ha	£ per acre
Establishment Costs:	over two years	
Materials	14,000	5,670
Labour	12,000	4,856
Total Establishment Costs	**26,000**	**10,526**
Subsequent Annual Costs:		
Materials	1,000	405
Labour (growing)	4,000	1,619
Harvesting*	500	202
Total Variable Costs	**5,500**	**2,226**

* Harvesting costs are very yield dependent. Growers without wineries will also have transport costs.

Prices: Grape prices will vary according to the variety and the vintage and whether growers are under contract or not. Prices range from £600 to £2,000/tonne delivered to a winery with still varieties being less valuable and good Pinot Noir or Chardonnay for sparkling wine at the higher end. In recent years prices have been high and many in the industry feel that these will fall as recently planted vineyards start producing grapes.

Wine prices (retail) vary widely but are likely to be in the range £6 to £10 per bottle for typical still white wines, and up to £14 for red wine. Sparkling wines retail between £15 and £25 per bottle (and a few more than that) but it is more costly to produce and requires significant storage time (2-5 years). A retail price for still wine of at least £7.00/bottle is necessary to break even for most enterprises.

e.g. £7.00 less 20% VAT and £1.81① duty = £4.02②

Less own winery costs (materials and labour) £2.50 per bottle③ = £1.52.

At 8.65 tonnes per ha and 950 bottles per tonne = £12,491/ha (£5,055/acre).

① Sparkling wine of 8.5% or more has a duty rate of £2.32 per 75cl bottle; still wines £1.81 per 75cl bottle

② If wines are sold via a wholesaler and/or retailer, gross profit margin of at least 10% (wholesaler) and 30% (retailer) on duty-paid prices must be allowed for.

③ Having still wine made under contract costs at least £3 a bottle. Sparkling wine will be at least £6/bottle, plus storage costs.

Acknowledgements: Thanks to - Stephen Skelton MW, Viticultural Consultant, 1B Lettice Street, London, SW6 4EH. Tel: 07768 583 700. www.englishwine.com United Kingdom Vineyards Association, Mr Robert Beardsmore, General Secretary, PO Box 1193, Bottisham, Cambridge, CBN25 9UY. Tel: 01223 813 812

2.   GRAZING LIVESTOCK

DAIRY COWS

Holstein Friesians (per cow per year)

Yield Group (1)	Low	Average	High	Very High
Milk Yield per Cow (litres) (2)	5,500	7,000	8,000	9,000
	£	£	£	£
Milk Value per Cow (3)	1457	1855	2120	2385
Plus Value of Calves (4)	118	118	117	117
Plus Value of Cull Cows (5)	100	100	100	100
Less Cost or Market Value of Replacements (6, 7)	£350	350	350	350
Output	1326	1723	1987	2252
Concentrate Costs (8)	220	418	594	792
Miscellaneous Variable Costs (10)	218	224	232	243
Gross Margin before deducting Forage Variable Costs (inc. Bought Fodder)	888	1081	1161	1217
Margin of Milk over Concentrates (MOC) (9)	1238	1437	1526	1593

Gross Margins per Cow and per Hectare (acre) at 4 different stocking rates (11)

Performance Level	Low	Average	High	Very High
1. **At 1·75 cows per forage hectare (low):**				
(0·57 forage hectares (1·4 acres) per cow)				
Forage Var. Costs & Bulk Feeds per Cow (11)	150	150	150	150
Gross Margin per Cow	738	931	1011	1067
Gross Margin per Forage Hectare	1291	1630	1770	1868
Gross Margin per Forage Acre	522	659	716	755
2. **At 2 cows per forage hectare (average):**				
(0·5 forage hectares (1·25 acres) per cow)				
Forage Var. Costs & Bulk Feeds per Cow (11)	176	176	176	176
Gross Margin per Cow	711	905	985	1041
Gross Margin per Forage Hectare	1423	1810	1970	2082
Gross Margin per Forage Acre	575	732	796	842
3. **At 2·25 cows per forage hectare (high):**				
(0·45 forage hectares (1·1 acres) per cow)				
Forage Var. Costs & Bulk Feeds per Cow (11)	193	193	193	193
Gross Margin per Cow	694	888	968	1024
Gross Margin per Forage Hectare	1562	1997	2177	2303
Gross Margin per Forage Acre	631	808	880	931
4. **At 2·5 cows per forage hectare (very high):**				
(0·4 forage hectares (1 acre) per cow)				
Forage Var. Costs & Bulk Feeds per Cow (11)	210	210	210	210
Gross Margin per Cow	677	871	951	1007
Gross Margin per Forage Hectare	1693	2177	2377	2517
Gross Margin per Forage Acre	685	880	961	1018

1.   *Yield group per cow:* Increases in this are usually (though not necessarily) associated with more intensive farming operations. Intensification focuses on higher gross

41

margins per hectare, whilst extensification on higher gross margins of other resources. Increase in concentrate feeding (kg/litre) and other inputs have been assumed as yields rise: see note 8.

2. *Yield.* The yield is annual herd production divided by the average number of cows and calved heifers in the herd. The average yield given (7,000 litres) is an estimated national figure for sizeable herds of black and white cows in 2012. The average yield for organic milk producers is around 6,500 litres.

3. *Milk Price:* This is assumed (as an average for the 2012 calendar year) to be 26.5p per standard litre, after deducting transport costs. It incorporates adjustments for milk composition and seasonality assuming an average-sized herd. Smaller herds achieve a lower price. The average price received by individual producers depends on seasonality of production and compositional quality.

Output and Gross Margin Change from a 0.25p/l price change per Cow

Low	Average	High	Very High
±£13.75	±£17.50	±£20.00	±£22.50

Seasonality Price Adjustments. These are diverse between the various dairy companies. An increasing number of companies no longer operate conventional seasonal adjustments but instead have payment systems that encourage a level monthly production, with a range of deductions and bonuses related to the individual producer's spring and autumn deliveries. The average adjustments for a selection of companies operating conventional adjustments are as follows in 2011/12:

April	May	June	July	Aug	Sept	Oct	Nov	Dec	Jan– Mar
–2	–3	–2	0	+1.5	+2	+2	+1.5	+0	0.00

Some companies also offer a premium for a level delivery option if supplies in a calendar month are within 10% of an agreed daily volume; the premium is typically 0·2 ppl. The trend towards new production profile payments is continuing, with more and more co-ops and companies introducing them, along with more individual pricing mechanisms.

Compositional Quality Payments:

Constituent values vary widely between buyers and months. As an example, the average values for the major dairies, in July 2011 were:

Butterfat: between 2.0p and 2.5p per litre per 1 per cent; average 2.2p.

Protein: between 2.8p and 5.1p per litre per 1 per cent; average 4.0p.

The *standard litre* is 4·15% butterfat and 3·35% protein.

Proportional Split of Dairy Breeds and milk Compositions

	Cows %	Butterfat %	Protein %
Holstein Friesian.........................	96	3·93	3·20
Ayrshire..................................	1·4	4·1	3·33
Jersey.....................................	1·3	5·39	3·87
Guernsey.................................	1·0	4·66	3·57
Dairy Shorthorn.........................	0·3	3·86	3·29
All Breeds................................		3·94	3·23

Data from Dairy Co data from Defra.

Within Breed Quality Variation. For Holstein Friesians without going to extremes the range can easily be: 3.5% to 4.1% butterfat and 3.1% to 3.4% protein. The difference in value between these two levels combined is about 2.5p per litre depending on milk contract. This is being achieved by both breeding and feeding for different milk quality to meet varying contractual requirements.

Hygiene Price Adjustments. These vary widely between the different dairy companies. A mid-2011 example is as follows:

A. *Bactoscan (bacteria measure)*

Bactoscan Reading	Price Adjustment (ppl)
0- 50,000	+0.5
51-100,000	nil
101-200,000	− 2
Over 200,000*	− 6

*1st month, -10p subsequent months.

B. *Somatic Cell Count (Mastitis)*

Count	Price Adjustment (ppl)
0-250,000	+ 0.3
251-325,000	Nil
326-400,000	− 1.5
Over 400,000*	− 6

*1st month -10p subsequent months.

Several milk buyers have no bonus for top hygiene bands, they expect suppliers to deliver top quality milk in order to receive the standard litre price.

C. *Antibiotics.* Milk in a consignment that fails an antibiotics test is usually worth lp/litre.

Organic milk. Organic milk price fluctuates over a large range depending on supply and demand. Farm-gate organic milk price currently about 4ppl more than conventional farm-gate price. Organic milk price for 2011 is forecast at 30.5ppl. Organic dairy feed is £280/tonne for 2011; this is 3.3ppl more expensive than conventional feed.

4. *Value of Calves.* Average annual value per cow at 10-20 days old, allowing for 5% mortality and an average calving index of 385 days.

Average value comprised as follows:

Dairy bull calf	(dairy x dairy)	£ 45
Dairy heifer calf	(dairy x dairy)	£200 (non-freemartin)
Cross bred bull	(beef x dairy)	£160
Cross bred heifer	(beef x dairy)	£140
Average		£118 after mortality

High yield herds normally have less beef genetics so dairy bull calves are less valuable than from lower yielding herds.

5. *Value of Cull Cows.* £400 allowing for casualties and a 25% per year replacement rate.

6. *Cost of Replacements.* £350 is £1,400 per down-calving heifer (purchase price or market value (mainly home-reared)) and a 25% per year replacement rate.

7. *Herd (Cow) Depreciation* thus averages £250 per cow per year, i.e., 25 per cent of £1,000 (i.e., £1,400-£400).

Net Replacement Cost = £132 per cow per year, i.e., herd depreciation (£250) less value of calves (£118).

Bull. AI is assumed in the tables; bull depreciation would be approx. £150 a year (£1,500 purchase price less £750 cull value, 5-year herd life); tight calving pattern: 60 cows per bull, well spread calving pattern: 100; 10 to 20 tonnes silage, 0·75 tonnes concentrates a year. Very high yield herds may use more expensive (dairy) bulls reaching £2,000 purchase price).

8. *Concentrate Costs.*

Amounts:	Yield Group	Low	Average	High	Very High
	kg/litre (approx.)	0.182	0.271	0.338	0.400
	tonnes/cow	1.00	1.90	2.70	3.60
	pence / litre (ppl)	4.00	5.97	7.43	8.80
	pence/ marginal litre*		13.20	17.60	19.80

* *This is the additional cost of feed between yield groups, and the cost of the additional feed divided by the additional litres production.*

Concentrate Price: taken (for 2012) as £220 per tonne, which is an average of home-mixed rations and purchased compounds of varying nutritive value, averaged throughout the year. Use of blends and straights are currently about 5-6% cheaper at £210/tonne average and compounds £230/tonne.

A difference of £5 per tonne has approximately the following effect on margin over concentrates and gross margin per cow, on the assumptions made regarding the quantity fed at each performance level:

Low	Average	High	Very High
±£7.50	±£10.00	±£13.00	±£16.25

Seasonality: Typically, specialist spring calving herds (60% or more calvings between January and May) use 0.09 kg per litre / 630 kg (£104) per cow per year less concentrates compared with autumn calving herds (60% or more calvings between August and December). See further note 12 below.

Typical Monthly Variation in Concentrate Feeding (kg per litre, 7,000 litre herd)

Winter		Summer	
October	0.30	April	0.27
November	0.33	May	0.16
December	0.33	June	0.16
January	0.33	July	0.22
February	0.33	August	0.24
March	0.30	September	0.27
Average winter: 0.32		Average summer: 0.22	
	Weighted average whole year: 0.28		

The distribution on farm varies according to factors such as seasonality of calving, milk yield, summer grazing productivity, the quantity and quality of winter bulk feeds, and turnout and housing dates. The March figure in particular will be affected by type of soil and seasonal rainfall.

Yield with no concentrates and good quality silage: approximately 4000 litres for spring calvers.

9. Margin over Concentrates and Concentrates per litre

The emphasis in the initial tables should be laid on the differences between the margin of milk value over concentrates per cow; the same large variation can occur with widely differing combinations of milk yield and quantity of concentrates fed.

In the following table, at each yield level figures are given for *(a) margin of milk value over concentrates* per cow (£) and (b) *concentrates per litre* (kg) at seven levels of concentrate feeding.

Margin Over Concentrates (£) and Concentrates per Litre (kg)

Yield Level	Low		Average		High		Very High	
Milk yield per cow (litres)	5,500		7,000		8,000		9,000	
	(a)	(b)	(a)	(b)	(a)	(b)	(a)	(b)
Concentrates per cow	£	kg	£	kg	£	kg	£	kg
1.0 tonne (£220)	1,238	0.18	1,635	0.14	-	-	-	-
1.5 tonne (£330)	1,128	0.27	1,525	0.21	1,790	0.19	-	-
2.0 tonne (£440)	1,018	0.36	1,415	0.29	1,680	0.25	1,945	0.22
2.5 tonne (£550)	-	-	1,305	0.36	1,570	0.31	1,835	0.28
3.0 tonne (£660)	-	-	-	-	1,460	0.38	1,725	0.33
3.5 tonne (£770)	-	-	-	-	-	-	1,615	0.39
4.0 tonne (£880)	-	-	-	-	-	-	1,505	0.44

At £220/tonne, 1kg feed costs 22.0p. This means that using 0.44kg feed per litre would cost 9.68p for every litre of milk.

10. *Miscellaneous Variable Costs (average)*

	£
Bedding*	70
Vet. and Med**	64
A.I. and Bull Hire**	30
Recording, Consultancy, Consumables, Dairy Stores	60
Total	**224**

* Straw varies from 0.4 to 1.5 tonne per cow.

** Both Vet and Med and A.I. and Bull Hire tend to increase with higher milk yield. This explains the higher variable costs in the higher milk yield data.

11. *Stocking Rate and Forage Costs.* The stocking rates given assume that nearly all requirements of bulk foods – both winter and summer – are obtained from the forage area, i.e. little is bought in. On average about 55 per cent of the forage area (or production) is grazed and 45 per cent conserved. Note that as the stocking density increases, gross margin per cow falls, but gross margin per hectare rises.

The first two forage costs are as for grass gross margins in the Forage Variable Costs on page 83. Seed costs clearly depend on the percentage of permanent pasture, if any, the length of leys, etc.

Dairy Herd Forage Costs

Cows per Ha (Acre)	1.75 (0.7)	2.00 (0.8)	2.25 (0.9)	2.5 (1.0)
N Kg/Ha (units/acre)	140 (112)	180 (143)	220 (175)	260 (207)
P_2O_5 Kg/Ha (units/acre)	25 (20)	30 (24)	35 (28)	40 (32)
K_2O Kg/Ha (units/acre)	45 (36)	50 (40)	55 (44)	60 (48)
Fertiliser £/Ha	£192	£240	£287	£334
Seed £/Ha	£15	£33	£41	£50
Ag-chem £/Ha	£8	£12	£15	£22
Forage Cost £/ha (£/Acre)	**215 (87)**	**284 (115)**	**343 (139)**	**406 (164)**
Total Forage cost £/Cow	£123	£142	£152	£162
Bulk Feed £/cow	£27	£34	£41	£48
Total forage £/cow inc Bulk	**£150**	**£176**	**£193**	**£210**

An increase in stocking density can be obtained not only by intensifying grassland production, as above, but also by buying in winter bulk fodder (assuming the same level of concentrate feeding in both cases). Theoretically, a zero-grazed farm buying in forage needs no land. In this situation, the gross margin per hectare would be extreme (and meaningless).

Overheads such as labour and depreciation on buildings are likely to increase per hectare and fall per cow as stocking density rises. Management challenges occur with higher stocking rates such as poaching which can be alleviated with good cow tracks. In addition the Nitrate Vulnerable Zone regulations must still be met.

12 *Seasonality.* Price and concentrate feeding differences according to the seasonality of production have already been outlined in notes 3 and 8.

Under similar levels of management mainly autumn calving herds average up to 1,000 litres more milk/cow/year than mainly spring calving herds but feed around a tonne more concentrates per cow/year; spring calving herds should normally only be feeding about 0.15 kg/litre. The average milk price would be expected to be higher for autumn calving herds, but the difference is less than might be supposed and has been steadily reduced with better prices being paid for summer milk.

13. *Quota.* The milk quota policy will end on 31 March 2015. To make gentle transition to this date, more quota is being allocated to all producers (see chapter III Section 1 for details). UK milk production is now so far below total quota restrictions, the regime is irrelevant and quota has no value.

14. *Labour:* see page 169.

15. *Building Costs:* see page 208.

Costs of Milk Production per Litre (Holstein Friesians)

	Average (pence)		Premium (pence)	
Concentrates	5.97		5.08	
Forage and Bought Bulk Feed	2.52		2.82	
Vet. & Med.	0.91		0.61	
Other Variable Costs	2.29		1.6	
Total Variable Costs		11.69		10.11
Labour: direct (milking etc.)	3.97		3.31	
: field/farm work	1.15		0.79	
Power and Machinery	5.01		3.27	
Rent/Rental Value	1.21		1.14	
General Overheads	1.30		1.11	
Total Fixed Costs		12.64		9.62
Net Replacement Cost *(Herd Dep'n)*		3.57		2.79
Total		**27.90**		**22.51**

1. *The average variable costs* per litre are derived from the data (and therefore the assumptions made) in the main per cow cost table using the 7,000l per cow data and 2 cows/ha. The labour cost is linked to page 169. The average fixed costs are as for the medium-sized farm data on page 197, with adjustments made to allow for the greater use of resources by dairy cows compared with followers (and possibly cereals). Rent is based on the figure on page 203

2. The 'Premium' figures are as estimated for the average of the most profitable 10% of herds, with lower than average costs per cow (except forage costs).

3. *Labour* includes farmer and any unpaid family labour.

4. *Power and machinery* cover all machinery and equipment costs, including the use of farm vehicles, etc.

5. *General overheads* similarly relate to the whole farm, including property repairs.

6. Neither interest on capital nor any management charge has been included.

Channel Island Breeds

Performance level (yield)	Low	Average	High	Very High
Milk Yield per Cow (litres) (1)	4,150	5,000	5,550	6,250
	£	£	£	£
Milk Value per Cow (2)	1245	1500	1665	1875
Concentrate Costs (3)	198	308	385	528
Margin of Milk over Concentrates (MOC)	1047	1192	1280	1347
Herd Depreciation less calf value (4)	170	170	170	170
Miscellaneous Variable Costs (5)	218	224	232	243
Gross Margin per cow before deducting Forage Variable Costs	659	798	878	934
Forage Variable Costs (inc. Bought Fodder)	146	153	160	167
Gross Margin per Cow	513	645	718	767
Gross Margin per Forage Hectare (6) (2.4 cows per ha: 0.42ha/cow)	1232	1549	1724	1842
Gross Margin per Forage Acre (1.05 cows per acre: 0.97acre/cow)	499	627	698	746

1. *Yield.* Average of Jerseys and Guernseys. See Note 2 for Holstein Friesians (page 42). Guernsey yield averages slightly higher than Jerseys and Jerseys achieve a higher butterfat and protein (see page 42).

2. *Milk Price.* This is 30p per litre (average of Jerseys and Guernseys), i.e. 3.0p above Holstein Friesian milk; (32p Jersey milk, 28p Guernsey). In addition to the higher price obtained through the higher compositional quality for Channel Island milk some companies pay a premium for Channel Island milk.

3. *Concentrate Costs.* The price taken (for 2011) is £220 per tonne.

Amounts:	Yield Group	Low	Average	High	Very High
	kg/litre	0.217	0.28	0.315	0.384
	tonnes/cow	0.9	1.40	1.75	2.40
	pence / litre (ppl)	4.77	6.16	6.94	8.45
	pence/ marginal litre*		12.94	14.00	20.43

   * *This is the additional cost of feed between yield groups, and the cost of the additional feed divided by the additional litres production.*

4. *Net Annual Replacement Value*: (i.e. Value of Calves less Herd Depreciation) were calculated as follows:

	£ per cow in herd
Cost of replacements: 25% of herd per year @ £1,000	250
Less Value of culls: 25% of herd per year @ £200 (allowing for casualties)*	50
Herd Depreciation	200
Annual Value of Calves**	30
Net Annual Replacement Cost	170

   * Cull cow prices for Guernseys are about £40 higher than for Jerseys.

   ** Allowing for calving index of 390 days and calf mortality; mixture of pure bred calves and beef crosses. Guernsey calves, especially crosses, fetch more than Jersey calves, averaging perhaps £10 more per head and substantially more for some Guernsey beef crosses.

5. *Miscellaneous Variable Costs.* See Note 10 for Holstein Friesians (page 45).

6. *Stocking Rate.* See, in general, Note 11 for Holstein Friesians (page 45). The effect of varying the stocking rate on gross margin per forage hectare is as follows:

Gross Margin per Cow before deducting Forage V.C.s

Cows per Forage Hectare	Forage Hectares (acres) per cow	Gross Margin per cow before deducting forage V.Cs				Forage V.C. £ per cow*
		Low £659	Average £798	High £878	Very High £934	
		Gross Margin £ per Forage Ha (acre)				
2.1	0.48 (1.18)	1226 (497)	1518 (615)	1686 (683)	1804 (731)	75
2.4	**0.42 (1.03)**	**1232 (499)**	**1566 (634)**	**1758 (712)**	**1892 (766)**	**146**
2.7	0.37 (0.91)	1362 (552)	1737 (704)	1953 (791)	2105 (852)	155
3.0	0.33 (0.82)	1474 (597)	1891 (766)	2131 (863)	2299 (931)	168

* A small amount of purchased bulk fodder is assumed, increasing with the stocking rate as follows (per cow): low £27, average £34, high £41 very high £48.

At the average stocking rate given above for combined Channel Island breeds (2.4 cows per forage hectare) the average figure for Jerseys would be approximately 2.55 and that for Guernseys 2.25 cows per forage hectare.

Ayrshires

Performance level (yield)	Low	Average	High	Very High
Milk Yield per Cow (litres) (1)	5,300	6,000	6,700	7,400
	£	£	£	£
Milk Value per Cow (2)	1484	1680	1876	2072
Concentrate Costs (3)	270	347	432	527
Margin of Milk over Concentrates (MOC)	1215	1334	1444	1545
Herd Depreciation less calf value (4)	158	158	158	158
Miscellaneous Variable Costs (5)	218	224	232	243
Gross Margin per cow before deducting Forage Variable Costs	839	952	1054	1144
Forage Variable Costs (inc. Bought Fodder)	146	153	160	167
Gross Margin per Cow	693	799	895	978
Gross Margin per Forage Hectare (6) (2.4cows per ha: 0.42ha/cow)	1664	1919	2147	2346
Gross Margin per Forage Acre (1.05cows per acre: 0.97acre/cow)	674	777	870	950

1. *Yield.* See Note 2 for Holstein Friesians (page 42).

2. *Milk Price.* See in general, note 3 for Holstein Friesians (page 42). The price assumed in the above table is 26.5p per litre. The compositional quality of milk from Ayrshires is higher than for the black and white breeds.

3. *Concentrate Costs.* See notes 8 and 9 for Holstein Friesians. In the above table, the levels of feeding kg/litre (and tonnes per cow) are as follows: low 0.25kg/l (1.225 tonne/cow), average 0.275kg (1.575t), high 0.30kg (1.965t), very high 0.325 (2.397t); price £220 per tonne.

4. *Net Annual Replacement Value*: i.e. Value of Calves less Herd Depreciation is calculated as follows:

	£ per cow in herd
Cost of replacements: 25 per cent of herd per year @ £1,000	250
Less Value of culls: 25 per cent of herd per year @ £250	
(allowing for casualties)............	63
Herd Depreciation..	188
Annual Value of Calves*.....................................	30
Net Annual Replacement Cost	158

*Allowing for calving index of 385 days and calf mortality; mixture of pure bred calves and beef crosses.

5. *Miscellaneous Variable Costs.* See Note 10 for Holstein Friesians (page 45).

6. *Stocking Rate.* See, in general, Note 11 for Holstein Friesians (page 45).

Shorthorns. The above data could be used for Shorthorns, although one would expect their average yield to be about 5% lower, their cull and calf prices to be higher and their stocking rate to be slightly lower – similar to Holstein Friesians.

DAIRY FOLLOWERS

(per Heifer reared)

A. Holstein Fresians

Performance Level	Low	Average	High
	£	£	£
Value of heifer (allowing for culls) (1)	1260	1260	1260
Less Value of calf (2)	200	200	200
Output	1060	1060	1060
Variable Costs:			
Concentrate Costs (3)	273	248	223
Miscellaneous Variable Costs (4)	141	128	115
Total Variable Costs (excluding Forage)	414	376	338
Gross Margin per Heifer, before deducting Forage Variable Costs	646	684	722
Forage Variable Costs (5)	122	129	134
Gross Margin per Heifer	525	555	588
Forage Hectares (Acres) per Heifer reared (6)	0.95 (2.3)	0.73 (1.8)	0.58 (1.4)
Gross Margin per Forage Hectare (7)	552	766	1022
Gross Margin per Forage Acre	224	310	414

B. Channel Island Breeds

Performance Level	Low	Average	High
	£	£	£
Value of heifer (allowing for culls) (1)	900	900	900
Less Value of calf (2)	30	30	30
Output	870	870	870
Variable Costs:			
Concentrate Costs (3)	232	211	190
Miscellaneous Variable Costs (4)	127	115	104
Total Variable Costs (excluding Forage)	359	326	293
Gross Margin per Heifer, before deducting Forage Variable Costs	511	544	577
Forage Variable Costs (5)	110	116	120
Gross Margin per Heifer	402	428	456
Forage Hectares (Acres) per Heifer reared (6)	0.68 (1.7)	0.58 (1.4)	0.50 (1.2)
Gross Margin per Forage Hectare (7)	595	744	912
Gross Margin per Forage Acre	241	301	369

N.B. on average Channel Island heifers calve about three months younger than Holstein Fresian Heifers

C. Ayrshires

Performance Level	Low	Average	High
	£	£	£
Value of heifer (allowing for culls) (1)	800	800	800
Less Value of calf (2)	30	30	30
Output	770	770	770
Variable Costs:			
Concentrate Costs (3)	246	223	201
Miscellaneous Variable Costs (4)	130	118	106
Total Variable Costs			
(excluding Forage)	375	341	307
Gross Margin per Heifer, before			
deducting Forage Variable Costs	395	429	463
Forage Variable Costs (5)	88	93	96
Gross Margin per Heifer	307	336	367
Forage Hectares (Acres) per Heifer			
reared (6)	0.68 (1.7)	0.58 (1.4)	0.50 (1.2)
Gross Margin per Forage Hectare (7)	455	585	733
Gross Margin per Forage Acre	184	237	297

1. *Heifer values* are based on the purchase price of down-calving heifers, allowing for culls. Most heifers are home-reared. If heifers are reared for sale, the price of whole batches is likely to be lower than the values given in the tables, by 10 or 15 per cent. On the other hand the purchaser will often take the batch a few months before the average expected calving date, thus reducing feed and area requirements for the rearer.

2. *Calf Value;* is based on the cost of a heifer dairy calf (hence worth considerably more than the average calf sold from the dairy enterprise) and known not to be a freemartin. It accounts for mortality of 5%.

3. *Lower levels of concentrate* costs are the combined result of more economical feeding and a lower average calving age. (Other things being equal, including the overall level of management, a lower calving age requires higher levels of feeding.) Average (Holstein Friesians) = £71 to 3 months (see Calf Rearing on page 54) plus 290 kg calf concentrates @ £230/tonne and 500 kg @ £220/tonne = £240 per calf.

4. *Miscellaneous* variable costs include bedding (£70): straw requirements average approx. 1 tonne per heifer reared, but are variable, depending on time of year and age when calved, as well as system of housing and extent of out-wintering. Vet. and med. approximately £44 per heifer reared.

5. *A "replacement unit"* (i.e. calf + yearling + heifer) equals about 1·25 livestock units with an average calving age of 2 years 4 months. The three stocking rates used above are equivalent to approximately 1.2, 0·9 and 0·7 forage hectares (0.48, 0.37, 0.31 acres) respectively per Holstein Friesian cow (Livestock Unit).

6. *Forage variable costs.* Grass for both grazing and conservation, at £98-153/ha including a small amount of bought and bulk food (£8, £13, £18 a head).

7. *Much higher gross margin figures* per hectare can be combined by intensive grazing methods, particularly if combined with winter feeding systems which involve little dependence on home-produced hay or silage (cf. Note 11, last three paragraphs, page 45).

8. *Contract Rearing*: see page 68.

9. *Labour*: see page 169.

SELF-CONTAINED DAIRY HERD: COWS AND FOLLOWERS

At average annual replacement rates (25 per cent of the milking herd), nearly one-third of a replacement unit is required for each cow in the herd, i.e. roughly one calf, yearling and heifer for every three cows (including calved heifers), allowing for mortality and culling. At average stocking rates for both, this means more than 1 hectare devoted to followers for every 3 hectares for cows. Since surplus youngstock are often reared and frequently the stocking rate is less intensive the ratio often exceeds 1:2 in practice. 1: 2·75 is about the minimum where all replacement heifers are reared, unless their winter feeding is based largely on straw and purchased supplements, or unless there is a combination of long average herd life and early calving, i.e. at 2 years old or just over.

The table below shows the combined gross margin per forage hectare (acre) for the whole herd (i.e., Cows and Followers Combined); (at four levels of performance, including four commensurate levels of stocking rate, for the dairy cows; and three levels of performance, including different stocking rates, for the followers) are as follows, assuming a 2:1 land use ratio (dairy cow area: followers area); (Holstein Friesians only). It is linked to the schedules on pages 41 and 51:

Gross Margin per Forage Hectare for Cows and Followers Combined

			G.M per Forage Hectare (acre) Dairy Cows			
			Low £	Average £	High £	Very High £
G.M. per			1291 (523)	1810 (733)	2177 (882)	2517 (1019)
Forage	Low	552 (224)	1045 (423)	1390 (563)	1635 (662)	1862 (754)
Hectare (acre)	Ave.	766 (310)	1116 (452)	**1462** (592)	1707 (691)	1933 (783)
Followers	High	1022 (414)	1202 (487)	1547 (627)	1792 (726)	2019 (818)

As an example, the above table indicates that at the average level of performance and stocking rate for both cows and followers, the whole dairy gross margin per hectare (acre) figure is £1,481 (600) compared with £1,810 (733) for the dairy cows alone, a reduction of 18 per cent.

If more than the assumed (minimum) number of dairy followers are kept and the ratio is 1·5:1 (i.e. 40% of the dairy herd forage area is devoted to followers rather than a third) the gross margin for the whole forage area figure (on the assumption again of average performance) falls to £1,180 (478), which is a reduction of 35 per cent compared with cows.

BEEF

There are numerous different systems for producing beef in the UK which are heavily influenced by factors such as feed and forage, breeds, housing, sale weights, market outlets, labour availability and enterprise scale. By virtue, the financial performance of beef enterprises are infinitely variable, more so than any other sector of UK agriculture. The enterprise gross margins shown on the following pages represent some of the most common types of beef systems with output prices and costs based on 2012 budgets.

Calves

The values in the table below are for 2012 and relate to dairy bulls or beef cross calves of average quality, less than three weeks old. These values have been used in the budgets for the following beef systems. There is significant regional and seasonal variation in calf prices.

Calf Values of various Beef Cattle

	Bulls	Heifers
Holstein Friesians (HF)	50	
Hereford Cross	160	120
HF/Continental Cross	210	170

Calf Rearing

	3 months	6 months
	£	£
Value of Calf	305	405
Less Calf Purchase (1)	198	198
Output	**107**	**207**
Variable Costs:		
Milk Substitute (2)...	33	33
Concentrates (2)..	38	105
Hay (3)...	1	13
Miscellaneous Variable Costs (4)..................	22	34
Total Variable Costs	**94**	**185**
Gross Margin per Calf Reared	**13**	**22**

1. *Calf Purchase*: Assumes equal number of male and female calves (Holstein Friesian/Continental beef cross, 1-2 weeks old). £190 average price, plus 4% mortality assumed, mainly in first 3 weeks.

2. *Milk substitute*: 20 kg @ £1,650/tonne = £33.00. Calf concentrates: to 3 months, 160 kg @ £240/tonne = £38.00; to 6 months, additional 290kg @ £230/tonne = £67. Calves fed on machine or lib milk systems will use more milk powder.

3. *Hay*: 10kg to 3 months, 190kg to 6 months.

4. *Misc.* Variable Costs include veterinary and medicines: £12 (3 months), £15 (6 months); bedding: £6 (3 months), £10 (6 months); plus ear tags etc.

5. *Weights*: at start = 45 to 50 kg; at 3 months = 115 kg; at 6 months = 245kg. Contract rearing charge (both 0 to 3 months and 0 to 6 months): £12 per week. Direct labour cost: approximately £25 per head to 3 months, £40 per head to 6 months.

6. *Labour requirements* (all beef systems): see page 169.

Suckler Cows

Single Suckling (per Cow): Lowland (1)

System	Spring Calving		Autumn Calving	
Performance Level (2)	Average	High	Average	High
	£	£	£	£
Value of Calf Sold (3)	470	525	622	655
Calf Sales / Valuation per Cow (3)	427	489	566	609
Less Cow and Bull Depreciation				
Calf Purchases (4)	96	96	109	109
Output	**331**	**393**	**458**	**500**
Variable Costs:				
Concentrate Costs (Cow and Calf)	43	36	74	67
Other Variable Costs (5)	79	56	90	64
Total Variable Costs (excl. forage)	**121**	**91**	**164**	**131**
Gross Margin per Cow, before				
deducting Forage Variable Costs	210	302	294	369
Forage Variable Costs	104	106	133	136
Purchased Bulk Feeds	12	10	20	16
Gross Margin per Cow	**94**	**186**	**141**	**218**
Cows per Hectare	1.80	2.20	1.65	2.00
Forage Hectares (Acres) per Cow	0.56	0.45	0.61	0.50
	(1.37)	*(1.12)*	*(1.50)*	*(1.24)*
Gross Margin per Forage Hectare (Acre)	**170**	**409**	**233**	**435**
	(69)	*(165)*	*(94)*	*(176)*

1. *System*: Relates to performance per cycle. i.e. for the production period. Assumed 390 days average calving interval.

2. *Performance level:* relates to variations in both outputs and inputs.

3. *Value of Calves:* Assumed sale weights; spring calving = average 280kg, high 309kg, autumn calving = average 371kg, high 385kg. Calf sale ages; autumn calving = average 250 days average, 240 days high, autumn calving = average 365 days, high 340 days. Sale prices; £1.68/kg liveweight for average performance herds, £1.70/kg liveweight for high performance herds. Prices are average for steers and heifers. *Calves reared* per 100 cows mated: average 91, high 93.

4. *Assumptions.* Herd life: spring calving, 8 years; autumn calving, 7 years. Purchase price £1,300, average cull value £700. Calves purchased: average per 100 cows mated: spring calving 2, autumn calving 3; at £190. Bull: purchase price £3,500, cull value £500; (one bull per 35 cows on average; 5-year herd life). Dairy cross beef cows have better fertility performance than continental pure bred cows, but lower cull sale prices.

5. *Misc.: vet & med*: spring calving £24, autumn £27; bedding: spring calving £39, autumn £44; *miscellaneous*: spring calving = average £16, high £17, autumn calving = average £19, high £20. *Straw*: where yarded in winter, straw requirements average 0.7 tonnes per cow for spring calvers and 0.8 tonnes for autumn calvers.

6. *The Forage Area* includes both grazing and conserved grass (silage and hay). The higher stocking density implies better use of grassland. Higher stocking rates can also be achieved by buying in more of the winter bulk fodder requirements, or by winter feeding largely on arable by-products, including straw. Purchased bulk fodder and/or

straw balancer concentrates will reduce gross margin per cow but increase gross margin per hectare.

7. *Headage Payment*: A payment is made in Scotland on three-quarter breed beef calves from Suckler Cows. Payments under the Scottish Beef Calf Scheme in 2010 were £52.19 per head (£104.37 per head for the first 10 calves claimed). 2011 rates will be determined at the end of the calendar (scheme) year.

8. In lowland conditions rearing two or more calves per cow is an option, but needs substantially greater labour input. Output is raised by fostering a second purchased calf onto a cow soon after calving, with little impact on costs of keeping the cow. The cow breed needs to be of a quiet temperament and have enough milk to rear two calves.

Single Suckling (per Cow): Upland / Hill

System	Spring Calving		Autumn Calving	
Performance Level	Average	High	Average	High
	£	£	£	£
Value of Calf (2)	458	476	611	629
Calf Sales / Valuation per Cow (3)	412	438	550	579
Less Cow and Bull Depreciation and				
Calf Purchases (4)	110	110	124	124
Output	**302**	**328**	**426**	**455**
Variable Costs:				
Concentrate Costs (Cow and Calf)	46	39	76	69
Other Variable Costs (5)	83	84	95	96
Total Variable Costs (excl. forage)	**129**	**123**	**171**	**165**
Gross Margin per Cow, before				
deducting Forage Variable Costs	173	205	255	290
Forage Variable Costs	83	88	124	130
Purchased Bulk Feeds	14	12	22	18
Gross Margin per Cow	**76**	**104**	**109**	**142**
Cows per Hectare	1.60	1.90	1.25	1.50
Forage Hectares (Acres) per Cow	0.63	0.53	0.80	0.67
	(1.54)	*(1.30)*	*(1.98)*	*(1.65)*
Gross Margin per Forage Hectare (Acre)	**121**	**198**	**136**	**213**
	(49)	*(80)*	*(55)*	*(86)*

1. *System*: Relates to performance per cycle. i.e. for the production period. Assumed 390 days average calving interval.

2. *Performance level:* relates to variations in both outputs and inputs.

3. *Value of Calves:* Assumed sale weights; spring calving = average 273kg, high 280kg, autumn calving = average 364kg, high 370kg. Calf sale ages; autumn calving = average 273 days average, 280 days high, autumn calving = average 364 days, high 370 days. Sale prices; £1.68/kg liveweight for average performance herds, £1.70/kg liveweight for high performance herds. Prices are average for steers and heifers. *Calves reared* per 100 cows mated: average 90, high 92.

4. *Assumptions.* Herd life: spring calving, 8 years; autumn calving, 7 years. Purchase price £1,300, average cull value £650. Calves purchased: average per 100 cows mated:

spring calving 2, autumn calving 3; at £190. Bull: purchase price £4,000, cull value £500; (one bull per 35 cows on average; 4-year herd life). Dairy cross beef cows have better fertility performance than continental pure bred cows, but lower cull sale prices.

5. *Misc*: *vet. & med.*: spring calving £25, autumn £28; bedding: spring calving £41, autumn £48; *miscellaneous*: spring calving = average £17, high £18, autumn calving = average £20, high £21. *Straw*: where yarded in winter, straw requirements average 0.75 tonnes per cow for spring calvers and 0.85 tonnes for autumn calvers.

6. *The Forage Area* includes both grazing and conserved grass (silage and hay). The higher stocking density implies better use of grassland. Higher stocking rates can also be achieved by buying in more of the winter bulk fodder requirements, or by winter feeding largely on arable by-products, including straw. Purchased bulk fodder and/or straw balancer concentrates will reduce gross margin per cow but increase gross margin per hectare.

7. *Headage Payment*: A payment is made in Scotland on three-quarter breed beef calves from Suckler Cows. Payments under the Scottish Beef Calf Scheme in 2010 were £52.19 per head (£104.37 per head for the first 10 calves claimed). 2011 rates will be determined at the end of the calendar (scheme) year.

Store Cattle

Maintenance / Keeping of Young Store Cattle **(per head) (1)**

	Summer Keeping	Winter Keeping
	£	£
Store Sales (2)	663	657
Less Purchased Store (incl. mortality) (3)	400	400
Output	**262**	**256**
Variable Costs:		
Concentrates	4	62 (4)
Other Variable Costs (5)	18	67
Total Variable Costs (excluding Forage)	**22**	**129**
Gross Margin per Head, before		
deducting Forage Variable Costs	240	127
Forage Variable Costs	36	14 (6)
Gross Margin per Head	**204**	**114**
Animals per Hectare	5.75	
Forage Hectares (Acres) per Head	0.17	
	(0.43)	
Gross Margin per Forage Hectare (Acre)	**1,172**	
	(474)	

1. *System*: Buying dairy cross steers and heifers at 6 months old for keeping / rearing. Animals spend a further 6 months in system before sale / transfer to a finishing enterprise.

2. *Sales*: 402kg liveweight @ £1.65/kg for summer finishing, 398kg liveweight @ £1.65/kg for winter finishing.

3. *Purchases*: Both systems 245kg purchase weight @ £1.65, plus 1% mortality.

4. *Concentrates*: 270kg concentrates @ £230 per tonne.

5. *Variable Costs*: Summer finishing = *vet. & med.* £9, misc. £9; winter finishing = vet. & med. £11, *straw* £44, *misc.* £12.

6. *Forage Costs*: Based on 2.9 tonnes per head grass silage consumption. Only silage variable costs are considered and therefore overhead costs of silage production need to be considered. Similarly, bought in silage will significantly increase the forage costs over those shown.

Finishing Cattle

Finishing of Dairy Bred Store Cattle (per head) (1)

	Summer Finishing	Winter Finishing
	£	£
Finished Sales (2)	1,016	1,027
Less Purchased Store (incl. mortality) (3)	663	669
Output	**352**	**358**
Variable Costs:		
Concentrates	27	152 (4)
Other Variable Costs (5)	42	96
Total Variable Costs (excluding Forage)	**69**	**247**
Gross Margin per Head, before		
deducting Forage Variable Costs	283	110
Forage Variable Costs	54	18 (6)
Gross Margin per Head	**230**	**93**
Animals per Hectare	4.00	
Forage Hectares (Acres) per Head	0.25	
	(0.62)	
Gross Margin per Forage Hectare (Acre)	**919**	
	(372)	

1. *System*: Finishing of dairy bred store cattle (as shown in previous margin – *summer finishing cattle will have been winter stores and vice versa*). Purchased / transferred in at 12 months old and finished over 7 months (210 days for summer finishing, 220 days winter finishing). Summer finishing takes place entirely out at pasture whilst winter finishing is a housed system or the production period.

2. *Sales*: Finished sale weights of 598kg liveweight for summer finishing and 604kg liveweight for winter finishing. Sale price of £1.70/kg in both systems.

3. *Purchases*: Purchase / transfer in weight of 398kg and 402kg for summer and winter finishing respectively. Cost in both cases £1.65/kg plus 1% mortality allowance.

4. *Concentrates:* 660kg concentrate @ £230 per tonne.

5. *Variable Costs*: Summer finishing = vet. & med. £9, misc. £33, winter finishing = *vet. & med.* £17, *straw* @ £39, *misc.* £40.

6. *Forage Costs*: Based on 3.7 tonnes per head grass silage consumption. Only silage variable costs are considered and therefore overhead costs of silage production need to be considered. Similarly, bought in silage will significantly increase the forage costs over those shown.

Finishing of Suckler Bred Store Cattle (per head) (1)

	Summer Finishing	Winter Finihsing
	£	£
Finished Sales (2)	1,093	985
Less Purchased Store (incl. mortality)	502	645
Output	**591**	**340**
Variable Costs:		
Concentrates (3)	59	124
Other Variable Costs (4)	45	103
Total Variable Costs (excluding Forage)	**104**	**227**
Gross Margin per Head, before		
deducting Forage Variable Costs	487	113
Forage Variable Costs	47	16 (5)
Gross Margin per Head	**440**	**96**
Animals per Hectare	4.20	
Forage Hectares (Acres) per Head	0.24	
	(0.59)	
Gross Margin per Forage Hectare (Acre)	**1,849**	
	(748)	

1. *System*: Beef suckler progeny purchased / transferred in at 8 months old for summer finishing and 12 months old for winter finishing (*summer finishing cattle will be from spring calving suckler cows and winter finishers from autumn calving suckler cows*). Summer finishers = 300 days in system, winter finishers = 180 days in system.

2. *Sales*: Summer finishing 639kg liveweight, winter finishing 576kg liveweight. Sale price of £1.71/kg in both systems.

3. *Concentrates*: Summer finishers consuming 255kg, winter finishers 540kg. Concentrate price of £230 per tonne.

4. *Variable Costs*: Summer finishing = *vet. & med.* £9, *misc.* £36, winter finishing = *vet. & med.* £17, straw @ £44, *misc.* £42.

5. *Forage Costs*: Based on 3.4 tonnes per head grass silage consumption. Only silage variable costs are considered and therefore overhead costs of silage production need to be considered. Similarly, bought in silage will significantly increase the forage costs over those shown.

Maize & Grass Silage Beef Finishing **(per Head Produced)**

System (1)	*Dairy X Progeny*		*Suckler Progeny*	
Performance Level	Average	High	Average	High
	£	£	£	£
Finished Sales (2)	1,112	1,206	1,110	1,221
Less Purchased Store (incl. mortality) (3)	400	400	465	514
Output	**712**	**806**	**645**	**707**
Variable Costs:				
Concentrates (4)	151	143	98	91
Misc Variable Costs (5)	90	92	97	99
Total Variable Costs (excl. Forage)	**241**	**234**	**195**	**190**
Gross Margin per Head, before				
deducting Forage Variable Costs	471	572	450	517
Forage Cost (6)	90	81	84	76
Gross Margin per Head	**381**	**491**	**366**	**441**

1. *System*: An intensive finishing system utilising a housed forage based system of grass silage and maize silage with heavy finished weights. Dairy cross progeny purchased transferred at 6 months old and suckler progeny at 8 months old. Dairy cross finishing period of 365 days and suckler progeny at 305 days. The gross margins are higher than in other finishing enterprises but overhead costs (fixed costs) will also be high in comparison.

2. *Sales*: Dairy cross = average 647kg liveweight @ £1.72/kg, high 701kg liveweight @ £1.72/kg. Suckler progeny = average 658kg liveweight @ £1.72/kg, high 718kg liveweight @ £1.73/kg.

3. *Mortality*: 1% mortality assumed.

4. *Concentrates*: Dairy cross = average 657kg, high 621kg, suckler progeny = average 427kg, high 397kg. Concentrates @ £230 per tonne.

5. *Variable Costs*: Miscellaneous costs assumed to be proportionally higher than the store and suckler finishing enterprises shown previously. Assumed 6% premium for average performance and 4% for high performance.

6. *Forage Costs*: Based on silage intakes of; Dairy cross = average 1.90 tonnes maize silage and 1.85 tonnes grass silage, high 1.70 tonnes maize silage, 1.70 tonnes grass silage. Suckler progeny = average 1.80 tonnes maize silage and 1.70 tonnes grass silage, high 1.62 tonnes maize silage, 1.50 tonnes grass silage. The silage costs relate to the total operational cost of growing and harvesting the forage, but not the costs incurred in preparing/mixing rations. Bought in silage will increase the forage costs over those shown.

Cereal Bull Beef (**per Head**)

System (1)	Continental Cross Holstein/Friesian Bulls		Holstein Friesian Bulls	
Performance Level	Average	High	Average	High
	£	£	£	£
Finished Sales (2)	853	910	784	865
Less Calf Purchase (3)	214	213	51	51
Output	**639**	**697**	**733**	**814**
Variable Costs:				
Concentrates (4)	444	430	444	430
Other Feed	18	17	18	17
Other Variable Costs (5)	112	110	112	110
Total Variable Costs	**573**	**557**	**573**	**557**
Gross Margin per Head	**66**	**140**	**160**	**258**

1. A traditional cereal based system for finishing cattle. Animals are housed throughout the production period and fed on a barley concentrate and straw based ration. Production period typically from 2 weeks old to 14 months old.

2. *Sales:* Cont cross bulls = average 530kg, high 555kg; Dairy bulls, average 475kg, high 515kg. Prices: Cont cross bulls, average £1.61/kg liveweight, high £1.64/kg liveweight; Dairy bulls, average £1.65/kg, high £1.68/kg. All year round production is assumed. Average slaughter age is 15 months, with killing out percentages ranging from 54% to 59%, with the better conformation continental cross bulls achieving higher percentages.

2. *Purchases:* £210 for continental cross male calves at 3 weeks of age including mortality; £50 for dairy bulls including mortality. Mortality, average 2%, high 1.5%.

3. *Concentrates:* £96 calf rearing (to 12 weeks: see page 54) + finishing ration. Finishing ration: 17 parts barley @ £130 per tonne, 3 parts concentrate supplement @ £230 per tonne; plus £12 per tonne milling and mixing cost. Total, £157 per tonne.

    Barley ration quantity; average 2,225kg, high 2,140kg (excluding calf feed to 12 weeks – see page 54).

    Margins are very sensitive to calf price and feed price movements. A £10 per tonne feed price movement equates to a margin change of £22 per head.

4. *Variable Costs:* Veterinary and medicine = average £18, high £16, Straw = average and high £50, miscellaneous = average and high £44.

Veal

Veal consumption is very low in the UK - only a small fraction of the per capita consumption in France for example. Continental demand is mainly for white veal, produced in individual veal crates, a system that is illegal in the UK. There is no live calf export activity from the UK to the continent for veal production owing to animal welfare concerns and the risk of spreading Bovine Tb.

There is some activity in UK 'welfare friendly' domestic veal production where calves are kept in groups in straw yards producing heavier calves with 'pink' meat known as 'Rose Veal'. This is a premium product and is considerably more expensive than imported 'white veal'.

SHEEP

Spring Lambing Flocks

Lowland Spring Lambing per Ewe (selling lambs off grass)

Performance Level	Low	Average	High
Lambs Reared per Ewe put to Ram (1)	1.30	1.57	1.74
Finished Lamb Liveweight (kg)		41.0	
Finished Lamb Liveweight Price (£/kg)		1.82	
Store Lamb Price (£/head)		58.0	
Average Price per Lamb (£) (2)	68.6	72.1	75.6
Sales:	£	£	£
Lamb sales...	89	113	131
Wool (3)...	2.5	2.5	2.5
Cull Ewes and Rams (4)..................	13.2	13.2	13.2
Sub Total	104.7	128.7	147.2
Less Ewe and Ram Replacements (4)	35.2	35.2	35.2
Output per Ewe	**69.5**	**93.4**	**111.9**
Variable Costs:			
Concentrates (54kg ewes, 8kg lambs) (5)	18.9	14.0	11.2
Vet and Med (6).............................	9.9	10.4	12.5
Miscellaneous (7)...........................	14.4	14.4	14.4
Total Variable Costs (excluding Forage)	**43.17**	**38.8**	**38.07**
Gross Margin per Ewe, before			
deducting Forage Variable Costs	**26.3**	**54.6**	**73.9**
Forage Variable Costs (inc bought-in			
Forage and Keep) (8)	10.2	12.9	17.4
Gross Margin per Ewe	**16.1**	**41.7**	**56.4**
Stocking Rate (Ewes with Lambs per forage			
Hectare (acre))	8 (3.0)	10 (4.0)	11 (4.5)
Gross Margin per Forage Hectare	121	417	621
Gross Margin per Forage Acre	49	169	251

1. *Rearing Performance Data:*

	Low	Average	High
Ewes in Lamb	90%	93%	95%
Lambing Percentage	160%	185%	201%
Lambs born /100 ewes	144	172	191
Young Lamb Deaths	6%	5%	5%
Older Lamb Deaths	4%	4%	4%
Total Lamb Losses	10%	9%	9%
Lambs sold / 100 ewes put to ram	130	157	174

These performance figures are assumed for flocks of mature ewes, i.e. shearlings and older. Where ewe lambs or mainly shearlings are included in flock performance adjustment needs to be made. The breed will obviously have a large effect on lambing percentage, liveweight gains and carcase grades.

2. *Lamb Prices.* Prices for lambs sold for slaughter are based on the forecast for the 2012 season and assumes a continuation of the robust EU export market without restrictions.

An average market price of £1.82/kg liveweight (equivalent to £3.95/kg deadweight) has been used giving £74.62 per finished lamb at an average liveweight of 41kg.

The average budgeted price in the table above allows for 15% sold as stores. Store price is assumed at £58 per head. Low performance is £3.50 a lamb less, high £3.50 per lamb more for variations caused by differences in weights, time of marketing and proportion sold finished or retained as stores.

3. *Wool*: The wool price has improved year on year from 2009. Reasonable, clean wool yields now mean that a small margin can be made over the cost of shearing. Budget price assumed for lowland flocks is £2.50 per ewe, based on a price of £1.40/kg at 1.8kg/ewe. Variations between flocks will occur due to ewe breed affecting wool quality and ewe size affecting weight of wool produced.

4. *Flock Depreciation:* (i.e. Market price of replacements less value of culls). It is assumed that 19% of the ewe flock is culled each year @ £68 each and that, allowing for 4% mortality, 23% are purchased or home-reared at £140 each. Rams: 1 per 45 ewes, 3.5 year life, purchased @ £480, sold @ £50. The net cost (flock depreciation) is £22 per ewe per year. *Cull ewe prices vary considerably depending on the weight and 'fleshiness' of the ewes. Cull values tend to be highly variable but remain high, partly at least through a strong, consistent demand from the UK ethnic sector. No other changes in flock valuation are assumed.*

5. *Concentrate Feeding*: Concentrate finishing of late season lambs has been common, but there has been a swing to sell as stores (for finishing on winter forage crops) rather than finish on high cost concentrates. Late season grass availability influences the store trade.

6. *Veterinary and Medicine:* includes allowance for wormer (ewes and lambs), vaccines, fly strike chemicals and foot treatments.

7. *Miscellaneous Costs:* include contract shearing @ £1.25/ewe, scanning £0.75/ewe and ewe and lamb tags £1.40/ewe (assuming slaughter batch tags are used), carcase disposal £2.00/ewe, straw £1.45/ewe, minerals and licks etc £1.45/ewe, marketing, levy and transport £6.10/ewe.

8. *Forage Costs*: Based on intensity of grassland. Only variable costs are considered and therefore overhead costs of forage production need to be considered. Similarly, bought in grass keep and forage may increase the forage costs over those shown.

9. *Other Costs:*

    a.   *Prices of Specialised Equipment*

Troughs (2.75 m)	£35 to £55
Racks (2 to 3 m)	£200 to £225
Foot Baths (3 m)	£100 to £150
Shearing Machines	£450 to £950
Lamb Creep Feeders	£350 to £750
Weigh Crate	£475 to £750
Mobile Handling System	£2,500 to £8,500

    b.   *Fencing:* Approximately £5.75 per metre *for posts, sheep netting, 2 strands of barbed wired and labour inclusive.*

    c.   *Labour*: see page 157.

Upland Spring Lambing per Ewe (**selling lambs off grass**)

Performance Level	Low	Average	High
Lambs Reared per Ewe put to Ram (1)	1.24	1.42	1.61
Finished Lamb Liveweight (kg)		39.0	
Finished Lamb Liveweight Price (£/kg)		1.75	
Store Lamb Price (£/head)		50.0	
Average Price per Lamb (£) (2)	61.6	65.1	68.6
Sales:	£	£	£
Lamb sales...	76.3	92.7	110.3
Wool (3)..	2.4	2.4	2.4
Cull Ewes and Rams (4)..................	11.7	11.7	11.7
Sub Total	90.4	106.8	124.4
Less Ewe and Ram Replacements (4)	35.2	35.2	35.2
Output per Ewe	**55.1**	**71.6**	**89.1**
Variable Costs:			
Concentrates (55kg ewes, 10kg lambs) (5)	19.81	14.7	11.74
Vet and Med (6).............................	9.12	9.6	11.52
Miscellaneous (7)...........................	13.05	13.1	13.05
Total Variable Costs (excluding Forage)	**41.98**	**37.3**	**36.31**
Gross Margin per Ewe, before			
deducting Forage Variable Costs	**13.1**	**34.3**	**52.8**
Forage Variable Costs (inc bought-in			
Forage and Keep) (8)	9.7	11.1	14.2
Gross Margin per Ewe	**3.4**	**23.2**	**38.6**
Stocking Rate (Ewes with Lambs per forage			
Hectare (acre))	4 (1.5)	9 (3.4)	10 (4.0)
Gross Margin per Forage Hectare	13	197	386
Gross Margin per Forage Acre	5	80	156

1. *Rearing Performance Data*:

	Low	Average	High
Ewes in Lamb	90%	93%	95%
Lambing Percentage	158%	172%	190%
Lambs born /100 ewes	142.2	159.96	180.5
Young Lamb Deaths	8%	6%	6%
Older Lamb Deaths	5%	5%	5%
Total Lamb Losses	13%	11%	11%
Lambs sold / 100 ewes put to ram	124	142	161

These performance figures are assumed for flocks of mature ewes, i.e. shearlings and older. Where ewe lambs or mainly shearlings are included in flock performance adjustment needs to be made. The breed will obviously have a large effect on lambing percentage, liveweight gains and carcase grades.

2. *Lamb Prices*. Prices for lambs sold for slaughter are based on the forecast for the 2012 season and assumes a continuation of the robust EU export market without restrictions (and therefore a continuation of the autumn 2011 euro to sterling exchange rate).

An average market price of £1.75/kg liveweight (equivalent to £3.80/kg deadweight) has been assumed giving £68.25 per finished lamb at an average liveweight of 39kg.

The average budgeted price in the table above allows for 17% sold as stores. Store price is assumed at £50 per head. Low performance is £3.50 a lamb less, high £3.50 per lamb more for variations caused by differences in weights, time of marketing and proportion sold finished or retained as stores.

3. *Wool*: The wool price has improved year on year from 2009. Reasonable, clean wool yields now mean that a small margin can be made over the cost of shearing. Budget price assumed for lowland flocks is £2.40 per ewe, based on a price of £1.40/kg at 1.7kg/ewe. Variations between flocks will occur due to ewe breed affecting wool quality and ewe size affecting weight of wool produced.

4. *Flock Depreciation:* (i.e. Market price of replacements less value of culls). It is assumed that 19% of the ewe flock is culled each year @ £60 each and that, allowing for 4% mortality, 23% are purchased or home-reared at £140 each. Rams: 1 per 45 ewes, 3.5 year life, purchased @ £480, sold @ £50. The net cost (flock depreciation) is £23.50 per ewe per year. *Cull ewe prices vary considerably depending on the weight and 'fleshiness' of the ewes. Cull values tend to be highly variable but remain high, partly at least through a strong, consistent demand from the UK ethnic sector. No other changes in flock valuation are assumed.*

5. *Concentrate Feeding*: Concentrate finishing of late season lambs has been common, but there has been a swing to sell as stores (for finishing on winter forage crops) rather than finish on high cost concentrates. Late season grass availability influences the store trade.

6. *Veterinary and Medicine:* includes allowance for wormer (ewes and lambs), vaccines, fly strike chemicals and foot treatments.

7. *Miscellaneous Costs:* include contract shearing @ £1.25/ewe, scanning £0.75/ewe and ewe and lamb tags £1.40/ewe (assuming slaughter batch tags are used), carcase disposal £2.00/ewe, straw £1.35/ewe, minerals and licks etc £1.45/ewe, marketing, levy and transport £4.85/ewe.

8. *Forage Costs*: Based on intensity of grassland. Only variable costs are considered and therefore overhead costs of forage production need to be considered. Similarly, bought in grass keep and forage may increase the forage costs over those shown.

Rearing Ewe Lambs

Purchasing ewe lambs and rearing over winter & summer for breeding

Sales:	£ Per Ewe
Sale Price / Transfer Value	140.00
Wool	2.10
Sub Total	142.10
Less Purchase Price / Transfer Value (2)	90.00
Losses & Culling (3)	3.75
Output per Ewe	**48.35**
Variable Costs:	
Vet and Med (4)............................	7.90
Miscellaneous (5)..........................	4.85
Total Variable Costs (excluding Forage)	**12.75**
Gross Margin per Ewe, before	
deducting Forage Variable Costs	**35.60**
Forage Variable Costs (inc bought-in	
Forage and Keep) (6)	7.53
Gross Margin per Ewe	**28.07**
Stocking Rate (Ewe lambs per forage	
Hectare (acre))	12.5 (5.1)
Gross Margin per Forage Hectare	351
Gross Margin per Forage Acre	142

1. *System:* Involves rearing or purchasing ewe lambs suitable for further breeding. Animals are purchased / transferred in late summer / autumn, grazed and outwintered, grazed on in the following summer before sale / transfer out in the autumn (i.e. 12 month system). *The terminology for this system varies between regions; gimmers, thieves, shearlings and tegs all relate to the same age of female sheep.*

2. *Purchase Price*: Assumes better quality ewe lambs are acquired @ £90 per lamb.

3. *Losses and Culls:* 3% losses and 3% culled (for meat) @ £85 as unsuitable for breeding.

4. *Veterinary and Medicine*: includes wormer, fly strike chemicals, vaccines and miscellaneous treatments.

5. *Miscellaneous Costs*: Shearing @ £1.25/head, minerals @ £1.60/head, carcase disposal @ £2/head

6. *Forage Costs*: Based on low intensity of grassland. Only variable costs are considered and therefore overhead costs of forage production need to be considered. Similarly, bought in grass keep and forage may increase the forage cost over that shown.

Finishing Store Lambs

Purchasing store lambs and finishing late autumn & winter

Sales:	£ Per Lamb
Sale Price (1)	79.55
Less Purchase Price / Transfer In Value	52.00
Losses (2)	3.12
Output per Ewe	**24.43**
Variable Costs:	
Concentrates (3)	4.95
Vet and Med (4)..	3.80
Miscellaneous (5)..	8.75
Total Variable Costs (excluding Forage)	**12.55**
Gross Margin per Lamb, before	
deducting Forage Variable Costs	**11.88**
Forage Variable Costs (inc bought-in	
Forage and Keep) (6)	6.87
Gross Margin per Lamb	**5.01**
Stocking Rate (lambs per forage	
Hectare (acre))	28.0 (11.3)
Gross Margin per Forage Hectare	140
Gross Margin per Forage Acre	57

System: lambs are batch bought in the autumn at or shortly after weaning in September or October, then drawn out and sold as they are ready in smaller groups from then through to March the following year.

1. *Sales*: Assumes 43kg liveweight @ £1.85/kg.

2. *Losses*: assumed @ 6%.

3. *Concentrates:* 22kg per lamb @ £225 per tonne

4. *Veterinary and Medicine*: Allows for wormer, clostridial vaccines and miscellaneous treatments.

5. *Miscellaneous*: Including transport, marketing, minerals, carcase disposal.

6. *Forage Costs*: Based on very low cost winter grazing and a stubble turnip crop. Only variable costs are considered and therefore overhead costs of forage production need to be considered. Similarly, bought in grass keep and forage crops will increase the cost over that shown.

GRAZING AND REARING CHARGES: CATTLE AND SHEEP

Grazing charges vary greatly according to the quality of the pasture, access, fencing and infrastructure. Local supply and demand also affect the value of grazing charges. The following figures are typical (estimated for 2012):

Summer Grazing (per head per week)

Store Cattle and in-calf heifers over 21 months, dry cows, and fattening bullocks over 18 months.	£3.50 - £4.50
Heifers and Steers, 12-21 months	£2.50 - £3.50
6-12 months Cattle	£2.00 - £2.75
Cattle of mixed ages	£2.50 - £3.50
Ewes	50p - 60p

Winter Grazing (per head per week)

'Strong' Cattle	£2.25 - £3.50
Heifers	£2.00 - £3.00
Sheep.	40p - 50p

Note: the above figures assume the farmer on whose land the livestock are present does all the fencing and shepherding. Where the owner of the stock does the fencing, shepherding, etc., the figures may be halved, or be even less depending on local demand.

Grass Keep

Most typically around £86-£173/hectare (£35-£70/acre), with the best £185-£271 (£75-£110/acre) and lower quality keep making £50-£75 (£20-£30/acre).

These figures are highly variable, especially between one part of the country and another, and even between one parish and another. The charge can be very high where the pasture is good, the supply scarce and the demand strong. Good fencing, electricity supply, mains water etc adds a premium to grass keep as does the quality of grassland and any licensor fertiliser applications. Grazing may be offered to livestock keepers at very little or no charge where the need for maintainance of grassland is the driving factor (e.g. amentiy value, requirement to cross comply or meet Agri-environment scheme agreements, value of cattle and sheep to 'clean-up' pasture or to provide beneficial mixed grazing). The length of grazing period offered will also influence the premium of grass keep (e.g. grazing until 30th September or until 31st December) as will permission to take a grass crop from the land (hay, haylage, silage).

The Nitrate Vulnerable Zone (NVZ) rules in England has also increased demand for grass keep in some areas where dairy enterprises are commonplace – an additonal acreage may help some producers to keep within the livestock manure loading level.

Winter Keep (Cattle per head per week)

Grazing + 9 kg hay and some straw	£9.50
Full winter keep in yards	£8.50-£11.00
Calf rearing for beef (0 to 12 weeks or 0 to 6 months)	£12.00

A typical rental for labour, buildings and maintenance diet would be £8.50 per head per week. These rates apply where feed to achieve maintenance plus some growth is supplied plus labour and buildings and bedding where applicable. A typical rental for labour, buildings and a maintenance diet would be £6.50 per head per week.

Heifer Rearing Charges

There have historically been two types of arrangements:

1. Farmer X sells calf to Rearer at agreed price; the calf is then Rearer's responsibility and he pays for all expenses and bears any losses. Farmer X has first option on heifers, which he buys back two months before calving. Approximate price: £800 above cost of calf for Holstein Friesians. Rearer fetches calf; Farmer X supplies transport for heifer. *This system is now less common due to low interest rates cheapening borrowing enabling breeders to retain ownership of heifers throughout their life.*

2. Farmer X retains ownership of calf, but sends it to a specialist rearer. Approximate rearer charges range from 110 to 120 pence per head per day although may vary depending upon cattle, system and location. Usually the owner of the cattle is responsible for transport costs and the choice and cost of vaccine programmes. The cost of semen for artificial insemination of the heifers is usually incurred by the owner and paid for over and above the standard rearing charge. The rearer is responsible for all standard rearing costs including for normal veterinary services and worming etc. and any animal losses (unless due to Tb or Bluetongue). *Model agreements are available from industry associations and advisors.*

Contract rearing on behalf of a third party may appeal to some producers who wish to reduce borrowing exposure and / or lower capital investment in a business. A well laid out contract rearing arrangement will also provide greater cost and income clarity to both the rearer and owner and therefore reduce the risk exposure to both businesses. It also enables each business to focus and specialise to achieve optimum performance without being distracted by other enterprises. Biosecurity issues are becoming increasingly paramount where an agreement is set up. In many cases the owner of heifers will require exclusive occupancy of a rearer's farm without cattle owned by the rearer or others being present.

RED DEER

A. Breeding and Finishing	Per 100 Hinds
Sales:	£
45 Stags (15-18 months) : 55kg dw @ £4.50/kg...................	11,138
35 Hinds (15-18 months) : 45kg dw @ £4.50/kg	7,088
8 Cull Hinds @ £130..	1,040
Average Annual Value of Cull Stags....................................	100
Less Average Annual Cost of Replacement Stags...........................	200
Output	**19,165**
Variable Costs:	
Concentrates @ 4.0 tonnes @ £220/tonne............................	880
Vet and Med...	484
Miscellaneous..	400
Total Variable Costs	**1,764**
Gross Margin before deducting Forage Costs	**17,401**
Forage Variable Costs (5.5 Hinds per hectare @ £0/ha).................	2,853
Gross Margin per 100 Hinds...	**14,548**
Gross Margin per Forage hectare (5.5 hinds/ha)........................	800
Gross Margin per Forage acre (2.2 hinds/ac).............................	324

B. Selling Store Calves to Finishers	Per 100 Hinds
Sales:	£
45 Stag Calves @ £120/head (45 kg liveweight)...................	5,400
35 Hind Calves @ £110/head (40 kg liveweight)...................	3,850
8 Cull Hinds @ £130...	1,040
Average Annual Value of Cull Stags.....................................	100
Less Average Annual Cost of Replacement Stags........................	200
Output	**10,190**
Variable Costs:	
Concentrates @ 1.3 tonnes @ £220/tonne.............................	286
Vet and Med...	279
Miscellaneous...	200
Total Variable Costs	**765**
Gross Margin before deducting Forage Costs...............................	**9,425**
Forage Variable Costs (6.5 Hinds per hectare @ £0/ha).................	2,414
Gross Margin per 100 Hinds...	**7,011**
Gross Margin per Forage hectare (6.5 hinds/ha)........................	456
Gross Margin per Forage acre (2.6 hinds/ac).............................	184

Lowland systems assumed. Hind replacements home-reared in systems A and B.

Herd Life: hinds, 12 years; stags, 6 years; 33 hinds per stag. Calves reared per 100 hinds: 90. Purchase price of breeding stock (good quality): hinds £350 plus, yearling hinds £275 plus, stags £500 plus.

C. Finishing Stag Calves

	Per 200 Stags
Sales:	£
195 Stags (15-18 months) : 55kg dw @ £4.50/kg.................	48,263
Less Purchases : 200 @ £120 per head..	24,000
Output	**24,263**
Variable Costs:	
Concentrates @ 12.0 tonnes @ £220/tonne............................	2,640
Vet and Med...	600
Miscellaneous..	975
Total Variable Costs	**4,215**
Gross Margin before deducting Forage Costs..............................	**20,048**
Forage Variable Costs (11.0 Stags per hectare @ £0/ha)................	0
Gross Margin per 200 Stags...	**20,048**
Gross Margin per Forage hectare (11 stags/ha).........................	1,103
Gross Margin per Forage acre (4.5 stags/ac)..............................	446

The venison prices reflect projected sales for 2011 to wholesale buyers. Higher prices will be obtained for direct sales to consumers (e.g. farm shops and farmers' markets) and caterers, but extra costs will normally be incurred.

D. Deer Park

	Per 300 Hinds
Sales:	£
120 Stags (15-18 months) : 55kg dw @ £4.00/kg.................	26,400
110 Hinds (15-18 months) : 50kg dw @ £4.00/kg.................	22,000
5 Cull Hinds @ £210..	1,050
5 Live Stag Sales @ £1,000.....................................	5,000
Output	**54,450**
Variable Costs:	
Concentrates @ 12.0 tonnes @ £220/tonne............................	2,640
Vet and Med...	500
Miscellaneous...	300
Total Variable Costs	**3,440**
Gross Margin before deducting Forage Costs	**51,010**
Forage Variable Costs (3.0 Hinds per hectare @ £101/ha).............	10,100
Gross Margin per 300 Hinds...	**40,910**
Gross Margin per Forage hectare (3 hinds/ha)............................	409
Gross Margin per Forage acre (1.2 hinds/ac)..............................	166

Sales are based on skin-on carcases bought by a game dealer/butcher.

Forage costs include 200 bales of silage and grass costs.

Sources of further information: The British Deer Farmers Association, PO Box 7522, Matlock, DE4 9BR Tel: 08456 344 758 www.bdfa.co.uk

Acknowledgements: Thanks to - Ali Loder, Strathdon Deer www.strathdondeer.co.uk; Nigel Sampson, Holme Farmed Venison www.hfv.co.uk

HORSES: LIVERY

The horse industry is now reported to be the second biggest employer in the rural economy. Prior to the economic downturn it was also one of the fastest growing. Over the last 3 years growth is unquantified but anecdotal evidence suggests that the horse population has been static. Although there are other equine enterprises that farm businesses can operate, by far the most common is providing accommodation for horses; i.e. livery. There are many different forms of livery and the charges, therefore, vary widely also. This is apart from the effects of local supply and demand, which can lead to large price differences from one area to another. However, three fairly standard forms are offered on farms:

Grass Livery. Keep at grass, preferably with shelter, water supply and secure area to keep tack and store feed. Some grass livery will provide an exercise arena and off-road riding. Charges average £30 per week; range £20-£50.

DIY Livery. The owner still has full care of the horse but has the facilities of a stable, grazing, and in some cases an all-weather exercise arena. The owner is responsible for mucking out, turning out, grooming, exercising and all vet./med. care and the cost of all feed and bedding. Charges average £40 per week; range £25-£55.

DIY Plus Livery. As the above, except that the yard manager is responsible for certain tasks, such as turning out and feeding. Charges average £45 per week; range £30-£60.

In addition there is *Full Livery.* The yard supplies a complete service to the horse owner including tasks such as grooming and exercise. Services provided by the yard may be fitted to the needs of a horse/owner. Few farm-based liveries would offer such a high level of management. Full livery charges average £120 per week; with a range of £80-£160.

The above are only guidelines. There is a wide variation both within, and between regions.

Other Costs:

Grazing. Variable costs will average some £55 per horse per year. Average stocking rates are 0·8 ha (2 acres) for the first horse and 0·4 ha (1 acre) for each horse after.

Hay. Average price £4.00 per conventional bale (approximately 20kg) (range £3-£6.00), depending on the season. It has to be good quality. Average consumption is one to two bales per horse per week; less in the summer depending on the grass quality/quantity and the work of the horse. Some horses now have haylage; more expensive, dust free and higher fibre and energy/protein levels; less required per head.

Concentrate Feed. Can range from almost nil to 3.0-4.0kg per day depending, amongst other factors, on breed, size and intensity of work. Compound feed 30 to 45p per kg.

Bedding. Averages around £8 per stabled horse per week, with some horses stabled year round and others having significant turnout in the summer, which reduces bedding cost. Typical cost £300-£400 per year. Straw might cost only half as much; however, more expensive, but preferable, alternatives (such as wood shavings, shredded paper and hemp fibre) are now increasingly being used.

Vet. and Med. Averages approximately £160 per horse per year. Some yards include worming of the horse in the livery cost.

Rates. Livery is a non-agricultural use, and therefore any buildings being used for the enterprise are liable to business rates.

The supply of livery yards appears to be increasing, from both farms diversifying and other yards setting up. Filling a yard is, consequently, becoming more difficult. The level of service and facilities expected by customers has increased. There is a trend towards greater professionalism in the running and management of livery yards. Livery contracts should be exchanged showing clearly the responsibilities of each party. Comprehensive third party insurance is also important.

To be successful, a livery enterprise needs higher quality facilities than farm livestock. To the owner the horse can be anything from a highly trained athlete to a family pet. Horses are expensive: even modest quality horses cost between £1,500 and £3,000. Good customer relations and an effective security system (including burglar and fire alarms) are crucial to success, as is good market research and effective advertising.

A full livery yard will require stables, a secure room to store tack, a vermin-proof hard feed store, storage for hay and bedding, a muck heap, a riding arena and parking provision with room for horse boxes. Planning permission is required for the conversion of an existing building to stabling or the erection of new, purpose-built stables. Permission is also required for construction of an all weather arena used for training horses and exercising them in bad weather. Hay and straw should be stored away from the stables and downwind of them to minimise the fire risk. A hard standing area with a water supply and good drainage should be provided for grooming and washing down the horses.

Good ventilation in the stables is crucial as horses are prone to respiratory diseases caused by spores and dust. Provision should be made for owners to soak hay in clean water before feeding it, to reduce respiratory problems.

Fences must be sound and free of protruding nails, wire etc. Ideally fields should be fenced using post and rail, but this is expensive. Barbed wire should be avoided wherever possible or should be 'protected' with an offset electrified fence. Fields should be divided into smaller paddocks to reduce the possibility of fighting between incompatible horses and to separate mares and geldings. Paddocks may be divided using two or more strands of electrified tape or rope but wire is not advisable as it is not easily visible to the horse.

Off-road riding opportunities on the farm are a real asset. The farmer may provide riding trails, a jumping paddock, or a cross country course. An all-weather ménage for exercising horses, possibly with floodlighting, is highly desirable, and some livery yards have horse walkers too. Good facilities can be rented out to individuals or organisations such as pony clubs. It is sometimes possible to link up with nearby farms to increase the length of riding tracks available.

Construction Costs. The cost of conversion of existing buildings will depend on their quality; prefabricated hardwood and steel internal stable partitions can be purchased from upwards of £900 per stable, depending on size and specification. Free standing timber stables cost between £1,000 and £2,000 (plus base), depending on size and quality. As horses are fairly destructive animals (they both kick and chew) better quality stables will often prove more economic in the long run. All weather arenas (20 metres by 40 metres) cost between £10,000 and £25,000; construction is a specialist job as good drainage is essential; a badly constructed arena is worthless.

Contact*:* Further financial information on horse enterprises, including riding schools and equestrian centres, is available in 'Equine Business Guide', 5th Edition, 2005, edited by Richard Bacon, Warwickshire College; Tel. 01926 318 338.

OSTRICHES

Introduction

Ostrich production was introduced to the UK during the 1990s. Today, production is limited to a few small farmers, working individually, selling most meat through farmers' markets and restaurants. There is minimal processing infrastructure in the UK. Slaughter is carried out under contract in, dedicated ostrich plants and red meat slaughter plants with a ratite (flightless bird) license.

Ostrich are produced primarily for their meat, with their skins (for leather), fat and feathers also providing revenue potential. Skins are generally sold in minimum numbers of 200 so it can require long-term storage to build up sufficient numbers.

Adult breeding stock are normally kept in trios of one male and two females, but pairs and colonies are not unusual. A trio will require about 0.2 ha (0.5 acre) well drained land for grazing and exercise: they must be able to run. A stout hedge or smooth wire fence of 1.7 metres high should surround the enclosure. Adult birds need shelter from wind and rain, and a dry floor on which to sleep. Domesticated ostrich are generally docile and easily handled.

The following provides production data and margins. There are two systems costed here, the production of chicks from trios, and fattening the chicks. More information can be downloaded from BDOA at: http://www.ostrich.org.uk/johnnix.htm.

Production

The table is a guide to two production systems, layers and fatteners:

Laying Bird Trios

Performance Level	Low	Medium	High
Eggs – per hen per year	55	65	80
Hatching - %	65%	75%	85%
Surviving Chicks - %	50%	70%	85%
Total Chicks per hen	18	34	58
Financial Data per Trio			
Sales:			
Chicks Per Year	36	68	116
Chick Income (1)	536	1024	1734
Output per Trio	**536**	**1024**	**1734**
Variable Costs:			
Concentrates (2).....................................	552	736	851
Miscellaneious (3)...............................	30	30	30
Bird Depreciation (4)..........................	93	93	93
Total Variable Costs	**675**	**859**	**974**
Gross Margin per Trio	**-139**	**164**	**760**
Stocking Rate 1 Trio per 0.2 ha			
Gross Margin per Ha	**-695**	**822**	**3798**

Notes:

1. *Chick Income:* Chicks sold out at £15 per head

2. *Concentrate feed:* £230/tonne. Low production birds eat 2.4 tonnes per trio, average = 3.2 and high production birds 3.7 tonnes/trio

3.   *Miscellaneous:* includes vet & med., forage etc.

4.   *Bird Depreciation costs:* replacement for a trio £1,400 over 15 year's productivity

Historically, skin was the ostrich's primary product. Now, meat is the highest value, especially if marketed into the restaurant sector. This clearly requires marketing expertise. Doubling meat yields and halving the time to reach slaughter transforms the economics as is shown below. Many systems involve a high cost building and fencing layout which should be taken into consideration with the economics of the gross margins shown here.

Slaughter Birds

Performance Level	Low	Average	High
Days to Slaughter	425	300	200
Sales:	£	£	£
Meat: (1)..	270	315	360
Value of Skin (2)................................	50	50	50
Less Day Old Chick (3)............................	15	15	15
Output per Bird	**305**	**350**	**395**
Variable Costs:			
Concentrates (4)...................................	188	174	104
Other Rearing Costs (5)......................	104	85	56
Slaughter, Processing etc.	75	75	75
Marketing	5	5	5
Total Variable Costs	**372**	**339**	**240**
Gross Margin per Bird	**-67**	**11**	**155**
Gross Margin per year per bird	**-58**	**13**	**284**

Notes:

1.   *Meat:* £9/kg, 30kg, 35kg and 40kg meat for low to high performance levels.

2.   *£50 per hide,*

3.   *Chicks* bought in at £15 each (see schedule above) but varies from £10 to £22

4.   *Concentrates:* Price of feed rises as performance rises (£240, £320 and £370/t) but consumption per bird falls from 2kg/day to 1.12kg/day.

5.   *Other Costs:* includes depreciation of site, vet. & med. and miscellaneous

Contact: British Domesticated Ostrich Association (BDOA), 33 Eden Grange, Little Corby, Carlisle, CA4 8QW. (Tel.: 01228 562 946); www.ostrich.org.uk

WILD BOAR

Wild Boar is farmed in the UK on about 50 farms, with a population of roughly 1,750 sows. They produce a firm dark meat with a characteristically 'gamey' flavour which is in demand particularly from the hotel and restaurant trade.

Wild Boar come under the Dangerous Wild Animals Act and farms must be licensed by the Local Authority. There is no uniformity of fee or conditions to be met, but typically licences cost £100-£150 and are renewed annually following a farm inspection. Enclosures must be secure with strong fencing: a minimum height of at least 1.8m is usually specified and most authorities require 30-80cm below ground plus an additional strand of electric fence inside the main fence. The estimated minimum cost of fencing using approved contractors is from £13.00 per metre erected plus the hire of a digger. All gates and access areas must be kept padlocked.

Wild Boars live in groups of up to 10 sows per boar. They are nearly always kept outdoors, often on arable land (as outdoor domestic pigs), although rough land with natural vegetation, such as scrub, or best of all, woodland, is ideal and require basic housing, such as arcs. Large arcs are suitable for a group of gestating sows, or sows running with maturing boarlets. Sows should have access to an individual shelter for farrowing and the first few days of lactation. If good vegetation is available sows may make their own farrowing nest away from the main group with satisfactory results.

Stocking rates vary according to land type but about a hectare would be needed for 5 sows and a boar. They forage but need additional balanced ration (additive free pig concentrate is suitable but specially formulated feeds are available) with supplementary vegetable material. Root crops may replace some concentrate. Wild boar mate and farrow naturally and have few health problems, so little if any intervention is needed. Gilts mature at 18 months. In the wild breeding occurs in the autumn and early winter and the sows farrow from February to March after 4 months gestation. Farmed sows can give two litters in most years. Young sows produce 2 to 3 boarlets and mature sows 6 to 8. A well-run enterprise should average 7 boarlets per sow per year raised to maturity. Wild boar can live from 12 to 15 years, but in a commercial herd the sows are usually culled at 7 to 8 years.

Boarlets remain in the family group until they are all weaned together at 8 to 12 weeks (16 at the outside). Although some (usually smaller) producers leave growers to mature in family groups, they are generally separated into grower/finisher groups on grass or in open barns. Wild boars take 9 to 18 months to reach a slaughter weight of 75-85 kg. This produces a 45-50 kg carcase. The carcase has more shoulder and less hind-quarter than a domestic pig. It can be butchered like a domestic pig or without the skin like venison. The meat from male animals 2 years old or over is too strong, except for sausages, but sows up to 8 years old still have an acceptable carcase and a good cull value. Abattoirs need to have wild boar specified on their licence and many expect them to be difficult to handle.

Labour requirements are low, owing to the 'hands off' nature of wild boar management. One person should manage a herd of 30-40 sows plus fatteners.

In spite of the large and apparently unsatisfied demand for wild boar meat, as with other alternative enterprises, there is no organised marketing system and producers have to develop their own outlets. There are some wholesale butchers and game dealers who will take whole carcases in significant numbers, but many producers organise their own processing into a variety of pre-packed products and arrange their own retailing. Wild boar production can be successful both as a secondary enterprise on a farm or as a stand-alone operation.

Wild Boar Gross Margin

Finished Boarlets per Sow per Year......................................	7 (6 - 9)
Finished Carcase Weight (over 15 months)...........................	45 - 50 kg
Price per kg deadweight..	£3.00 - £4.50

Sales:	£
Meat sales per Sow per Year...	1,247
Less Depreciation per Sow per Year (1)......................................	30
Output per Sow	**1,217**

Variable Costs:	
Concentrates sow (2)...	205
fatteners (@ £72 each).................................	504
Bedding..	11
Vet, Med and Licence.......................................	31
Miscellaneous (inc. Water and Electricity)...........................	11
Total Variable Costs per Sow	**762**
Gross Margin per Sow	**455**

1. Cost of sow £400, cull value £200, herd life 7 years, plus share of boar
2. Including share of boar

Capital Costs *Housing and fencing - £4,000 per hectare (£1,620 per acre); pure-bred boar - £300-£600; pure-bred sow - £250-£500.*

Acknowledgement: Thanks to - Dr Martin Goulding www.britishwildboar.org.uk

GOAT DAIRYING

Performance Level	Low	Average	High
Milk Yield (litres) per Goat (1)	500	800	1,200
Sales:	£	£	£
Milk Value (2).....................................	200.0	320.0	480.0
Value of Kids (3)................................	2.8	3.6	3.6
Less Livestock Depreciation (4).................	27.7	27.7	27.7
Output per doe	**175.1**	**295.9**	**455.9**
Variable Costs:			
Concentrates (5)...................................	63.3	101.2	151.8
Miscellaneous (inc. Vet and Med).......	55.0	55.0	55.0
Forage Variable Costs (6)...................	54.0	86.4	129.6
Total Variable Costs	**172.3**	**242.6**	**336.4**
Gross Margin per Doe	**2.9**	**53.3**	**119.5**
Stocking Rate (Goats per Forage Hectare (acre) - zero-grazed system).................	6.5 (2.6)	8.0 (3.2)	9.5 (3.8)
Gross Margin per Forage Hectare..............	19	427	1,135
Gross Margin per Forage Acre...................	8	173	459

1. *Yield:* Per 300 day lactation, kidding each year. Autumn kidders tend to yield less.

2. *Price:* 40p per litre; seasonal variation from 33p in June to 53p in November. 12.5% solids delivered.

3. *Kid(s):* Prolificacy relates to age, breed, seasonality and feed level. Assumptions: low 140%; average and high 180%. There is very little trade in kids for meat (£2 per kid assumed).

4. *Culls and Replacements:* Replacements at £180/head; culls £17.50, average life 6 years. Bucks: 1 per 40-50 does. Does normally mate in autumn; gestation 150 days; young goats can be mated from 6 months.

5. *Concentrates:* Average 0.55 kg concentrate per litre, at £230 per tonne.

6. *Forage:* Average 0.9 kg DM forage per litre at £95 per tonne DM (part purchased, part home-grown). Goats can be grazed but are normally storage fed to avoid problems with worms, fencing, milk taints and pneumonia. Farmers able to produce maize silage will have a better forage conversion ratio.

7. *Miscellaneous:* Bedding £12, vet and med. £24 (includes treatment for out-of-season breeding, vaccination against Johnes and humane disposal of unsaleable kids), sundries £19.

8. *Stocking rate:* Based on home-grown forage.

9. *Labour:* 1 full-time person per 100 goats is a guide, but very dependent on technology employed.

10. *Markets:* Herd sizes in the UK range from 50 to 3,000 milking does. Average herd size is growing as established producers expand with the market at about 15% average annual growth. Successful businesses have been built on producer processing and retailing, as bulk purchasers of goats milk are few and far between. Prolificacy and technical improvements allow higher annual growth than the market and there is a cycle in milk and stock prices.

Contact: *The British Goat Society* www.allgoats.com registers pedigree animals and publishes a monthly newsletter.

Acknowledgements: The above information originally supplied by *Dr. T. Mottram*, Silsoe Research Institute, Bedford MK45 4HS, amended since by the author.

SHEEP DAIRYING

Performance Level	Low	Average	High
Milk Yield (litres) per Ewe per Year	225	375	450
Sales:	£	£	£
Milk Value (1)...............................	202.5	337.5	405.0
Value of Lambs (2)............................	56.6	56.6	56.6
Wool......................................	2.4	2.4	2.4
Cull Ewes and Rams (3).....................	4.5	4.5	4.5
Output per Ewe	**266.0**	**401.0**	**468.5**
Variable Costs:			
Concentrates (4)...............................		208.9	
Miscellaneous (inc. Vet and Med).......		18.0	
Forage Variable Costs (5)....................		25.0	
Total Variable Costs		251.9	
Gross Margin per Ewe	**14.1**	**149.1**	**216.6**
Stocking Rate (Ewes with Lambs per forage Hectare (acre))....................................		11 (4.5)	
Gross Margin per Forage Hectare..............	155	1,640	2,383
Gross Margin per Forage Acre....................	63	664	964

1. Price: 90p per litre at farm gate (range from 80p-105p per litre).
2. *Lambing %:* 175%. Assume a 300 Friesland ewe flock. Retain 60 ewe lambs for flock replacements. Sell 390 finished lambs reared from 2 days old (inc. 15% mortality) at £38. If meat-type terminal sires used then cross-bred lamb values increase to £63.
3. *Cull ewes:* Assumed 18% culled at £25.00 per head (average, including mortality).
4. *Concentrates:* Milking ewes: 200 days at 1.5 kg/head/day, 100 days at 0.5 kg/head/day; cost £200-240 /tonne. Ewe lamb replacements and artificially reared finished lambs at £65/head.
5. *Forage costs:* Quality silage: 1 tonne per milking ewe (or hay equivalent). Grazing: early grass in March/April; good grazing on leys or pasture; similar for dry stock and lambs.

Fixed Costs per Ewe: Labour (paid) £73; Power and Machinery £22; Property Costs £12; Other £13; Total, excluding Finance and Rent, £120.

Capital Costs of Equipment: Complete milking unit for 300 ewes (including yokes, bulk tank, dairy equipment, installation): £12,000-£25,000. A small 50 ewe unit can be put together for under £10,000. Any building works would be additional to the above costs.

Acknowledgement: thanks to - Anthony Hyde, FRICS, FBIAC, ARAgS.

ANGORA GOATS

Angora goats produce mohair; angora rabbits produce angora; cashgora is produced by angora cross dairy goats; cashmere is produced by improved feral goats (valuable 'down' has to be separated from guard hairs; thus, with cashmere production, 'yield of down' must not be confused with 'weight of clip' as percentage down is low and can vary widely). Goat meat is called 'chevon'.

UK mohair output is currently around 5 tonnes per year, which indicates a population of between 1500 and 2,000 animals. The figures below are for a commercial enterprise. Many UK angora flocks are kept on a semi-commercial or hobby basis, in which case different criteria may apply – does retained longer, mortality rates lower, doe/buck ratio different. Currently (2011) the world price of mohair is reaching record levels due to a world shortage of Angora Goats and demand from China. The figures used in the calculations are based on prices achieved in 2010.

Performance:

Kids per Doe per Year (1)..	1.4
Fibre: Doe/Buck, 2 clips, 3.2 & 4.5kg/clip respectively (2).......	6.8 kg
Kids (1.4), first and second clips (3)................................	5.0 kg
Whethers/Replacement Does (0.9), third clip (3).............	3.15 kg

	£
Fibre Sales:	
Doe/Buck: 6.8kg @ £6.00/kg (3)..	40.6
Kids: 5.0kg @ £10/kg (3)..	50.4
Whethers/Replacements: 3.2kg @ £7/kg (3)............................	22.1
Stock Sales:	
Does: 0.5 females sold for breeding @ £120 each (1)(4)...........	60.0
Whethers: 0.7 males sold for meat @ £40 each (1)(4)...............	28.0
Culls: 0.17 does @ £40 each (1)(4)...	6.8
Skin Sales:	8.7
Less Replacements (Buck only) (4)...	1.5
Output per Doe	**215.0**
Variable Costs:	
Concentrates (5)	41.3
Vet and Med (6)...	8.0
Miscellaneous (6)..	18.0
Total Variable Costs per Doe	**67.3**
Gross Margin per Doe before Forage Costs..	**147.7**
Forage Variable Costs (7)...	21.5
Gross Margin per Doe..	**126.3**
Gross Margin per Forage hectare...	1,262.7
Gross Margin per Forage acre...	511.0

1. 1.5 kids born alive per doe mated; 2% mortality to each clip. Of 0.7 surviving doe kids, the majority (0.5) are sold for breeding, the remainder (0.2) are retained for replacements. Culls (0.17) and casualties are equal to the number of replacements (unless the flock size is changing). Progeny are sold after 2 clips for breeding or after 3 clips for meat. Stock may be retained for further shearing. This has become more common, as the demand for breeding stock is small, fibre quality has improved and there is little market for meat.

2. The data for Breeding Does include output and inputs for breeding bucks. Assumes 25 does to one buck.

3. Angora goats are usually clipped twice a year. Yield increases over first four clips, but quality decreases with age. Prices can be volatile, being dependent on fashion and on the world market dominated by South Africa and Texas. Demand and prices are highest for the high quality kid fibre <25 microns in diameter.

   The following yields and prices have been used:-

   Clip 1 = 1.1 kg at £10.60 per kg; clip 2 = 2.5 kg at £10.60 per kg; clip 3 = 3.5 kg at £7.60 per kg. Adult doe: 3.2 kg, adult buck 4.5 kg at £6.00 per kg.

   British Mohair Marketing arranges a collection once a year, currently in September. Recently (2010), the entire collected clip was containerised and shipped to South Africa where it was sold by auction by Cape Mohair Ltd. The prices thus achieved were considerably better than those previously attained in the UK and easily covered the increased handling expenses. Membership of BMM costs £30. (Some producers improve their return by processing and using the fibre themselves or selling to local spinners. Commercial processing costs are significant: combing about £2.50 per kg and spinning about £15 per kg).

4. *Stock sales.* Breeding stock in commercial flocks are culled after seven years on average. Subsequent shearing stock culled after a further 4 clips. Value of all cull stock: £40 each. Depending on quality, the skin can be worth £10 before curing or up to £120 after curing. Replacement costs: does, £100; bucks, £300. Shearing stock, £20 (as transfer from breeding enterprise). Show quality stock command a premium.

5. *Skin Sales:* From cull does and males sold for meat @£10.00

6. *Concentrates.* Quantities: Kids - 50 kg to clip 2, 15 kg to clip 3; Adults - breeding adults 90 kg per year, shearlings 40 kg per year.

7. *Veterinary* costs can be high. *Miscellaneous* costs include £2.50 to £3.50 per shearing per head (it may be more) and bedding materials.

8. *Forage:* 10 does per hectare at £215 per hectare forage (grass) variable costs.

9. Angora goats require more management than sheep. Fencing requirements are similar but housing costs rather higher. Margins are particularly sensitive to the value and number of breeding stock sold, yield and value of fibre, kidding percentage and meat values. There is a market for meat from older animals but no reliable market has yet been developed specifically for younger animals. Angoras are probably most successfully run as a subsidiary enterprise on a farm rather than a stand alone operation.

Contact: *British Angora Goat Society*: www.britishangoragoats.org.uk

Acknowledgements: Stephen Whitley, Corrymoor Angoras, Stockland, Honiton, Devon EX14 9DY socks@corrymoor.com www.corrymoor.com

CAMELIDS

Llamas, alpacas, guanacos and vicunas are collectively known as Camelids. Originally they all came from Central America. They are all members of the same family and are related to Bactrian and Dromedary camels. Camelids are herd animals and should not be kept in isolation but will live happily with other animals.

Llamas

The llama is the largest of the Camelids, weighing up to 180kg (400lbs) and standing 1.25m (4ft) at shoulder height. Llamas are strong animals traditionally used as pack animals and kept in the UK for trekking or pets. They have a life span of 15-20 years.

Llamas can be kept at stocking rates of 10-12/ha (4-5/acre). They are generally hardy animals but benefit from an open fronted shelter. They eat grass and hay, with occasional supplements. They can be bought from a few hundred pounds.

Alpaca

Alpacas are smaller with a shoulder height of 1m (3ft) and weigh around 70kg (155lb). They produce an outstanding quality fleece. Its fibres are very fine and exceptionally strong. An annual shearing will produce an average fleece of 2.5kg which, when cleaned can sell for;

- Baby Alpaca £8 per kg (22 micron or below)
- Fine Alpaca £5 per kg (23-27 micron)
- Coarse Alpaca £0.75 per kg (28-32 micron)

Alpacas require shearing either annually or biannually, depending on breed type , Huacaya (95% of UK alpacas, tight curly locks) or Suri, (with longer curly locks like a Wensleydale sheep).

Alpacas should be kept at 12–20 per hectare (5-8/acre). They are hardy animals well suited to the UK climate, but require shelter from rain. They graze all year, with additional hay and occasional supplements.

An alpaca can cost anything from £250 for non breeding stock to £15,000. Price will vary according to genetics, age, fertility, fibre quality and colour. The alpaca gestation period is up to 11 months.

The earning potential of an Alpaca is dictated by the quality of its fleece and through breeding as there is no commercial alpaca meat industry in the UK. Animals with low quality fleeces may have a value as pets or even flock guards. Alpaca fleece is a luxury fibre thus only the highest quality fleeces and stock command good prices.

GRAZING LIVESTOCK UNITS

Dairy cows	1.00	Lowland ewes		0.11
Beef cows (excl. calf)	0.75	Upland ewes		0.08
Heifers in calf (rearing)	0.80	Hill ewes		0.06
Bulls	0.65	Breeding ewe hoggets:		
		½ to 1 year		0.06
Other cattle (excl. intensive beef):		Other sheep, over 1 year		0.08
0-1 year old	0.34	Store lambs, under 1 year		0.04
1-2 years old	0.65	Rams		0.08
2 years old and over	0.80			
Breeding sows	0.44	Broilers		0.0017
Gilts in pig	0.20	Other table chicken		0.004
Maiden gilts	0.18	Turkeys		0.005
Boars	0.35	Ducks, geese, other poultry		0.003
Other pigs	0.17	Horses		0.80
Cocks, hens, pullets in lay	0.017	Milch goats		0.16
Pullets, 1 week to point of lay	0.003	Other goats		0.11

Source: as advised by DEFRA for the Farm Business Survey.

1. *Total livestock units on a farm* should be calculated by multiplying the above ratios by the monthly livestock numbers averaged over the whole year.

2. *The ratios are based on feed requirements.* Strictly speaking, when calculating stocking density, allowances should also be made for differences in output (e.g. milk yield per cow or liveweight gain per head), breed (e.g. Friesians v. Jerseys) and quantities of non-forage feed consumed.

FORAGE VARIABLE COSTS

£ per hectare (acre) / year	Dairy Grass (1)	Other Grass (1)	Grass Clover Ley	Forage Maize (2)	Kale
Yield tonnes/ha (tons/acre)	50 (20)	45 (18)	40 (16)	40 (16)	45 (18)
Seed per year	33 (13)	15 (6)	19 (8)	170 (69)	50 (20)
Fertiliser	240 (97)	192 (78)	51 (21)	189 (77)	193 (78)
Sprays	12 (5)	8 (3)	14 (6)	42 (17)	48 (19)
Total	284 (115)	215 (87)	84 (34)	401 (163)	291 (118)
Length of Ley (Years)	4	7	5		
Cost per tonne fresh weight	5.69	4.77	2.11	10.04	6.48

	Fodder Beet	Forage Rape	Maincrop Turnips	Stubble Turnips	Swedes
Yield tonnes/ha (tons/acre)	70 (28)	35 (14)	65 (26)	35 (14)	70 (28)
Seed	130 (53)	20 (8)	42 (17)	14 (6)	156 (63)
Fertiliser	253 (102)	140 (57)	184 (75)	152 (62)	184 (75)
Sprays	154 (62)	23 (9)	50 (20)	26 (11)	52 (21)
Total	537 (217)	183 (74)	276 (112)	192 (78)	392 (159)
Cost per tonne fresh weight	7.67	5.22	4.25	5.50	5.60

Notes

1. *Intensively silaged and grazed grass* may have higher fertiliser costs to as much as £327/ha (132/acre) for some dairying systems (based on N:P:K of 225:60:75). Seed costs vary according to the proportion of permanent pasture and length of leys. Fertiliser is often less on permanent pasture, depending on management style which also affects stocking rates and productive levels per animal.

2. *Contract work on maize, silage and cultivations:* Refer to Page180.

3. Standing maize crops are typically sold for £600 to £700/ha (£243-283/acre) but can be as high as £850/ha (£350/acre), depending on the potential yield of the crop and local supply and demand.

4. *Labour:* forage and conservation labour, pages 157

5. *Conservation machinery:* page 174.

Whole Crop (feed wheat). Variable costs are as for combined crop (page 5) plus contract harvesting and clamping at £175 per ha (£71/ac.). Fresh yield averages 27.5 tonnes per ha (11 t/ac.) harvested in late June at 35% dry matter. Urea treatment (for higher dry matter) for whole-crop alkalage: £7/treated tonne. For urea treated grain, add £14.70 per tonne. Standing wheat in 2011 sold for between £800 (324/ac) and £1,000/hectare (400/ac), on expectations of forage shortages. Normally prices are nearer the lower end of this range.

Plastic wrap for bagged silage = £4.30/ round bale (120cm).

Net wrap for bales = £0.50/round bale.

TOTAL COSTS OF PRESERVED FORAGE

Cost of Preserved Forage	Clamped Grass Silage	Wrapped Grass Silage	Hay	Clamped Maize
Variable Costs	284	284	215	401
Mowing		30.9	30.9	
Turning		16.3	32.6	
Raking		16.7	16.7	
Harvesting & Clamping	293	-	-	176
Drilling	8	8	5	44
Land Preparation	25	25	14	100
Fertilising & Spraying	28	28	28	27
Land Rent	200	200	200	200
Land based Costs £/Ha	838	609	542	948
Total Costs £/fresh t	16.76	12.19	12.04	23.71
Fresh DM	18%	18%	18%	
Preserved DM	25%	25%	85%	
Sub-total £/t Preserved	23.28	16.93	56.84	23.71
Baling £/bale	0	2.6	2.6	
Wrap £/bale	0.0	4.3	0	
sheet £/t				1.00
Bale Weight		600	400	
Total Costs £/t Preserved	**23.28**	**28.43**	**63.34**	**24.71**

Notes:

1. *Variable Costs:* Linked to previous schedule, grass silage using 'Dairy Grass', hay using 'Other Grass'.

2. *Operational Costs:* Taken from contractor's charges, page 180, land preparation and drilling divided by length of rotation.

3. For simplicity, all costs are charged to the forage, despite possible late season grazing.

Sale Value of hay and (far less common because of its bulk) silage vary widely according to the region and season (supply/demand situation), quality and time of year:

a. *Hay* (pick-up baled) has an average ex-farm sale value of £130 to £170 per tonne. Seed hay (main range November to May £100 to £120) and £65-£85 for meadow hay (main range November to May £70 to £80); prices are higher in the west than the east and more after a dry summer (giving low yields of grass). Prices tend to be higher for horses as quality is higher. Big bale hay is £20 to £30/tonne cheaper.

b. *Grass silage* is typically about £35 a tonne delivered (higher when forage is very short in an area and *vice versa*), maize silage approx. £30 a tonne.

Relative Costs of Grazing, Conserved Grass, etc.

	Yield DM tonnes/ha (acre)	Cost per tonne DM (£)	MJ per kg DM	Pence per MJ of ME in DM
Grazed Grass	9.0 (3.6)	£61	12.8	0.47
Kale (direct drilled)	6.8 (2.7)	£133	11	1.21
Forage Turnips (direct drilled)	3.7 (1.5)	£169	10.2	1.66
Grass Silage	9.0 (3.6)	£80	10.9	0.74
Big Bale Silage	9.0 (3.6)	£98	10.8	0.91
Hay (1)	8.1 (3.3)	£75	8.8	0.85
Brewer's Grains (2)	-	£146	11.7	1.25
Concentrates (3)	-	£256	12.8	2.00

(1) at £63/t (2) at £35/t (3) 14% CP 14% Moisture, delivered in bulk, £220/t

1. *In interpreting the above figures* for use in planning feed use on farm, it is important to remember that own land, labour and capital for equipment are included here for home-produced fodder but not for purchased feed, and much more storage is required

2. *The consumption of fodder* is limited by its bulk although this very much depends upon its quality/digestibility.

3. *The cost of forage* will vary enormously depending on growing conditions, soil fertility and type, intensity of farming practice and management ability.

FODDER CROPS, GRASSES, CLOVERS AND ENVIRONMENTAL SEEDS

Seed Prices (For 2012) and Seed Rates

Crop	Price £/Kg	Seed Rate Kg/Ha	Cost £/Ha
Grass Leys			
1 year leys	£2.80-3.40	35-55	98 - 185
2 year leys	£3.15	35	110
3-4 year leys	£3.50	35	125
4-6 year leys	£3.80	35 - 40	133 - 150
Long-term ley	£4.37	32	140
Permanent Grass	£4.90	32.5	160
Mixed and Clover Leys			
White Clover ley	£4.30	30	130
Red Clover ley	£4.55 - 5.10	30	137 - 154
Timothy/M. Fescue ley	£4.25	31kg	135
Fodder Crops			
Fodder Kale	£11.50	5-7.5	55 - 86
Swedes	£50	Precision drill 0.7	35
		seed drill 3.7	185
Stubble Turnips	£4.50	3.75 kg drilled,	17
		5.0 kg broadcast	22.5
Maincrop Turnips	£13.50	3.75 kg drilled,	50
		5.0 kg broadcast	67.5
Rape	£2.70	10	27
Mustard	£2.60	20	52
Rape and Turnip mix	£4.60/kg mix	1.25 kg rape	
		3.75 kg turnips	23
Kale, Swede & Turnips	£20/kg mix	1.5 kg kale,	75
		0.5 kg swede	
		1.75 kg turnips	
Fodder Beet			185 - 200
Cover Mixes, Environmental and Equine			
Game Cover mixture	£4.60	25	115
Game Maize	£3.70	27.5	100
Forage Maize: Silage			130 - 175
Vetch/Tares	£2.00	75 to 125 kg	150 - 250
Quinoa & Kale mix	£11.50	7.5	87
Field Corner mixture	£15	25	280
Horse grazing	£3.85 - 6.70	35kg	135-235
Gallop mixture	£4.00	100-250	400 – 1,000

Crop	Price £/Kg	Seed Rate Kg/Ha	Cost £/Ha
Individual Varieties			
Westerwold Ryegrass	£2.80	35 kg	100
Italian Ryegrass	£2.80	35 kg	100
Perennial Ryegrass	£3.80	25 to 40 kg	95 - 150
Hybrid Ryegrass	£3.40	35 kg	120
Cocksfoot	£4.85	20 to 25 kg	97 - 120
Red Clover	£7.80	15	117
White Clover	£10.00	7 kg	70
Timothy	£4.00		
Meadow Fescue	£3.60		
Sweet Vernal	£80.00		
Reed Canary Grass	£21.00	7.5 kg	160
Lucerne	£7.80 (inoculated)	20 kg	150
Sainfoin	£3.40	70 to 90 kg	238 - 300
Millet	£2.72	25	68
Sunflower	£6.00	25	150
Sorghum	£4.90	20	98

Acknowledgement: Particular thanks to - Cotswold Seeds 0800 252 211

3.   PIGS, POULTRY, TROUT, RABBIT

PIGS

Breeding and Rearing *(to 37kg liveweight)*

Performance Level	*Average*		*High*	
	per sow	per pig	per sow	per pig
	£	£	£	£
Weaners: (ave) 22.3 (1) @ £47 (3)..........	1048	47.00		
(high) 25.4 (2) @ £47 (3).........			1194	47.00
Less Livestock Depreciation (4)...............	54	2.42	64	2.54
Output	994	44.58	1130	44.46
Variable Costs:				
Food (5)...	694	31.11	717	28.24
Miscellaneous (6).............................	107	4.8	115	4.53
Total Variable Costs	801	35.91	832	32.77
Gross Margin (per year)	**193**	**8.67**	**298**	**11.70**

1. *Weaners per sow:* - average: 9.90 reared per litter, 2.25 litters per year = 22.3 weaners per sow per year. (The average has now recovered following falls in the early 2000's due to the wasting diseases PMWS and PDNS. Productivity improvements are also being made).

2. *Weaners per sow:* - high: 10.80 reared per litter, 2.35 litters per year = 25.4 weaners per sow per year. For Outdoor Breeding performance figures see page 92.

3. *Price:* assumed pig cycle average. (See General Prices on page 90). Prices for 37kg weaners have varied from £15 to £60 during the past decade. They had been between £30 and £40 for some years prior to mid-2008, but rose with the general improvement in pig prices. They were above £50 per pig in early 2010 but fell to below £45 as profitability declined. Some improvement is expected over the next 12 months.

4. *Average livestock depreciation* assumes an in-pig gilt purchase price of £195, a cull value per sow of £105 and a 47% replacement rate (i.e. approximately 6 litters per sow life). Sow mortality 4%. Boars (1 per 24 sows) purchased at £700 (40% a year replacement), sold at £100. 'High' compared with 'Average': higher gilt purchase prices, higher replacement rate and slightly fewer sows per boar assumed.

5. *Food:* total food per sow of 2.55 tonnes breaks down as:

	Tonnes	Value £/t	Total Cost
Sow	1.30	225	293
Boar	0.05	225	11
Weaner feed	1.20	325	390
Total	**2.55**	**272**	**694**

High performance: lower sow feed but extra piglet rearing feed for additional weaners. Piglets weaned at average 3.75 weeks, 7.5kg weight.

6. *Miscellaneous Average:* vet. and med. £40, transport £10, straw and bedding £15, miscellaneous £15, electricity and gas £15, and water £12.

7. *Direct Labour Cost* per sow: average £230, good £183; per weaner: average £10.30, good £7.20.   This figure does not include labour used for 'overhead' activities – repairs etc. For further fixed costs information see page 197.

8. *Building Costs:* see page 208.

Feeding (from 37 kg liveweight): per pig

Average Performance	Pork £	Cutter £	Bacon £
Sale Value......................................	91.80	107.00	121.70
Less Weaner Cost (1)...............................	47.00	47.00	47.00
Mortality Charge...............................	1.20	1.30	1.40
Output	43.60	58.70	73.30
Variable Costs:			
Food...	28.30	38.60	49.50
Miscellaneous....................................	5.75	6.25	6.75
Total Variable Costs	34.05	44.85	56.25
Gross Margin	**9.55**	**13.85**	**17.05**
Liveweight (kg)...................................	77	90	103
Deadweight (kg)...................................	58.5	69	79
Killing Out %.....................................	76%	77%	77%
Price per Deadweight (p).............................	157	155	154
Price per Liveweight (p).............................	119.3	118.8	118.1
Food Conversion Rate...............................	2.65	2.72	2.80
Food per Pig (kg)...................................	105	143	183
Average Cost of Food per tonne (£) (2)........	£270	£270	£270
Food Cost per Kg l/w Gain (p).....................	71.55	73.44	75.60
Liveweight Gain per Day (kg).....................	0.72	0.75	0.78
Feeding Period (weeks)..............................	7.8	10.0	12.0
Mortality (%)......................................	2.6	2.8	3.0
Direct Labour Costs per Pig (£)....................	5.70	6.70	7.80

High Performance (same pig price)

Food Conversion Rate................................	2.5	2.55	2.6
Food per Pig (kg)...	99	134	170
Food Cost per Pig (£5/t less than ave.)..........	26.17	35.48	45.13
Food Cost per Kg l/w Gain (p).....................	66.25	67.58	68.90
Gross Margin per Pig	**11.55**	**16.85**	**21.35**
Direct Labour Costs per Pig........................	4.40	5.00	5.60

1. *Weaner cost* assumes on farm transfer. If purchased (i.e., feeding only) transport and purchasing costs have to be added: these are very variable but average about £2.00 per weaner.

2. *Average of home-mixed and purchased compounds:* There can be big variations in feed costs per tonne between farms, according to whether the food is purchased as compounds or home-mixed, bought in bulk or in bags, size of unit, etc.

3. *Labour:* see page 157.

4. *Building Costs:* see page 212.

5. *Sensitivity Analysis.* The effect of changes in important variables are as follows:

Change in Gross Margin (£)	Porker	Cutter	Baconer
Price: 5p per kg dw difference 2.93		3.45	3.95
Food Cost per tonne: £10 difference 1.05		1.43	1.83
Food Conversion Rate: 0.1 difference ... 1.07		1.42	1.77

Combined Breeding, Rearing, and Feeding: per pig

	Pork £		Cutter £		Bacon £	
Performance Level*	Ave.	High	Ave.	High	Ave.	High
Sale Value	91.80	91.80	107.00	107.00	121.70	121.70
Sow and Boar Deprcn	2.42	2.54	2.42	2.54	2.42	2.54
Mortality Charge	1.20	1.30	1.30	1.40	1.40	1.50
Output	**88.18**	**87.96**	**103.28**	**103.06**	**117.88**	**117.66**
Food	59.41	54.44	69.71	63.74	80.61	73.34
Miscellaneous	10.55	10.28	11.05	10.78	11.55	11.28
Total Variable Costs	**69.96**	**64.72**	**80.76**	**74.52**	**92.16**	**84.62**
Gross Margin per Pig	**18.22**	**23.25**	**22.52**	**28.55**	**25.72**	**33.05**
Gross Margin per Sow	**406**	**591**	**502**	**725**	**573**	**839**
Labour Costs per Pig	16.00	11.57	17.00	12.17	18.10	12.77
Labour Costs per Sow	357	294	379	309	404	324

*   Performance levels refer to breeding and rearing differences as on the previous 2 pages and, for feeding, differences in food conversion rate, food costs and labour cost only.

Prices - General

Pig prices are notoriously difficult to predict. Over the last four years the GB average pig price (DAPP Eurospec) has ranged from 100p per kg deadweight to over 155ppkg. The vast majority of UK pigs are taken to baconer weight. The level shown in the finisher margins for baconers above, of 154p, is an estimated average for late 2011 through 2012. This assumes some improvement in markets from the levels seen at the time of writing. The finished pig price is highly dependent on the £/€ exchange rate.

Further Performance Data

Source: The Meat and Livestock Commission's 'Pig Yearbook 2011' (data for the year ended December 2010).

		Performance Level	
Breeding	Average	Top Third*	Top 10%*
Sow replacements (%).................................	49.3	52.2	54.5
Sow sales and deaths (%)...........................	49.2	48.1	49.3
Sow mortality (%)......................................	3.6	2.5	3.3
Litters per sow per year..............................	2.25	2.34	2.39
Pigs reared per litter..................................	9.8	10.8	11.5
Pigs reared per sow per year.......................	22.1	25.2	27.7
Weight of pigs produced (kg)......................	7.2	7.4	7.4
Average weaning age (days)........................	26.7	23.4	26.1
Sow feed per sow per year (tonnes).............	1.23	1.19	1.17
Feed per pig reared (kg)..............................	56	47	43
Sow feed cost per tonne (£).........................	163	162	170
Sow feed cost per sow per year (£)..............	174	188	187
Feed cost per pig reared (£)........................	8.12	7.43	6.96

* selected on basis of pigs reared per sow per year.

Rearing	Average	Top Third*	Top 10%*
Weight of pigs at start (kg)..........................	7.4	7.4	7.5
Weight of pigs produced (kg)......................	34.6	35.1	30.9
Mortality (%)...	2.7	2.5	4.2
Feed conversion ratio..................................	1.75	1.46	1.19
Daily Gain (g)...	486	519	498
Feed cost per tonne (£)................................	297	269	260
Feed cost per kg gain (p).............................	49.0	36.0	23.0
Feed cost per pig reared (£)........................	12.89	10.33	5.86

Feeding	Average	Top Third*	Top 10%*
Weight of pigs at start (kg)..........................	38.0	35.2	38.5
Weight of pigs produced (kg)......................	103.9	105.2	108.5
Mortality (%)...	3.0	3.2	2.7
Feed conversion ratio..................................	2.95	2.68	2.80
Daily Gain (g)...	766	792	818
Feed cost per tonne (£)................................	177	169	140
Feed cost per kg gain (£).............................	52.2	42.6	35.9
Feed cost per pig reared (£)........................	34.86	29.97	25.49

* selected on basis of feed cost per kg liveweight gain.

Feed conversion ratio for rearing and feeding combined, from 7.5kg to 107kg liveweight is approximately 2.50.

Outdoor v Indoor Performance

Breeding	Outdoor	Indoor
Sow replacements (%)....................................	39.2	47.6
Sow sales and deaths (%)..............................	38.2	41.5
Sow mortality (%)...	1.1	1.4
Litters per sow per year................................	2.25	2.25
Pigs reared per litter.....................................	9.3	10.2
Pigs reared per sow per year..........................	21.0	23.0
Weight of pigs produced (kg)........................	7.1	7.4
Average weaning age (days)..........................	26.5	26.9
Sow feed per sow per year (tonnes)...............	1.33	1.18
Feed per pig reared (kg)................................	65	51
Sow feed cost per tonne (£)...........................	160	163
Sow feed cost per sow per year (£)	180	172
Feed cost per pig reared (£)...........................	9.34	7.69

1. *Stocking Rate for outdoor pigs* is mainly between 12 and 25 per hectare (5 and 10 per acre), 20 (8) being the most common. Good drainage is essential. A low rainfall and mild climate are also highly desirable. In 2003, MLC's Agrosoft puts the cost of establishing a sow herd on a greenfield site at £1,800 per sow place for an indoor unit and about £600 per sow place for an outdoor unit.

2. *Data on the split* of indoor and outdoor herds is hard to come by. However, it is probable that well over a third of the UK breeding sow herd is now kept outdoors. A somewhat smaller proportion (probably <10%) of pigs are finished outdoors.

Further costing information can be found in 'Pig Production in England 2009-10' produced by Askham Bryan College, York on behalf of Rural Business Research. See www.ruralbusinessresearch.co.uk

Acknowledgement: The main data source for the margins within the Pigs section is the Pig Yearbook 2011 (AHDB), but the pig and feed prices are the author's responsibility.

EGG PRODUCTION

Brown egg layers; 55 week laying period, 2 week changeover period. This reflects current commercial practice

Level of Performance	Enriched Cages				Free Range	
	Average		High		Average	
	per bird	per doz eggs	per bird	per doz eggs	per bird	per doz eggs
	£	p	£	p	£	p
Egg Returns......................	14.18	53.5	14.71	53.5	20.75	83.0
Less Livestock Deprcn.....	3.58	13.5	3.58	13.0	3.67	14.7
Output	**10.60**	**40.0**	**11.13**	**40.5**	**17.08**	**68.3**
Variable Costs:						
Food..........................	11.39	43.0	11.39	41.4	13.25	53.0
Miscellaneous.............	1.95	7.4	1.95	7.1	1.90	7.6
Total Variable Costs	**13.34**	**50.3**	**13.34**	**48.5**	**15.15**	**60.6**
Gross Margin	**-2.74**	**-10.3**	**-2.20**	**-8.0**	**1.93**	**7.7**

1. *Hen-housed data* are used throughout, i.e. the total costs and returns are divided by the number of birds housed at the commencement of the laying period. IPPC permit charges have not been included. *Large variations* in input costs and returns occur.

Cage Production

3. *Yields assumed* per bird per year are:
   Average................ 318 (26.5 dozen)
   High................. 330 (27.50 dozen)

4. *The price* used, 53.5p per dozen, includes all quantity and quality bonuses. If sold direct (to local shop, add 35p/doz., if sold to consumers (farm-gate) add 65p/doz.

5. *Livestock depreciation* - average point of lay pullet is priced at £3.75 (16/17 weeks).

6. *Feed* is 45kg per bird at £253 per tonne. Feed cost is dependent on breed, housing and environmental conditions, quantity purchased and type of ration.

7. *Direct Labour Costs:* average £1.46 per bird, premium £1.11. See page 171.

8. *Housing Costs:* see page 213. Deadstock depreciation averages about £1.73 per caged bird. Deadstock depreciation is calculated over 57 weeks (55 week laying period plus 2 weeks clean out).

9. *Stocking density*: 750cm^2/bird (13.3 birds/m^2) in enriched cage systems; conventional cages (550cm^2/bird (18.2 birds/m^2)) prohibited from 1 Jan 2012

Free Range Production

10. *Egg yields:* 300 (25 dozen) and *average price:* 83p per dozen.

11. *Quantity of feed* used = 50 kg. Price £265 per tonne.

12. *Livestock depreciation* - the average point a lay pullet is priced at £3.67 (16/17 weeks).

13. *Direct Labour Costs*: average £4.30 per bird, dependent on degree of automation.

14. *Stocking density in house*: 1111 cm^2 /bird (9 birds per m^2) up from 855cm^2/bird (11.7 birds/m^2) as of 1 Jan 2012, stocking in multi-tier systems can be higher, if appropriate use is made of the height of the building.

    Stocking density outside the house; regulations allow 2,500 birds/ha (1,000/acre). Freedom Foods and the Lion Code allow 2,000 birds/ha (810/acre).

REARING PULLETS

Average per bird reared

	£
Value of 16/17 weeks old bird..	3.75
Less Chicks 1.01 (1) @ 66p (including levy)......................................	0.67
Output	**3.08**
Variable Costs:	
Food: 6.25 kg @ £240 per tonne...	1.50
Miscellaneous (2)...	0.88
Total Variable Costs	**2.38**
Gross Margin	**0.70**

1. *Chick Value:* Assumes 3 per cent mortality, but 2 per cent allowed in price.

2. *Miscellaneous:* Excluding transport (21p), but including full vaccination costs.

3. *Labour* (41p); *deadstock depreciation* (46p).

TABLE POULTRY

A **Broilers** (per bird sold at 41 days)	p
Returns: 2.2 kg per bird @ 87.0p per kg lw......................................	191.4
Less Cost of Chick..	32.0
Output	**159.4**
Variable Costs:	
Food: 4.2 kg @ £320 per tonne...	134.4
Miscellaneous...	18.2
Total Variable Costs	**152.6**
Gross Margin	**6.8**

1. Capital cost of housing and equipment: £6.65 per broiler space (depreciation cost approximately 5.7p per bird sold). Housing Costs: see page 213.

2. Labour: 5.4p, excluding catching and cleaning out (5.0p) but includes management; see page 171.

3. *Stocking density* 38kg/m^2, 263cm^2/kg

O.R. = Oven Ready

B All Year Round Turkey (per bird at 20 weeks, sexed stags)   £

Returns: 14.3 kg per bird @ £2.70 per kg O.R................................	38.6
Less Cost of Poult...	2.0
Output	**36.6**
Variable Costs:	
Food: 50 kg @ £285 per tonne..	14.3
Miscellaneous..	4.9
Total Variable Costs	**19.2**
Gross Margin	**17.4**

1. 10% mortality allowed in cost of poult figures.
2. Rearing turkeys all the year round now tends to be just in the hands of a few large and vertically integrated companies. Imports have outcompeted many small operators.

C Christmas Turkey (Traditional Farm Fresh - indoor reared)

	Light £	Medium £	Heavy £
Returns per bird sold........................	39.60	45.04	64.23
Less Cost of Poult............................	4.57	4.57	3.84
Output	**35.03**	**40.47**	**60.39**
Variable Costs:			
Food..	7.81	9.86	10.61
Miscellaneous................................	12.99	13.42	13.87
Total Variable Costs	**20.80**	**23.28**	**24.48**
Gross Margin	**14.23**	**17.20**	**35.92**
Killing Age (weeks).........................	18	22	22
Live Weight (kg).............................	6.6	8.0	12.4
Oven Ready Weight (kg)....................	5.4	6.6	10.2
Food Conversion.............................	3.2	3.4	2.4
Food per Bird (kg)...........................	20.8	27.0	29.5
Food Cost per tonne.........................	£375	£365	£360

1. *Mortality:* 7, 8 and 10% mortality allowed for in cost of poult figures for light, medium and heavy weights respectively.
2. *Performance Categories:*
    Light and medium = slow growing sexed hens.
    Heavy = stags (as hatched).
3. *Liveweight Price per kilogram*: small £6.00p/kg, medium £5.63 p/kg, large £5.18p/kg
4. *Miscellaneous costs* include processing (inc. plucking and eviscerating) and marketing

Note: With both turkey enterprises, considerable variations will occur between individual strains and because of different production systems and feeding regimes. Free range systems for example will show higher costs and returns. The figures should therefore be used only as rough guidelines.

D Large roaster chickens (per bird sold at 12 weeks; Christmas - males only)

	£
Returns: 4.8 kg per bird @ £3.40 per kg O.R.	16.32
Less Cost of Chick..	0.80
Output	**15.52**
Variable Costs:	
Food: 14.3 kg @ £328 per tonne..	4.69
Miscellaneous..	1.59
Total Variable Costs	**6.28**
Gross Margin	**9.24**

10% mortality allowed for in cost of chick figures.

E Ducks (Pekin type) (per bird sold at 7 weeks)

	£
Returns: 2.3 kg per bird @ £3.50 per kg O.R................................	8.05
Less Cost of Duckling...	0.63
Output	**7.42**
Variable Costs:	
Food: 11.3 kg @ £270 per tonne..	3.05
Miscellaneous..	2.15
Total Variable Costs	**5.20**
Gross Margin	**2.22**

Day-old costs allow for 10% mortality. There are very few indoor duck farmers left in the UK operating to this system, but they are large-scale.

F Geese (Traditional Farm Fresh - free range and dry plucked)

	£
Returns: 6.5 kg per bird @ £8.32 per kg O.R.................................	54.08
Less Cost of Gosling...	5.60
Output	**48.48**
Variable Costs:	
Food: 64 kg @ £270 per tonne...	17.28
Miscellaneous..	12.40
Total Variable Costs	**29.68**
Gross Margin	**18.80**

1. Day-old costs allow for 6% mortality.

2. 16kg feed wheat at £180/t and 48kg goose concentrate at £300/t

3. Farm gate output values used

4. Miscellaneous costs include processing / marketing

Acknowledgement: The figures in the whole of the poultry section are provided by John Newton, ADAS, Wergs Road, Wolverhampton.

RAINBOW TROUT (FRESHWATER)

	£ per tonne of fish
Returns: 1 tonne of fish @ £2.25 per kg...	2,250
Less 4000 fingerlings @ 8.0p each..	320
Output	**1,930**
Variable Costs:	
Food: 1 tonne @ £1200 per tonne...	1,200
Vet and med;..	130
Miscellaneous..	35
Total Variable Costs	**1,365**
Gross Margin	**565**

1. Fish growing to 350g from fingerlings at 4.5g.

2. Prices are estimated ex-farm to processor or wholesaler. Higher prices of up to £4.20 per kg can be achieved by selling direct to retailers, caterers and consumers at, say farmers markets, but significant additional costs are associated with such sales.

3. Fingerlings price: varies according to quantity ordered and time of year.

4. Average feeding period, 10 months. Mortality, from fingerling to market size, 15%. Food conversion ratio 1.1:1, having a very low maintenance requirement. The price for fish food is for a pigmented high oil expanded pellet.

5. Current capital costs for construction of earth pond unit approximately £80 per cubic metre, to include buildings, holding systems and installation of water supply and services, but excluding land.

6. Labour requirement: the basic norm has in the past been 1 man per 50 tonnes of fish produced per annum on a table fish farm, but to remain competitive farmers now need to produce at least 150 tonnes per annum of table fish per man.

The figures given are illustrative and don't reflect the complexities of trout farming. Trout farming varies in the UK from Cage Farming in Scottish lochs (freshwater and marine) to 'traditional' flow through earth/pond/concrete raceway river farming. Trout farming also encompasses both the table and restocking sectors, prices given above relate to the sale of fish for the table market. As such feed costs, conversion rates etc do vary which obviously has an effect on the costings for the enterprise. Differences in water temperature will also impact significantly on food conversion ratios, growth rates etc.

Acknowledgement: Thanks to - British Trout Association, The Rural Centre, West Mains, Ingliston, Edinburgh, EH28 8NZ. Tel: 0131 472 4080 www.britishtrout.co.uk

MEAT RABBITS

The consumption of rabbit meat in the UK is low, at less than 2oz per person per year, but most of this is imported where production costs are less where welfare standards are usually lower. There are very few buyers and processors of meat rabbits in the UK and do not cover all parts of the country, hence transport costs may have to be allowed for. It is important prospective producers research the market. An individual producer may develop local markets. The demand for rabbit meat is seasonal - more is eaten in winter than summer, which can pose marketing problems. Producers often adjust their production by 15 to 20% in summer to allow for this. There may be a market for the manure.

Commercial rabbit production is an intensive livestock enterprise and usually requires planning permission and building regulation approval from the Local Authority. The construction or conversion of a building to house rabbits is the main expenditure and must be done in accordance with Defra's Welfare Code. A meat rabbit unit needs to be weather- and vermin-proof, insulated, ventilated, well-drained, with lighting and a water supply. Housing can be fully environment controlled to give good feed conversion rates and better winter conditions for both stock and personnel, or be natural environment, which has lower capital and running costs and possibly keeps animals healthier.

Meat rabbits require a lot of maintenance. Health, hygiene and good stockmanship are crucial. One full time person can look after 250 – 300 does and their progeny. New Zealand White or Californian stock is used. Young does are bought in at 12 weeks and mated at 16-20 weeks. Bucks are bought at 16 weeks and first mated at 20 weeks. A ratio of one buck to 10-20 does is recommended. Gestation is 31 days. Average litter size is 8-9, of which 6-7 should be successfully fattened. Re-mating can be immediately post-partum or up to 6 weeks afterwards; the average is about 21 days. A doe can have a useful life of 10-12 litters over 18 months; less productive animals may be culled sooner. A mortality rate of up to 12.5% can be expected.

Young rabbits are weaned at 35-42 days at about 2.5-3 lb and then fed *ad-lib* until they are ready for marketing at 5.5-6.5lb liveweight at 11-13 weeks. Food conversion rate, including the doe's feed and a share of the buck's is around 4:1. A balanced ration can be obtained for about £250 per tonne in bulk but may cost up to £350 per tonne. A doe should produce around 50 meat rabbits each year but experienced producers would aim for 60-70.

4.   RENEWABLE ENERGY

GENERAL

The renewable energy sector is maturing rapidly as entrepreneurs and investors assess whether it offers opportunities for them or not. There are clearly farmers who have made good money from it, others who are breaking even, and others who have lost sums of capital. Correct investment appraisal is necessary for renewable energy projects just with any other. Land is fundamental to the renewable energy sector, it is capital intensive and requires an entrepreneurial approach to its implementation. Agriculture is therefore a natural partner for the sector.

Renewable energy is a relatively novel concept in industrial terms even though virtually all technologies are not new and are well understood. Wind power and wood heating clearly have long histories, as has anaerobic digestion having been harnessed by man for centuries. Even biofuels were available for the Second World War and second generation biofuels, whilst well understood are simply prohibitively expensive. What is new is the increasing focus on these technologies as a means to combating climate change.

The Renewable Energy industry is developing in response to incentives to cut the emissions of climate changing green house gases (GHGs) as a result of human activities. The main GHGs are:

- Carbon Dioxide (CO_2), which accounts for up to a quarter of the green house gas effect
- Methane (CH_4) accounts for between 4% and 9% of the effect but is about 25 times more potent by volume than carbon dioxide
- Nitrous Oxide, which, whilst very low in concentration in the atmosphere, is about 300 times more potent than carbon dioxide
- Water Vapour. Whilst this is the most voluminous and causes between a third and two thirds of the green house effect, human activity has a negligible effect on it.

In 2010, human activity in the UK accounted (provisionally) for 582 million tonnes of GHG emissions (CO_2 equivalent), 2.8% up from 564mt in 2009. Agriculture accounted for 49.5mt CO_2 equivalent, most of which comes from the enteric fermentation of ruminating animals (methane) and the use of (and manufacture) nitrogen fertilisers (nitrous oxides).

UK GHG Emissions 2009 (measured in million tonnes of CO_2 equivalence)

	GHG Total	Carbon Dioxide	Methane	Nitrous Oxide	Others
UK	564	474	44	34	11
UK Agriculture	49.5	4.1	18.0	27.4	0.0
Percentage	8.8%	0.9%	41%	80%	0%
GWP[1]		1	21	310	

1.   GWP is the Global Warming Potential over 100 years relative to 1 tonne CO_2
     Figures from Defra/DECC.

RENEWABLE ENERGY POLICY

The UK has a legally binding target under the Kyoto Protocol to reduce its GHG emissions to 12.5% below 1990 levels by 2012. There is currently no international agreement to replace Kyoto, largely because its ambition has proven difficult to achieve.

The EU's 2008 Climate Change Package became the 2009 Renewables Energy Directive. It aims to ensure the EU will achieve its self set 2020 climate change targets by setting binding targets:

- a 20% reduction in greenhouse gas emissions,
- a 20% improvement in energy efficiency, and
- a 20% share for renewables in the EU energy mix (the UK national target is 15%)
- of this target, biofuels and electricity should account for 10% of the EU's transport fuel consumption.

The UK 2008 Climate Change Act set legally binding targets for government, to steer it to achieve an 80% reduction of GHG emissions by 2050. It does this through additional targets; a 26% reduction of CO_2 emissions by 2020 and capped emissions over 5 year periods, 3 budget periods set at a time. The 2008 UK Energy Act implemented legislation that:

- Strengthened the Renewables Obligation with ROC bandings
- Allowed Government to introduce Feed-in-Tariffs
- Enabled Government to establish the Renewable Heat Incentive, RHI
- Provided Government with the authority to introduce Smart Metering

In July 2009, DECC published The UK's Low Carbon Transition Plan (LCTP). It is a White Paper laying out the Governments plans for meeting GHG reduction targets. Whilst the UK is expected to reduce emissions by 34% (of 1990 levels) by 2020, agriculture, which accounts for 7% of emissions, is expected to reduce its emissions by only 6%. Government recognises not only the industry is growing, but also will provide the resources for many renewable opportunities and also already stores vast amounts of carbon in soils and woodland.

In 2012, agriculture is expected to demonstrate to Government the industry's voluntary actions to address its GHG emissions by 2018. Government will then decide whether regulations should be implemented if current activities are insufficient.

Also published in July 2009 was the Renewable Energy Strategy which set out how the UK plans to meet its target of delivering 15% of UK energy by 2020.

The Renewables Obligation (RO)

The primary mechanism for encouraging electricity supply from renewable sources in the UK is the Renewables Obligation (RO). Renewables Obligation Certificates (ROCs) are issued to registered electricity generators for producing electricity from renewable sources at between ¼ and 2 per mega watt hour (MWh) depending on the generation type. This so called 'ROC banding' was introduced in April 2009.

Renewables Obligation Target, ROC Value and Non-Compliance Penalty

Year*	Renewables Obligation Target (ROCs per 100MW)	Non-compliance Penalty per MWh (buy-out price)	Average Value of ROCs
2010/11	10.4	£36.99	£48.10
2011/12	11.4	£38.69	£50.94
Annually thereafter to 2015/16	+1 15.4	Index linked increments	Market Price

ROCs are required by registered electricity suppliers to offset their annual RO target (an annually rising target of ROCs per 100MW of use). If they do not have sufficient ROCs to meet their target, they are charged £30/MWh for the difference (index linked to 2002/03 making £38.69 in 2011/12). This money is re-circulated equally to all certificates after each year-end, meaning ROCs are worth more than the penalty. Thus ROCs have a market value; their average price in June 2011 was £51.04/ROC. Electricity suppliers can fulfil their RO by purchasing ROCs from other generators. Farmers generating renewable electricity can sell the ROCs, having no obligation to keep them.

The introduction of 'ROC banding' meant some renewable electricity generation types 'earn' more ROCs per MWh than others as the next table illustrates. Also, any generator with a capacity of 50kW or less is classified as a micro-generator and earns 2 ROCs per MWh ('double ROCs') if operational pre July 2009.

Number of ROCS per MWh depending on Generation Type (non-exhaustive list)

Generation types	ROCs per MWh
Co-firing of biomass	0.5
Onshore wind	1.0
Hydro-electric	1.0
Co-firing of energy crops	1.0
Energy from waste with CHP	1.0
Co-firing of biomass with CHP	1.0
Dedicated biomass	1.5
Co-firing of energy crops with CHP	1.5
Anaerobic digestion	2.0
Dedicated energy crops	2.0
Dedicated biomass with CHP	2.0
Dedicated energy crops with CHP	2.0
Solar photovoltaic	2.0
Geothermal	2.0

Generators can also claim 1 LEC (Climate Change Levy Exemption Certificate) for each MWh of electricity produced. Utilities need to source these LECs so they can exempt business consumers from Climate Change Levy - which in 2010/11 is £4.85 on 1 MWh of electricity.

Feed-in Tariffs (FIT)

Designed to facilitate the administration and subsidy receipts of small-scale electricity generators, the Feed in Tariffs are aimed at encouraging the production of renewable electricity at all levels up to 5MW capacity. This is equivalent to a very large offshore turbine or a very large anaerobic digestion plant. Almost all farm-scale renewable energy schemes would therefore fit within the FIT scheme. The Tariffs work as follows:

- A renewable electricity generator receives a fixed payment for each kWh electricity generated; the 'Generation Tariff'. This is set at different levels depending on technology type, installation size and start date (see below).

- A guaranteed market payment of 3.1 p/kWh (2011/12) is available if required for its export to the wider market; the 'Export Tariff'.

- Generators can opt out of the Export Tariff by either selling electricity directly to an electricity consumer or making use of the electricity themselves.

- The FIT payments are made by the registered Electricity Suppliers, the cost of which is redistributed among all suppliers in a pro-rata manner.

- Generators with capacity below 50kW (known as micro-generators) are eligible for FIT, whilst installations between 50kW and 5MW have the option to choose between FIT and the RO.

- Generators choose between ROCs or FITs but cannot claim both.

This was implemented in April 2010. Generation Tariff rates for photo voltaic and wind technologies will reduce in subsequent years for new claimants as technology becomes cheaper. Tariffs are paid for 20 to 25 years after installation depending on technology. Generation and Export Tariffs are index linked.

The Generation Tariffs for large scale solar (Photovoltaic) generation were changed in August 2011 as Government deemed they were too generous. there was also a small increase in small scale AD generation. There is to be a review of all FITs in 2012

Generation Tariffs for FITs

Generation Technology	Scale	Generation Tariff p/kWh 1 Apr 11 to 31 Mar 12	Tariff Lifetime (years)
Anaerobic Digestion	< 250kW	14.0	20
	250 - 500kW	13.0	20
	> 500kW	9.4	20
Hydro	< 15kW	20.9	20
	15-100kW	18.7	20
	100kW - 2MW	11.5	20
	2MW-5MW	4.7	20
Photo Voltaic	< 4kW *New Build*	37.8	25
	< 4kW *Retrofit*	43.3	25
	4kW - 10kW	37.8	25
	10kW - 50kW	31.4	25
	50kW - 150kW	19.0	25
	150kW - 250kW	15.0	25
	250kW - 5MW	8.5	25
	Stand Alone *	30.7	25
Wind	< 1.5kW	36.2	20
	1.5kW - 15kW	28.0	20
	15kW - 100kW	25.3	20
	100kW - 500kW	19.87	20
	500kW - 1.5MW	9.9	20
	> 1.5MW	4.7	20
Micro Generators moving from the RO		9.4	To 2027

* Stand Alone Systems are those not attached to a building and not wired to provide electricity to an occupied building.

The Renewable Heat Incentive (RHI)

Heat accounts for 47% of all energy used in the UK. Government's target for 2020 is that 12% of this will come from renewable sources. The value of heat is low (possibly 1-2p/kWh thermal energy depending on local market) which rarely justifies the capital expenditure in the UK of harnessing heat or generating it from a renewable source. The RHI is designed to change this. It is being introduced in two phases, Phase 1 in July 2011, for non-domestic installations, the second for domestic installations. In the first year, Premium Payments are available to subsidise the cost of installing qualifying renewable heating systems for the domestic sector; metered payments will begin in 2012.

Tariffs are paid for 20 years to eligible technologies that have been installed since 15 July 2009 for each kWh of renewable heat generated. Payments are index linked.

The RHI is being administered by OFGEM.

Levels of Support for RHI

Tariff name	Eligible technology	Eligible sizes	Tariff rate (p/kWh)	Tariff duration (Years)	Support calculation
Small biomass	Solid biomass; Municipal Solid Waste (inc. CHP)	Less than 200 kWth	Tier 1: 7.6	20	Metering. Tier 1 annually up to Tier Break, then Tier 2 *.
			Tier 2: 1.9		
Medium biomass		200 kWth and above; less than 1000 kWth	Tier 1: 4.7		
			Tier 2: 1.9		
Large biomass		1000 kWth and above	2.6		Metering
Small ground source	Ground-source heat pumps; Water-source heat pumps; deep geothermal	Less than 100 kWth	4.3	20	Metering
Large ground source		100 kWth and above	3.0		
Solar thermal	Solar thermal	Less than 200 kWth	8.5	20	Metering
Bio-methane	Biomethane injection & biogas combustion, except landfill gas	Biomethane all scales, biogas combustion less than 200 kWth	6.5	20	Metering

* Tier Break is: installed capacity x 1,314 peak load hours, i.e.: kWth x 1,314

The Renewable Transport Fuel Obligation (RTFO) and Fuel Excise Duty.

Biofuels have the same duty payable as mineral fuels for most producers. A 100% duty exemption for small scale biofuel producers those producing up to but not exceeding 2,500l biofuel per year (notionally sufficient for home use) remains in place. There is a 20p/l duty discount for biodiesel produced only from waste cooking oil. This is until April 2012.

The RTFO started in 2008/9. For every litre of biofuel that excise duty is paid on, a Renewable Transport Fuel Certificate (RTFC) is issued. Companies supplying at least 450,000 litres of mineral fuel to the UK market annually (about 14 companies) must participate by incorporating an increasing proportion of biofuel into their sales, buying RTFCs from another biofuel provider or pay a 'buy-out' penalty (fine) of 30p/l. As a compelling incentive, the 'buy-out fund' generated is redistributed equally to every RTFC issued by the year-end. This means that the further away the UK is from hitting the annual target, the greater the incentive to incorporate as RTFC values rise. These subsidies are essential to make the industry viable, without them there would be no biofuel industry. The proportion of biofuels to incorporate rises annually. For 2011/12 the incorporation rate is 4% rising by 0.5% each year until it reaches 5% in 2013/14.

Fuel Excise Duty:	23-Mar 2011	1-Jan 2012
Petrol, Diesel & Biofuels *ppl*	57.95	60.97
Rebated gas oil (red diesel) *ppl*	11.14	11.72
Biodiesel for non-road use *ppl*	11.14	11.72
Natural Gas (inc. biogas) *p/kg* ◊	24.70	29.07

◊ *The duty differential applicable to biogas is equivalent to 40.88p on a litre of petrol. It will remain at this level until at least Budget 2012*

SUPPORT AND GRANTS

The **Energy Crops Scheme** is part of the Rural Development Programme for England and is managed by Natural England. It finances the establishment of Miscanthus and Short Rotation Coppice. The grant rate is 50% of planting costs. A minimum of 3 hectares can be claimed. See more on page 148.

The **Bio-energy Capital Grants Scheme** (England only), was part of a 5-year fund from 2006. It is thought unlikely to start again.

The **Wood Energy Business Scheme** (Wales) 2008-2013 is a capital grant scheme for wood fuel heating systems, wood powered CHP and equipment for wood fuel supply businesses. Farm and forestry businesses are generally ineligible as it is funded through the Convergence and Competitiveness Structural funds.

The **Bio-energy Infrastructure Scheme** (England) supported biomass feedstock sector (wood-fuel, energy-crops and straw) for heat, power and electricity end users. Round 3 ended in February 2010, and will not reopen.

LIQUID BIOFUELS

Liquid biofuels are road transport fuels produced from organic materials, including several mainstream farm crops. Biodiesel is produced from oilseed crops such as oilseed rape, soybeans and palm and is a replacement for mineral diesel. Bioethanol is a petrol replacement, produced from starch/sugar-based crops including wheat, maize and sugar beet or cane. Biofuels from cellulosic (woody) feedstock is possible referred to as 'second generation' biofuels. This would enable a higher energy return per hectare and the opportunity to process household, manufacturing and agricultural organic wastes. Its production is not financially viable so may be some years from large-scale commercial production.

Supply

About 40 million tonnes of road fuel is used in the UK (diesel exceeding petrol use by about 55:45). To meet the RTFO target in 2011/12, about 1.6m tonnes of biofuel is required (4%). The RTFO does not differentiate between biofuels so one may dominate the market. Splitting the market proportionately would require roughly 880,000 tonnes of biodiesel and 720,000t bioethanol. This would need 2.1m tonnes OSR or equivalent feedstock (at 42% extraction) covering 650,000 hectares (at 3.2t/ha) and 2.4m tonnes of wheat (or equivalent feedstock) covering 290 thousand hectares (at 8.25t/ha).

Farmers' options on whether to grow a crop to supply biofuel facility is simply by allowing the market to decide the buyer: As crops used in biofuel production are, in the most part, mainstream crops that could also be sold to other consumers, the processor that bids the farmer the highest value deal ought to win the contract. Clearly headline price is important, but also other contractual details including the risk of rejection or cost of claims, turnaround times etc should be considered. There are therefore no farm-level gross margins for biofuel crops.

BIOMASS FOR POWER

Energy crops are grown for heat and electricity generation or to produce transport fuels. They are considered 'carbon neutral' which means the carbon released on burning is only what they (recently) took up into the plant when growing, thereby not releasing additional carbon from fossil reserves beyond the requirements for fertiliser and chemicals, mechanical cultivation, harvest and transport to end-use location. Some are considerably more 'carbon-efficient' than others, with carbon costs of haulage, fertiliser, processing (such as chipping or biofuel synthesis) and processing establishments to account for.

This section covers crops that are grown to be burnt directly to produce heat and/or electricity. The plant material is pelleted, chipped, or baled and is generally either used in boilers in dedicated biomass power stations, or mixed with coal for co-firing in conventional power stations. Biomass includes short rotation coppice, Miscanthus, straw, canary reed grass and switch grass as well as forest residues.

Short Rotation Coppice

Short Rotation Coppice (SRC) is a fast growing species of willow or poplar that when harvested, chipped and dried can be used as a fuel for heat or power generation. In the UK most SRC is willow in part because of problems with mechanically planting poplar.

SRC willow needs ample moisture but grows on any cultivated land. It requires a seedbed similar to that of a conventional arable crop, with particular attention to weed control. Planting is in the spring using un-rooted cuttings at a rate of 15,000/ha. Rabbit (or deer) fencing may be necessary. Pest and weed control is essential until canopy closure is achieved in the second year. In the autumn after planting, most growers cut back the willow to encourage multi-stemmed stools. This allows herbicide application and encourages a more competitive canopy. Some growers omit this cut-back when weed control is good, thereby achieving a commercial harvest sooner. Crops are usually harvested on a 3 year cycle. In poor conditions it may be left for 4 years, but in good conditions possibly every 2 years. In best conditions, stems would grow too thick to harvest if left any longer. Crops should last more than 20 years. Most growers apply some fertiliser post harvest. Sewage sludge is commonly used as are animal manures. In general, approximately 60 kg/ha N is sufficient to maintain growth through the harvest cycle.

The harvested crop can be stored as billets or chips. Many processors grind and pellet the crop, increasing density and improving transport efficiency but adding to costs. Pellets flow better in automated fuel feed systems and are preferred for co-firing (with coal) as the willow has been milled prior to pelleting easing the load on the generator's mills. Pellets command a premium price over billets (6-8 inch lengths) and chips. SRC wood chip sells for around £60/odt (oven dried tonne) delivered, and, depending on contractual details, the consumer may organise delivery to the furnace. The first harvest should yield 10-20odt/ha, subsequent ones 21-27odt/ha.

The following gives a broad indication of likely planting costs and net annual returns. Account has been taken of the Energy Crops Scheme at 50% of costs

SRC Establishment Costs:	*£/ha*
Fencing (optional)	210
Pre-planting spraying	35
Post-planting spraying	74*
Fertiliser	45 ~
Cultivations	170 ∞

Planting...	365 ɔ
Cuttings...	780
Cut-back..	50
Energy Crops Scheme Grant (50%)........................	-865
Total Establishment...	*865*

* *This varies from £35 to £145 depending on weed presence and control management.*

˜ *RB209 recommends N:P:K of 90:55:72. This would cost £183/ha. Advisers suggest using biosolid or slurry only.*

∞ *estimate 25% of the site is subsoiled, fully ploughed, power harrowed at least once then rolled twice after planting.*

ɔ *including all cold storage of cuttings Haulage & travel for contactor*

Annual Net Returns: Output 25 odt/ha at £60 every third year; £500/year. Harvesting £300/ha plus £50 fuel, transport and handling £10/tonne harvested. Planting costs (including fencing etc) have been spread over the forecast period of the crop. This capital investment will be written off over the years the SRC is cropped. It should be amortised into its current value. Use the Amortisation Table in section VIII. SRC land remains eligible for the Single Payment.

Gross Margin for SRC Chips

	Per Harvest	Per Established Year
Average Harvest Yield (odt/ha)	25.0	25.0
	£	£
Yield: 25odt/ha at £60/odt	1500	500
Output:	**1500** (608)	**500** (203)
Variable Costs:		
Planting Cost**	130 (53)	43 (18)
Fertiliser/spray	48 (19)	16 (6)
Harvest	350 (142)	117 (47)
Transport & Handling***	250 (101)	83 (34)
Total Variable Costs	778 (315)	259 (105)
Gross Margin per ha (acre)	**722** (293)	**241** (98)

* *including the rise in yield in early years* ** *£865 spread over 21 years* *** *£18/odt*

Miscanthus (Elephant Grass)

Miscanthus is a perennial crop lasting 20 years grown for energy and fibre. It is indigenous to Africa and Asia. It is harvested annually with conventional farm machinery.

After suitable treatment, Miscanthus can be used as animal bedding, for paper making and biopolymer manufacture or be used to produce bio-degradable products, such as plant pots.

Miscanthus is grown throughout the UK on a wide range of soil types and pH values and benefits from ample water. The crop is propagated from rhizomes. Weed control is necessary at establishment and in the following spring. A mature crop suppresses weeds. There are no significant pathogens or pests in the UK so agro-chemical use is minimal

Fertiliser requirement is low. Leaf mulch recycles nutrient, but cannot replenish that removed from harvest. In the first year, there is little growth so fertiliser is not necessary.

Research suggests the mature crop removes 7kg P and 100kg K/ha/year. The plant being deep rooted may access minerals from deeper than most other crops. The mature crop removes about 75kg N/ha/year, some of this is replaced by soil mineralisation and aerial deposition. Sewage sludge is an ideal fertiliser. The Miscanthus gross margin below has a notional cost for imported slurry, biosolids or other organic manure.

The crop shoots in April, and grows into bamboo-like stems up to 4 metres high by late August. They contain solid pith. The foliage dies after the first frost and stems desiccate to 50% moisture during winter. The leafless canes are harvested in February-March, before shoots reappear. The robust rhizome network provides a platform for harvesting machinery. The harvest method depends on end use. For energy the crop is cut with a mower conditioner or modified forage harvester at 35% moisture and then baled 10 days later into 550-700kg Hesston bales at 16% moisture, the contractual benchmark moisture level. For other end uses a standard maize harvester can be used.

The price for Miscanthus ranges between £45 to £75 with £60 fairly standard for energy crop contracts. Note most contracts now use fresh harvested weight (normally 16% moisture) rather than the former 'oven dried tonnes'.

In year 1, only about 50 to 60% of the full yield is obtained. With the recent development of precision planting machinery for miscanthus evenly established crops are now being achieved, offering greater yields, average fresh weight of yield per hectare on light land is between 10 – 15t/ha and on medium to heavy land 13 – 20 t/ha.

There are somewhere between 6,000 to 10,000 hectares of Miscanthus in the UK although it is not measured. Small on-farm boilers, to produce heat and energy, have been developed which offer potential for Miscanthus growers. This will be fuelled by the Renewable Heat Initiative (see page 102). Planting and establishment costs are in the region of £2,000 per hectare. Some agro-chemicals will probably be required in the first 2 years. In the UK there is a 50% establishment grant for all costs in the first 2 years.

Miscanthus Gross Margin

Production level	Low	Average	High
Yield: tonnes per ha (tons per acre)	11 (4.5)	14.00 (5.7)	18 (7.3)
	£	£	£
Output	605 (245)	770 (312)	990 (401)
Variable Costs:			
Establishment *...........................		65 (26)	
Fertiliser.................................		20 (8)	
Harvest....................................		75 (30)	
Bale..	121 (49)	154 (62)	198 (80)
Total Variable Costs		314 (127)	
Gross Margin per ha (acre)	**324** (131)	**456** (185)	**632** (256)

* *Establishment costs of £2,462/ha (£997/ac) less the 50% Establishment grant shared between 19 productive years. Financial discounting has not been accounted for here.*

Acknowledgement: thanks to – Keith Wilson, International Energy Crops.

ANAEROBIC DIGESTION

Anaerobic Digestion (AD) is the digestion of non-woody organic material in the absence of oxygen by micro-organisms to produce biogas (a mixture of 40% carbon dioxide CO_2 and 60% methane CH_4) and digestate (a soil conditioner). The biogas is collected and normally used in a combined heat and power (CHP) generator to produce heat and electricity for use or sale. The biogas can also be purified by removing the CO_2 and contaminant gasses (less than 1%) making biomethane for use as road fuel or in place of natural gas. It is a natural process and is well understood by mankind having been harnessed for many years.

An extensive range of feedstock can be used. Livestock manure is cheap with high levels of micro-organisms but has a low biogas yield. Energy crops such as maize silage offer high yields and are commonly used in AD business models are expensive feedstocks so add substantially to operating costs. Non-farm waste streams from food processing companies or separated kitchen wastes offer a high return, with potential to earn revenue from gate fees. Regulatory controls and 'front-end processing requirements are far greater when importing others' waste streams, especially if animal by products are likely to be included pushing up capital costs and changing the business model substantially.

There are several types of AD plant, all suited to different situations and feedstocks. The rate of turnover of digestate is controlled by the rate at which feedstock enters the digester less the small (usually 3-10%) fall in volume from the production of biogas. Depending on feedstock and system used, digestion can take as little as a week up to 2 months in some circumstances.

Example On-Farm Feedstocks for Anaerobic Digestion

Feedstock	Biogas Yield m^3/t feedstock	Value of Biogas £/t feedstock*
Cattle/pig slurry	15 – 25	5.21 – 8.68
Poultry manure	30 – 100	10.40 – 34.50
Maize silage	190 – 220	66.00 – 76.00
Grass silage	150 – 200	52.00 – 69.00
Whole crop wheat	185	64.00
Maize grain	560	190
Rolled wheat grain	600	200
Crude glycerine	580 – 1,000	200 – 350
Rape meal	620	215
Fats	Up to 1,200	up to 400

* *13.0p/kWh Generation Tariff, 3.1p/kWh Export Tariff, 1p/kWh heat*

Policy

When biogas is used to generate electricity, it can be sold with Feed in Tariffs (see above) or 2 ROCs can be claimed per MWhe (Mega Watt hour of electricity) as part of the Renewables Obligation (see above). Biomethane for road transport is technically eligible for RTFCs (see Biofuels section above). AD also benefits from the Climate Change Levy and indirectly the Landfill Directive. AD does not facilitate NVZ implementation regulations.

Economics

The two major costs associated with AD are usually the capital set up and feedstock (if home grown or purchased feed is used). Operating and maintenance costs such as insurance, labour and utilities are usually low. An average size plant (2,500m³ digester and 450kW CHP generator) would cost in the region of £1.4-2 million to build and commission. Depending on feedstock, temperature and other settings, this size plant could digest in the region of 20,000 tonnes of feedstock per year with a 45 day retention time (spent in the digester) or 30,000t with a 30 day retention period.

Revenue from this system digesting 20,000 tonnes using the assumptions from the table above, an average gas yield per tonne of feedstock of 100m^3/tonne and an efficiency of 90% gas conversion would return income before costs and without gate fees of about £680,000 with FITs.

HYDRO POWER

Hydro power provides about 40% of all renewable electricity produced in the UK providing about 1,500MW capacity. One major benefit of hydro electricity over many of the other renewable power sources is that power supply is predictable and relatively constant (short of severe drought). Key factors that require careful measurement are the 'head' (total drop of water) and the flow.

Hydro, just like other renewable energy projects is capital loaded, expensive to install but cheap to operate. However, installation costs have fallen in recent years to around £3,000 to £6,000 per kWhe for small 'micro' hydro electric systems. Its price varies as each installation is unique. Capital cost and electrical capacity depend largely on the following:

- The head (maximum vertical fall) of water which is key as the higher the head, the smaller the turbine required to generate the same amount of electricity. Less than 10m is normally considered 'low head'.

- The flow rate of water. For small schemes it is measured in litres per second.

- How much construction is required and how much of it is done 'in-house'.

The cost of construction per kW tends to fall as capacity rises meaning the smallest projects take longest to repay their investment. Operational costs are low, generally 1-2% of capital setup. Access to sites is a factor affecting instalment.

WIND TURBINES

There are currently 3,411 operational wind turbines spread across 306 grid-connected wind farms throughout the UK (July 2011). Small scale turbines can have capacities of as little as 100 watts (W) up to models of 2-3 mega watts (MW) and 6MW for offshore turbines. Wind farms are becoming larger; the average size a decade ago was 7MW and is now 18.7MW, albeit with considerable offshore wind farm growth.

Wind turbines in good locations produce energy equivalent to their rated capacity for around 30% of the year. For example: for a turbine rated at 40kW this calculates as 40kW x 30% x 8760 (hours in a year) = 105,120 kWh per year (105.12MWh). If this electricity is sold at 28.4p per kWh with FITs, then a return of £29,854 per year is achieved.

Typical costs for a range of turbine capacities are in the region of the following table. Good quality constructions should have an operational life of 20 years.

Guideline Figures for Capital and Revenue of Wind Turbines

Capacity kW	Capital Cost	Annual Output (kWh)	Revenue/yr using FIT*
5.0	20,000	13,100	£4,010
11	68,000	28.900	£9,000
75	200,000	197,000	£56,000
250	650,000	657,000	£150,000
800	1,100,000	2,100,000	£273,000

* Relevant FIT price as in FIT Table on page 102.

The land surrounding a wind turbine is usually un-affected, apart from access required up to the base of the tower. A minimum wind speed of 5 meters per second (m/s) is required; they operate at their rated capacity at 11-15m/s. Many turbines have automatic shut-down mechanisms when wind speeds exceed about 25m/s to avoid damage. Selection of the correct turbine technology and size is important.

Planning permission is required and consultation with neighbours and stakeholders for all scale turbines. Wind farms (multiple large turbines) are built in association with developers as the costs and expertise required planning and preparing them is very high. Many schemes are operated by developers with land rented to them by the land owner for 20 years. In this situation, a rent will be payable to the landowner, usually at about 2-4% of income (£5,000 to £6,000 per mast per year is not uncommon plus similar construction access fees). Access to the turbines must be possible, but land between the turbines can be farmed normally. Other benefits like road improvements may also be included. An option to develop a site could be worth £1,000 to £5,000 per year.

A 11kW turbine will have a hub (mast) height of 15 to 18 metres, blade diameter of 9 metres and a 63m³ swept area. Tip height will be up to 22.5m. A large (800kW) wind turbine has a standard hub height of 76m, a height at the maximum blade position of 102m, and a blade diameter of 53m. The area of wind captured by this size blade is 0.88ha.

SOLAR POWER

Solar Photovoltaic (PV)

Solar PV panels generate electricity through the direct conversion of daylight. Panels can either be roof mounted, free-standing or integrated as a form of building material though solar slates, tiles or glass laminates.

Supply and installation costs for a 1kWe capacity system start at around £6,000, ranging up to £16,000 for a 4kWe capacity system. Little maintenance is required. There are companies that will 'rent' your barn roof for installation of solar PV if you did not wish to invest in equipment yourself.

Approximately 7-8m^2 of PV panels is required to generate 1kW of electricity. A typical panel weighs 13kg per m^2 so additional roof support may be required. Panels may last for 45 years but most manufacturers place a 25 year guarantee on panels and a 5 year guarantee on inverters.

For optimum results, modules should be south facing at an angle of 30-40 degrees and un-shadowed by trees or surrounding buildings. Productivity varies across the UK with levels between 1100 kWh per m^2 in the South West, to 800 kWh per m^2 in Scotland. Modules that are face East or West will drop in efficiency to 85%.

In England and Scotland most private PV installations do not require planning permission, unless the building is of conservation status, is in a designated area or is a large free standing system. Wales and Northern Ireland will need to seek planning permission from their local planning authority.

Solar Thermal

Solar thermal systems use the sun's energy to warm water through using either evacuated tubes or flat plate collectors fitted to a roof. A conventional or immersion boiler is then used to heat the water further.

Costs of a typical water heating system are £3,000 to £5,000. Most systems come with a 5-10 year warranty and require little maintenance. Savings are modest; the average system can provide one third of water needs, reducing heating bills by approximately £50-£85 per year.

In England most systems will not require planning permission unless the building is listed or within a designated area. Wales, Scotland and Northern Ireland will need to contact their local planning authority.

5.   OTHER ENTERPRISES

MUSHROOMS

The mushroom industry has changed considerably during the past few years. A significant number of businesses of all sizes and in different parts of the country have ceased production and few if any new growers have entered the business. Less than 75 firms remain in production. Those that remain are either highly efficient enterprises with strong links to supermarkets or small low cost family-run businesses selling largely to wholesalers. The reasons for this are static consumption levels and competition from cheap imports. There are a few organic mushroom producers who sell at a premium.

Among the firms that remain there have also been changes in the method of production. Traditionally, the majority of UK growers employed Phase 1 compost, which they pasteurised and spawn-ran on the premises, to fill moveable trays or shelves in their growing rooms. Currently, the most prevalent system (perhaps 70% of all growers) uses purchased Phase 2 compost (pasteurised, with spawn added). This is supplied in shrink-wrapped blocks but it is also available in plastic bags as well as in bulk. Phase 3 compost (fully spawn-run) in blocks or bags is used by some growers. Organic Phase 2 and Phase 3 compost is also available.

Type of Compost Used	*Phase 2*	*Phase 3*
	per tonne compost	
Mushroom Yield/tonne compost	250 kg	300 kg
	£	£
Mushroom Price/kg	1.80	1.80
Spent Compost/tonne	2.00	2.00
Output	**452.0**	**542.0**
Variable Costs:		
Compost (incl. delivery)	95.0	135.0
Casing	15.0	15.0
Operations & growing labour at 6p/kg	15.0	18.0
Supervision & picking labour at 48p/kg	120.0	144.0
Packing materials at 21p/kg	52.5	63.0
Packing labour at 10p/kg	25.0	30.0
Energy costs at 10p/kg	25.0	30.0
Other costs at 15p/kg	37.5	45.0
Total Variable Costs	**385.0**	**480.0**
Margin / tonne compost	**67.0**	**62.0**
Variable Costs / kg mushrooms	1.54	1.60
Margin / kg mushrooms	0.27	0.21

Note: All labour is included but labour for growing, if not picking and packing, could well be regular.

Output: Growers using Phase 2 compost will fill on an 8-week cycle and produce 6.5 crops per year. Phase 3 compost can be filled on a 6-week cycle and allows 8.5 crops per year. Yields are expressed as kg per square metre of bed or kg per tonne of compost. Commercial yields are 25-35kg/sq m of bed area per crop (250-350kg per tonne of compost) using Phase 2 or 3 compost, but only 18-20kg/sq metre (180-200kg/tonne of compost) using Phase 1. Phase 1 compost costs £25/tonne, Phase 2 £85/tonne and Phase 3 £125/tonne plus delivery which can add £6-15/tonne, depending on distance and size of load.

Labour costs: If Phase 2 or 3 compost is used, labour for growing amounts to around 10% of all labour costs while picking is 75% and packing 15%. Using Phase 1 compost labour cost for growing is significantly greater, perhaps 40p/kg or 40% of total labour, but the initial compost is cheaper.

Prices: Mushroom prices are in the range of £2.00/kg supplied to a supermarket to £1.00 or less sold on the wholesale market. Small growers marketing through a producer organisation would get around £1.60/kg delivered. At present 60% of the crop is sold by growers direct to supermarkets. Prices can be volatile and oversupply can lead to mushrooms being sold at a loss. Imports now account for 65% of all mushrooms sold in the UK, and 60% of the value of sales. Almost all imports are from the Netherlands and the Republic of Ireland.

Returns: The data suggest that ex-farm it costs £1.54 to produce 1kg of mushrooms using Phase 2 compost and £1.60 using Phase 3 compost. This does not take into account management or finance costs. The yield of the crop and the number of cycles each year are, of course, crucial.

Establishment Costs: A mushroom farm using Phase 2 compost on an 8-week cycle would require 8 rooms each with a 200sq m capacity. A farm using Phase 3 compost on a 6-week cycle would need 6 rooms of 200sq m capacity. In both cases one growing room would be filled each week using 20 tonnes of compost. To set up such a production system would require a capital investment of £200,000-£300,000 for the rooms, trays or shelves, heating and cooling systems, packing area, hard standings and equipment. If Phase 1 compost is used then buildings and equipment for composting, peak heating and spawning are also required.

Acknowledgement: Mushroom Growers Association, c/o Snowcap Mushrooms, Broadway, Yaxley, Peterborough, Cambs. PE7 3EF: www.mushroomgrowers.org.

LOG CABINS

A renewed interest in British short breaks and holidays has lead to a popularity surge of 'alternative' accommodation over the more traditional cottage rentals or caravan and camping. There are examples where log cabin rentals for tourism and leisure purposes have been extremely successful as farm diversification projects. As with any tourism and leisure based enterprise, location is everything and will determine the success (or failure) of the proposal. It will also determine the rental income and occupancy that can be achieved. There may also be potential for using log cabins as a substitute for 'permanent', traditional buildings for office, storage facilities etc.

Full planning permission will be required before the construction of any log cabin. It is recommended that professional support is sought in this respect prior to any expenditure on equipment / groundwork.

Build Costs

Prices for cabins vary considerably, primarily linked to the size and finish (quality) of the final build and the cost of routing any mains services. The figures below are a guide to log cabin purchase and build costs, but excluding fixtures and fittings which may add £85.00 to £125.00 of additional cost per m². Costs in routing mains services to the cabins will be greatly dependant on remoteness, topography, environmental restrictions etc and the extent of supplies required (bottled gas and septic tanks can be used in place of mains gas and sewage):

'Fishing' Log Cabin   30m² floor space plus sleeping 'loft'   £10,000 - £40,000

'Holiday let' Log Cabin   60m² floor space with 2 bedrooms   £20,500 - £52,500

For cabins larger than the examples above, add £240.00 to £300.00 per m² for every m² over and above the sizes stated

Rental Potential

Good occupancy rates of the cabins will be paramount to the viability of any investment. Annual occupancy rates will vary depending on location, seasonality of local attractions and level of discount given in the 'off' season. Rental incomes again vary considerably, but typically range from £250 to £1,100 per week, with the higher incomes being achieved where the cabins are located in more desirable locations i.e. near to areas popular for fly and course fishing, mountain biking, walking, coastal activities, tourist attractions etc. Single night stays and short breaks often command a higher income pro rata than weekly lets. The troubles in the wider economy have led to reductions in the more 'typical' tariff rate ranges as businesses realise the importance of maintaining occupancy levels.

COARSE FISHING

Coarse fishing is the most popular pastime in the UK with in excess of 1.5 million people expected to regularly coarse fish in 2011. There have been year-on-year increases in the number of people coarse fishing since 2000. This ongoing demand has lead to many farmers and landowners to explore ways of gaining extra revenue from the letting of fishing rights either on a half day, full day or seasonal basis.

Coarse fishing is a freshwater method of line fishing and in most cases is undertaken by using a rod and real or a 'pole' usually from the banks of a watercourse. Coarse fish species include Rudd, Roach, Bream, Barbel, Tench, Chub, Perch, Pike, Carp etc but exclude sea species and 'game' fish like salmon and trout (the latter of which are usually line caught by 'fly fishing'). Coarse fish are always returned to the water after catching, weighing etc. Freshwater coarse fishing facilities can include rivers, streams, canals and man-made or natural lakes, ponds and drains. The close season for coarse fishing is 15th March to 15th June inclusive each year although most canals and still waters are exempt from the close season. Anyone fishing must have a rod licence (available from the Environment Agency). Fishing permit prices vary widely depending on the location, quality of the fishing, species present etc, but will typically be as follows:

Half-Day Ticket (per rod)	£4.00 to £7.00
Full-Day Ticket (per rod)	£5.00 to £13.00
Season Ticket (per rod)	£50.00 to £180.00

Permit prices will be higher if the water is actively managed to attract more or certain fish species. Ponds and lakes can be initially or routinely stocked. Maintenance and landscaping of the water banks will also add a premium to a facility as will safe, secure car parking and easy access to fishing pegs (platforms). The number of fishing points available along a water (and therefore income potential) will vary, but as a guide spacing of at least 25m per peg is usually required.

GAME SHOOTING

Game shooting remains a popular activity and has in recent years become more accessible to a wider range of people. Game shooting refers to the shooting of game species which include both feathered and fur animals and large mammals in the case of deer. The most common feathered species shot in the UK include pheasant, partridge, duck, woodcock, snipe and grouse. Most feathered game species can be reared in captivity and then released or alternatively populations can be enhanced by different management techniques. There are strict and differing shooting seasons for a range of different species, both game and pests. Shooting activities are widely recognised for their significant contribution to countryside conservation in all areas of the UK.

'Driven' game shooting is the most popular method of game shooting in the UK whereby game birds are 'flighted' towards a standing line of guns. The quality and type of driven shooting available is hugely variable and mostly linked to climatic, landscape and management factors as well as the number of birds present. These variances also have a major impact on the cost of partaking in a shoot. As a guide, a 120 bird day driven shoot will cost in the range of £175 to £500 per gun (participant). It is usual for a driven shoot to have 7 or 8 guns with up to 8 'drives' in a day. An organised driven shoot will usually state how many birds are expected to be shot on a specific day, with any birds shot over and above this charged on a per head basis of circa £24 to £30 per bird in the case of pheasants.

The income potential from running a driven shoot is highly variable depending on the factors outlined above. The expensive nature of most driven game shoots is usually justified by the amount of work and cost involved in running a shoot (buying birds, feeding, structural equipment costs, game plot establishment, game keeper and beater's costs, shoot day hospitality etc) and so margins may be small given the investment required.

Further information: British Association for Shooting and Conservation – www.basc.org.uk

TURF

The market for turf remains reasonably healthy, despite the downturn in the home building industry. Competition within the sector is strong, particularly among the producers of general contract grade turf. The market is now predominantly supplied with seed sown turf or cultivated lawn turf. Pasture turf is still available in certain areas, but overall its importance is small and declining. Suitable pasture for turf lifting is hard to find and it can now be cheaper to grow cultivated turf than treat and prepare existing pasture. Special seed mixtures and cultivation techniques produce a range of types of turfgrass that can be matched to particular sites and uses. In some cases special soil mixes are provided for the site as well as the turf. The Turfgrass Growers Association (TGA) has introduced quality standards and buyers are increasingly specifying the precise type of turf they require. It is estimated that there are around 16,000 ha (40,000 acres) of turfgrass grown in the UK. Although several turfgrass companies were originally set up by farmers, the business has moved away from mainstream farming. However, farms may be involved in the following ways:

Selling existing pasture turf to a turf company

This is the traditional option but it now represents very little of the turf market and its share will continue to decline. The opportunity will be open to very few farmers indeed. The approach may be by the farmer to the company or vice-versa. Minimum 5-6 year ley/pasture generally needed for spring or autumn lifting, 8-10 year grass is better for summer cutting.

Important features: good root structure, number and type of weeds, level, well-drained, stone-free land; good access; timing (farmer wants lifting completed in time to drill next crop).

Payment varies between £750-£1,500 per hectare (£300-£600 per acre), but mainly £900-£1,200 per ha (£360-£480 per acre). There is usually an initial payment plus further payments as turf is lifted. There may be a penalty clause if lifting delays prevent subsequent timely drilling. Lifting can take from two months to even a year. It can be done at any time of year except when there is snow or frost on the ground. The turf company usually sprays against broadleaved weeds, fertilises and mows before lifting; the farmer may do these tasks, for payment. He may graze the land, for a rent, if lifting is delayed.

The effect on the land is not detrimental, the amount of topsoil removal is not much greater than other root crops; some say there are benefits (removal of accumulated pests, etc. in the top half inch of grass, roots and topsoil).

Some local authorities require planning consent for turf stripping. In some instances it has been refused on the grounds that pasture turf is not an agricultural crop. Cultivated turf, however, is deemed to be an agricultural crop. On tenanted land landlord's permission is necessary to cut pasture turf.

Farmer cutting, lifting and selling pasture turf himself

Extremely uncommon. The turf must be treated, as in option 1. A small turf cutting machine can be hired for about £60 a day. This slices off the turf which must then be cut into lengths and picked up by hand. Two or three workers are required. It is slow going even in good conditions. The wastage figure is commonly 10-20% of the area, perhaps more. To hire a machine which cuts and picks up the turf may be possible but the charge will be considerably more.

Turf has a short life once cut and stacked - a maximum 1 to 2 days in summer, 3 to 4 days in winter, depending on temperature.

Renting land to a turf company for production of cultivated turf

Turf companies rent land for turfgrass production in addition to using their own land. As before, well-drained, stone-free land with good access is required. Typically the land is rented on a per crop basis and one or two crops grown. A turf crop usually takes 12 to 18 months from preparation to harvest but autumn sown crops may be harvested within 12 months. Rent levels depend on the quality of the land, the provision of irrigation and the profitability of competing agricultural enterprises. Currently rents are in the order of £650-£1,200 per hectare per crop (£265-£485 per acre) or £500-£750 per ha per year (£200-£300 per acre).

Cultivated turf production

On their own land turf producers can grow turf continuously, taking a crop every 18 months to two years on average. On rented land (as in option 3), they take one or two crops and move on. Usually they produce a quick growing type of turf which sells quickly on rented land and cultivate more specialist and slower growing turf on their own land. A high level of agronomic expertise and considerable investment in machinery are needed and labour requirements are heavy. As the business is very competitive a high degree of marketing expertise is essential. While the bulk of the trade goes into general landscaping or garden centres there is an increase in the number of contracts where the quality and type of turf is specified. It is estimated that a turf farm would need to be 150-200 hectares (400-500 acres) or more in size to be viable – in order to justify the machinery and equipment necessary and to produce a succession of turf for the market. There are significant economies of scale. The cost of specialist machinery for turf production can be £350,000. The new one-man harvesting machine costs in the order of £120,000-£200,000 but significantly reduces labour costs.

Costs and Returns

Variable Costs plus Rent:	£/ha	(£/ac)
Seed	750-1,100	(300-445)
Fertiliser	400-800	(160-325)
Herbicide	90-150	(35-60)
Fungicide	100-210	(40-85)
Rent (for 15 months)	650-1,200	(365-525)
Total Costs	*1,990-3,460*	*(805-1,400)*

It may be necessary to irrigate and on occasions use netting to grow the grass through for certain sites.

Labour: Special seed bed preparation (including subsoiling and stone burying), regular mowing (twice a week May/June), picking up clippings, harvesting (2 men on harvester plus one loading lorry) between 0.2-0.4 hectares per day (0.5-1.0 acre). The new one-man harvester can do 2 ha (5 acres) a day.

Total costs of the order of £4,942-£7,413 per ha (£1,200-£3,000 per acre), approximately 56-83p per sq.m. (47-69p per sq.yd.)

Value of Turf (on the field)

	per sq. m	per sq. yd.	per ha*	per acre*
Pasture turf	38-43p	32-36p	£3,420-£3,850	£1,380-£1,570
Hardwearing, domestic general contract	75-95p	65-80p	£6,840-£8,550	£2,755-£3,470
Football, hockey, prestige landscape	115-145p	95-120p	£10,260-£12,825	£4,150-£5,200
High quality/specialist**	190-475p	160-405p	£17,100-£42,750	£6,910-£17,290

*   assuming 90% recovery, but some producers work on 85%.

** for some contracts the price may be higher.

Delivery charges 45-55p per sq.m for a full lorry load. Higher for smaller deliveries.

Acknowledgements: Turfgrass Growers Association, 133 Eastgate, Louth, Lincolnshire, LN11 9QG. Telephone: 01507 607722. www.turfgrass.co.uk. *Robert Laycock,* Dial Cottage, North End, Seaton Ross, York, YO42 4LX. www.robertlaycock.co.uk.

GOLF

The recession is having a major impact on golf in the UK. Many clubs are seeing reductions in turnover by up to 30%. There are only a handful of clubs with waiting lists unlike a few years ago when up to 7 years wait was common in the best clubs. Some clubs have managed to stem the attrition, mostly by abandoning joining fees or producing a series of flexible options on how to pay for memberships.

Golf experienced a boom associated with a growth in GDP and standards of living. The pressures of life today mean it is now less acceptable for a golfer to spend the whole of Saturday playing golf while the family stayed at home. Clubs are becoming more family orientated in an attempt to stop the loss in members and attract new membership. One of the easiest savings to make on the family budget is to cancel sports memberships. Many golfers switched to 'pay and play' rather than subscribe to a yearly membership. But this has not translated into increased business for pay and pay clubs. The latest research shows only the 70+ age segment increased activity, with all other age groups playing less. Most importantly, the biggest drop was in youngsters (and qualified teachers who were coaching them).

There are only two UK courses under construction, but numerous courses have been trying to upgrade old facilities to cope with the new competition. This strategy has worked to an extent, but the reduction in the overall market does not bode well for new investment. It seems that the only development has been in situations where hotels have been trying to add golf as a facility to improve occupancy or in specialist niches. Therefore, the need for agricultural land for golf development has ceased in all but a very few situations. Rises in agricultural land values means that the viability of any golf project is threatened by land costs alone, even for hotel companies.

A large number of courses have been sold, with the largest owner of golf facilities selling-off a significant proportion of its inventory. Range development has also virtually stopped with a declining marketplace. Financing golf developments is now virtually impossible although with courses selling at low prices there are an increasing number of overseas investors looking at buying courses in the UK.

Despite changes in the planning system, and more to come with the proposed localisation legislation, the biggest change seems to be Local Authorities accepting that there are now golf courses which are redundant and worrying about what to do with them.

Type of facility

- 18-hole 7000 yard plus course: 70-80 ha (*170-195 acres*) with Clubhouse and Pro Shop (600 sq. metres), parking, proper access and maintenance buildings. It takes between 1 and 2 years to construct.
- 9-hole course: 35-40 ha (*84-95 acres*).
- 9-hole Par 3 course: 7 ha (*17 acres*).
- 6-hole Par 3 or 4 course: 14 ha (*34 acres*).
- Driving range: 4 ha (*10 acres*).
- Pitch and putt course: 1.5 ha (*4 acres*).

Type of business organisation

To sell land with planning permission: The cost of development of an average new course will be significantly more than the value of the facility when it is complete. There is currently no premium over agricultural value unless the situation or planning consent offers something exceptional.

To let land to a developer/operator: Assuming the latter pays for constructing the course, a long lease will be required. Rental levels will depend on the expected profitability of the facility but currently, in our experience, leases are around £40-60,000 for an 18 hole course

To form a joint company with a developer/operator: This obviously means the farmer shares in the success or failure. The land would be all or part of the farmer's equity. A well constructed agreement is essential.

To develop and operate the course himself: The farmer would need good knowledge of golf and exceptional management ability besides access to substantial capital. In the present circumstances it is not to be recommended.

Construction methods and cost (by a specialist golf course constructor):

- 18-hole course (60-75 ha): £2.5m-£3.5m according to drainage, earthmoving and irrigation, but excluding green keepers building and machinery.
- 9-hole course (35-40 ha): £800,000-£1.2m.
- 9-hole par 3 course (7 ha): £600,000-£900,000.
- 6-hole par 3 or 4 course (14 ha): £500,000-£800,000.
- Driving range (4 ha): £250,000-£800,000, to include offices, storage, equipment, fencing and floodlighting.
- Full inventory of new machinery for 18-hole course: £500,000.
- Clubhouse (600 sq. metres): from £780,000 or £2.0m fitted out.
- Direct labour may reduce costs by around a third.
- Using own farm labour it is possible to reduce costs but it is very risky in terms of resultant course quality.

It is crucial to obtain professional advice at the outset for investment appraisal, feasibility study and a business plan. Changes to the national planning system places some obligation on Local Authorities to make allowance for the needs of all sports in their areas but in many emerging plans such information is often missing.

Large scale developments require Environmental Impact Assessments to be submitted with a planning application. These can cost anything from £70,000 to £140,000 on top of the golf designers and architects fees. The design and environmental fees are all at risk if planning approval is not gained.

Returns

Few courses or clubs are now profitable with many struggling to break even. Bankable rates of return on new courses are now extremely rare. It would have to be a special circumstance to recommend the construction of a new stand-alone golf development in the UK today. Associated residential development could make developments profitable, but even this is now debateable in the current climate.

Acknowledgement: International Design Group Studio 5.17, The Paintworks, Bath Road, Bristol BS4 3EH. Telephone: 0117 316 0591. www.idgplanet.com

BED AND BREAKFAST

Although there are no official statistics, it is estimated that up to 2,000 farms across the UK offer B&B. Some are seasonal and informally run but many are open for much of the year, inspected under the auspices of the National Tourist Boards and/or the AA, and are members of a Regional Tourist Board and/or an organisation such as Farm Stay UK.

A bed and breakfast enterprise can be rewarding in both financial and social terms. However, the person running the business should enjoy meeting people, have good social skills and be prepared to work long hours. Other members of the family must be willing to share their home with visitors and to lose a certain amount of privacy. In a crowded market, and with rising customer expectations, the standard of the product is increasingly important. The aim must be to provide a standard of accommodation equal to that found in hotels. This is likely to involve some refurbishment of the farmhouse; either before starting the enterprise, to upgrade an existing B&B to modern standards, or just ongoing repair of wear and tear.

Support for farm diversification into tourism is minimal but has recently transferred from the Development Agencies (RDAs) to DEFRA – see www.defra.gov.uk/rural/rdpe/ for more details. As with all new ventures, it is good practice, and essential if seeking additional finance, to create a well-thought-out business plan containing realistic projections.

Although they are not necessarily onerous for smaller operations, it is vital to know the planning, legislative and financial requirements involved in B&B provision. Details are available from VisitBritain in the '*The Pink Booklet' - a practical guide to legislation for accommodation providers'*. This is now available online at www.accommodationknowhow.co.uk/ Further information can be found on the VisitBritain corporate website at www.visitbritain.org. In addition, a great deal of help and advice is provided by National Tourist Boards – England, Scotland and Wales each have their own organisations. Lastly, there are Regional Tourist Boards.

Marketing is very important. It can be done through a national organisation, in local Tourist Information Centres, in newspapers and magazines, and by word of mouth. Some establishments produce an attractive brochure or card giving details of the B&B, its location, facilities, and quality standards rating. Copies are left at tourist information centres etc and sent to prospective visitors. The internet is an important tool for the promotion of farmhouse B&Bs. Indeed, nowadays it's almost imperative to have a website and e-mail address, whilst many operators are also subscribing to online booking and availability systems.

As there is considerable competition it is useful if the enterprise can offer something special or different such as accommodation for visitors' horses, a welcome for pets, or use of a tennis court or pool. Establishments that can accommodate bigger parties are gaining in popularity. The number of B&Bs offering an evening meal has tended to decline in recent years, but providing locally grown produce can also be a draw. If evening meals are not offered it helps to have good local restaurants and pubs to direct guests to.

To join a marketing organisation it is important for the B&B to have a Quality Assurance Standard rating. These are awarded either by the official National Tourist Board inspectorate (which in England is Quality in Tourism), or the AA. The rating is at one of five levels, expressed as stars. It is based on guest care and the quality of what is provided following an unannounced overnight inspection visit. The inspection fee depends on the number of bedrooms and the level of charges. The rated establishment gets a listing in the VisitBritain guides and on their internet site. In some areas, membership of a Regional Tourist Board is an option; this confers additional benefits including a reduction in inspection fees, access to legal advice, and discounted rates for promotional activities and training courses.

Prices charged will reflect the quality of accommodation and location but cannot be far out of line with other local B&Bs and small hotels. Prices can also vary depending on length of stay and time of year. The price range for one person per night ranges from £20 to over £50, but most fall into the range of £30-£40 on the basis of two adults sharing a room. A higher rate usually applies for single occupancy of a double room. There are regional differences with higher prices generally being charged in the south and east, and lower ones in the west and north.

The receipts from the enterprise can be calculated as follows: If the B&B is open for 40 weeks of the year at £35 per person per night, given a 60% occupancy rate the gross return per bed will be around £5,900. Most farmhouse B&Bs have 4-6 bed spaces, which would generate a gross return of between £23,500 to £35,000 p.a.

As every farmhouse B&B is different and some costs are difficult to apportion between guests and family, it is hard to provide realistic average costings. The following provides some pointers. Variable costs are food, electricity and heating, laundry, cleaning materials and additional help. There will also be regular redecoration costs, repairs, and replacement and renewal of glassware, china, cutlery, towels and bed linen. Variable costs if no non-family labour is used might average about 20% of the nightly charge. If casual labour has to be included variable costs could amount to 30-35% of the nightly charge.

Fixed costs will include insurance, business rates (if they apply), membership of a marketing organisation, regular advertising, repayments on any loans taken out for building and equipment to start the business and regular labour; they are likely to average 30-35% of charges.

Contact: Farm Stay UK, NAC, Stoneleigh Park, Warwickshire, CV8 2LG. Tel: 02476 696 909. www.farmstayuk.co.uk *VisitBritain,* 1 Palace Street London, SW1E 5HX. Tel: 020 8846 9000. www.visitbritain.org. *Quality in Tourism*, Security House, Alexandra Way, Ashchurch, Tewksbury, Gloucs, GL20 8NB. Tel: 0845 300 6996. www.qualityintourism.com.

CHRISTMAS TREES

About 8 million trees are sold a year in the UK: 7.5 million of them UK grown. Five years ago 80% were Norway Spruce, but this is now down to less than 25%, with Nordman Fir, which retains its needles longer, at 60% (95% in urban areas) and Fraser Fir, a US favourite, 12%. The most popular size has been increasing and is now 5 to 7 feet. Only 5% are sold rooted, although public interest in 'living trees' is now increasing.

Imported trees in the past have accounted for 20% of total sales, but imports for Christmas 2005 fell to a few hundred thousand, and this trend has continued in subsequent years. This has put pressure on supplies and resulting in higher wholesale prices. Christmas trees are not eligible for the Single Payment, and as a result, many growers throughout the EU have grubbed-up trees, or are not replanting. The supply of trees in mainland Europe has therefore been substantially reduced. UK Christmas tree growers, unlike those in other countries, have never received subsidies and have not cut back production significantly. In addition changes in the pound-euro exchange rate has made imports more expensive.

There are some 400 British growers across all parts of the country, with plantations ranging from less than one hectare to 1,000 ha. It is estimated that there are 60 million trees being grown, on some 25,000 ha. The average grower sells 6 to 7,000 a year from about 20 ha. The majority of sales are through the big garden centres, which require a uniform tree, netted and palletised, but there are successful 'choose and cut' operations and the enterprise works well on a farm with a farm shop. Producers need to sell 10,000 to 15,000 a year to justify buying machinery to assist in cultivation

The enterprise is slow to make a return. Norway Spruce is harvested in years 5 to 7, Nordman and Fraser Firs in years 7 to 9, making the enterprise vulnerable to changing market conditions. About 30% of the crop is harvested in the first harvesting year, 40% in the second, 30% in the third. All species need a well-drained site free from late frosts, with good access. As with any crop, the better the land, the better the crop.

	Nordman Fir		Norway Spruce	
	£/ha	(£/ac)	£/ha	(£/ac)
4000 5 to 7 foot trees per ha @ price of ..	£5.50 - 6.00 / ft		£4.50 / ft	
Output (average)	138,000	(55,848)	108,000	(43,707)
Variable Costs:*				
Plants	2,950	(1,194)	2,360	(955)
Planting	826	(334)	826	(334)
Fertiliser	916	(371)	687	(278)
Weed control	1925	(779)	1925	(779)
Pesticides	830	(336)	1230	(498)
Pruning and shaping	5005	(2,025)	2723	(1,102)
Harvesting	4675	(1,892)	4125	(1,669)
Marketing	13,800	(5,585)	10,800	(4,371)
Total Variable Costs	30,927	(12,516)	24,676	(9,986)
Gross Margin (whole period)	107,073	(43,332)	83,324	(33,721)
Gross Margin per year over 8 & 6 years ..	**13,384**	**(5,416)**	**13,887**	**(5,620)**

1. *Labour* assumed to be casuals.
2. *Rabbit fencing:* (£2 per m) and possibly deer fencing (£5.50 per m) are pre-requisites. Spacing is possible from 60cm x 60cm to 1.8m x 1.8m, but 1.2m x 1.2m is recommended. This gives 5,500 plants per ha allowing for 80% land loss for headlands, access, etc. Losses of 5 to 10% in the first year means 300-500

replacements are needed in second year. Norway Spruce transplants 30p-50p each, Nordman Fir 40-60p. Planting, by hand or machine, 12-15p/per plant.

3. *Variable Inputs:*

   Fertiliser in a split top dressing of 350 kg/ha 12:11:18 + Mg and TE in late March and mid-September.

   Herbicides for weed control: residual herbicide, as cereals, in first year; subsequently an over-spray in October/November plus spot weeding until the canopy closes over. Weed control costs have been affected by rising herbicide costs and are likely to be 35p/per plant over the life of the tree.

   Pesticides: aphicide three times a year for Norway Spruce, once for Nordman Fir at £35 per ha per application. Acaricide from year 3 to harvest: £200 per ha per year for Norway Spruce, £110 for Nordman Fir.

4. *Pruning and Shaping*: This is essential to produce the shape of tree the market demands. Norway Spruce: shaping 16.5p per tree per year from year 3 or 4. Nordman Fir: basal pruning in year 3 or 4 at 20p per tree plus shaping in the same year at 15p per tree and bud-rubbing every year except harvest at 5-10p per tree per year.

5. *Harvesting:* Done over 3 to 6 weeks, for dispatch Nov 20th to Dec 12th. A full-time person is needed per 3,000 trees sold, or one person per week per 400-500 trees. Cost: Norway Spruce 65-85p per tree, Nordman Fir 75-100p; Norway Spruce may be dipped or sprayed to reduce needle drop. Marketing costs around 10% of output.

6. *Machinery:* Inter-row plantation tractors £15,000-£65,000; stump clearing machines £7,000-£25,000; palletiser £13,000-£14,000; mist blowers £8,000-£10,000; hydraulic netting funnel £8,000-£10,000; manual netting funnel £175.

7. *Labour:* Planting and pruning can be done in January/February and tagging for height and quality in October/November. Thus it fits in well with combinable cropping.

The gross margins given are high, but these will only be achieved by a high level of expertise and commitment and the long period before any return is obtained must also be stressed, together with the risk this entails.

Acknowledgement: Thanks to - British Christmas Tree Growers Association, 13 Wolrige Road, Edinburgh, EH16 6HX. Tel: 0131 664 1100 www.bctga.co.uk.

OTHER DIVERSIFICATION

Well calculated diversification should be encouraged. Non-agricultural enterprises managed in conjunction with the farming operation can offer several benefits to the business. These include:

- Spreading risks of returns; if the economics of agricultural production declines, revenue from non-commodity based enterprises may boost business income.

- Resource efficiency; most farm systems have quieter and busier periods for staff and management which may be switched into other roles for examples.

- Increasing profit.

Any new enterprise will have its own risks associated with it. These must be clearly and objectively calculated (this will be a requirement if borrowed money is necessary). Each resource employed will have its own opportunity cost (what could it be earning if it was not being used for this new venture?). Cash (return on capital) is the obvious one, what could it earn in a high interest account? Labour is less straight forward. For example, a B&B might require minimal new capital under some circumstances, but tie somebody to the house at key times of the day, restricting other employment opportunities.

Before any major investment or change in business structure to incorporate new diversifications, business plans and market research to assess the likely income potential are critical. Most new enterprises require new skills (such as different production systems, new marketing and sales techniques). These take time and dedication to acquire. Developing new ideas and expanding a novel business venture can be exciting and time consuming; maintaining sufficient management time on the existing farm business is a common problem.

Nevertheless, many ventures exist where entrepreneurial skills have achieved notable success. Conversion of surplus farm buildings, for offices, workshops, retail and storage, has been the primary farm diversification activity up to date. A DEFRA survey found that 51% of farms had diversified activity in 2008/09, but if letting farm buildings is stripped out the percentage of diversified farms falls to 28%. It also shows that arable farms tend to be more diversified than livestock and farms in the South East are more diversified than elsewhere in the UK. Diversified enterprises might have a different VAT and taxation treatment. Check in advance with your accountant.

Some 'diversification' enterprises have been included above. There are many others, which include;

Novel Crops/Livestock
- Alpacas
- Herbs
- Carp and Crayfish
- Llamas
- Alpacas
- Quails
- Snails

Sporting
- Fisheries
- Game Shooting
- Stalking
- Clay Pigeon Shooting

Horses
- Riding School
- Trekking

Adventure Games
- Motor Sports
- Go-carting

Tourism
- Caravans / Camping
- Holiday Cottages

Barn Conversions
- Business Lets
- Dwelling Let

Vertical integration
- Yoghurt, Ice cream, etc.
- Meat sales
- Farm Shop

6.   FORESTRY

ESTABLISHMENT COSTS (BEFORE GRANT)

Unit Cost of Operations

Year/s	Operation	Cost (£)
1.	Trees for planting	
	(i) Bare rooted:	
	Conifers	200-260 per 1,000
	Broadleaves	380-480 per 1,000
	(ii) Rooted in small peat blocks:	
	Conifers	170-300 per 1,000
	Broadleaves	350-430 per 1,000
1.	Tree Protection	
	(i) Fencing (materials and erection)	
	Rabbit	5.31-6.49 per metre
	Stock	4.05-4.95 per metre
	Deer	7.02-8.58 per metre
	Deer and Rabbit	9.00-11.00 per metre
	Split post and rail	5·50-8.50 per metre
	(ii) Tree guards/shelters	
	Spiral and canes (450mm)	23-28 per 100
	Plastic tubes (1,200mm)	85-110 per 100
	Stakes	45-55 per 100
1.	Spot spraying	40-60 per 1,000 trees
1.	Hand planting	
	Conifers	180-220 per 1,000 trees
	Broadleaves *	135-165 per 1,000 trees
	Machine planting (loams and sand based on	
	2,250 plants per ha)	225-450 per ha
2-3.	Replacing dead trees **	
	Operation	60-120 per ha
	Plant supply	75-100 per ha
1-4.	Weeding per operation	
	Herbicide ***	45-55 per ha weeded
2.	Inter-row mowing	225-275 per ha

	Costs specific to location		Upland	Lowland
1.	Ground Preparation:	ploughing	132-209 per ha	66- 99 per ha
		mounding	275-385 per ha	275-385 per ha
1.	Drainage		88-110 per ha	—
1.	Fertilising		132-297 per ha	—

*   Includes cost of erecting guards/shelters.

**   Replacing dead trees (beating up) may be necessary, once in the second year and again in the third year. Costs depend on number of trees.

*** Up to 2 weeding operations may be necessary in each of the first 4 years in extreme situations. Costs are inclusive of materials.

Access roads may need to be constructed and can typically cost between £13,500 and £33,000 per kilometre (£21,700 to £53,000 per mile) depending on availability of road stone and the number of culverts and bridges required.

Total Establishment Costs up to Year 3

1. *Conifer—Lowland Sites:* On a fairly typical lowland site, requiring little or no clearing or draining, the approximate cost before grant of establishing a conifer plantation would be in the range £2,000-£3,500 per hectare. Up to 8 separate weeding operations may be required.

2. *Conifer—Upland Sites:* Establishing a similar conifer plantation on an upland site could cost £2,200 to £3,800 per hectare. Normally some form of site preparation and drainage is required but only one weeding operation may be necessary. Overall costs tend to be £110-£270 per ha less than on lowland sites.

3. *Hardwoods:* Costs of establishing hardwood plantations are highly dependent on the fencing and/or tree protection required. If tubes are needed the overall costs will be influenced by the number of plants per hectare. Costs could be in the range £2,000-£5,000 per ha. Site conditions normally mean that hardwoods being grown for timber production are restricted to lowland sites.

4. *Farm Woodlands:* Establishment costs for farm woodlands may be lower than those indicated for hardwoods in (3) above if lower planting densities are used. Initial establishment costs in the first year of about £2,800 per ha for woods under 3 ha and £2,500 per ha for woods of 3 to 10 ha would be typical.

5. *Size Factor:* Savings in fencing and other economies of scale may reduce average costs per ha by 10 to 20% where large plantations are being established.

6. *Method of Establishment:* A range of organisations and individuals undertake forestry contracting work and competitive tendering can help to control costs.

Re-Stocking Costs

Once trees on a site have been felled, the Forestry Commission usually requires the site to be restocked as a condition of awarding a felling licence. This can be done by replanting or through natural regeneration, leaving a proportion of the trees standing and using seed from these trees to re-stock. Minimal site preparation is usually required for natural regeneration. There is no grant for restocking woodland, although grant is available for 'regeneration' where the species mix is being altered. (see Grant section). The costs of establishment given above, and those for maintenance given below, are estimates for England. Costs in Scotland tend to be lower.

MAINTENANCE COSTS

Once trees have been established they normally require some maintenance and management work each year. For trees being grown primarily for timber production on a large scale, operations required may include ride and fence maintenance, pest control, fire protection, management fee and insurance premiums. Costs are normally £40-£60 per ha per annum depending on the size of the plantation and the complexity of management. In upland areas, fertiliser is occasionally applied once or more times in the first 20 years of the tree's life depending on the quality of the site. Estimated cost £110-£275 per ha, depending on elements applied. For trees being grown for sporting and amenity purposes, annual maintenance costs are likely to be less and may range up to about £11 per ha.

A brashing operation which involves removing branches up to two metres may be required for access reasons as the crop matures. Opening up inspection racks over 5-10% of the crop may cost £44-£77 per ha. Brashing 40-50% of the crop costs £180-£400 per ha.

PRODUCTION

Production is usually measured in terms of cubic metres (m^3) of marketable timber per hectare and will vary according to the quality of the site, species planted and thinning policy. Sites in lowland Britain planted to conifers typically produce an average of 12 to 18 m^3 of timber per ha per year over the rotation as a whole and would accordingly be assessed as falling in yield classes 12 to 18. Under traditional management systems, thinning begins 18 to 25 years after planting and is repeated at intervals of approximately 5 years until the wood is clear-felled at between 40 and 60 years. Approximately 40-45% of total production will be from thinnings. Broadleaves typically produce an average of between 4 and 8 m³ of timber per hectare per year and fall in yield classes 4 to 8. A felling licence must be obtained from the Forestry Commission before any felling takes place, unless a Forest Management Plan has already been approved by them. Grants are available for preparing a Forest Management Plan which covers a 20 year period (see Grants section).

Prior to a thinning sale the trees normally have to be marked and measured at an estimated cost of 75p - £1 per m³, which is equivalent to £175-£300 per hectare depending on species, crop density and age. For a clear-felling sale the cost can range from £300 to £400 per ha, or about £1.50 per m³ where a full tariff applies, i.e. where each tree is counted and sample measurements of individual trees are taken.

Felling permission is also required when more than 5m³ are to be removed in one calendar quarter. This requires an application to the Forestry Commission for a Felling Licence which will vary in complexity depending on the size and variety of the woodland.

PRICES

Prices for standing timber are extremely variable, depending on species, tree size and quality, ease of extraction from site, geographical location (nearness to end user), quantity being sold, world market prices and effectiveness of marketing method used. The use of wood for energy generation is beginning to open up a new market for poorer quality hardwood and conifer logs and forest residues.

Conifers

Coniferous Standing Sales Price for Great Britain from the Forest Enterprise Estate

Year to:	Average Price (Per m³ Overbark)		Fisher (5 yearly)	
	Nominal Terms (£)	Real Terms (2006 price in £)	Nominal Terms	Real Terms (2006 Price)
31-Mar-03	5.75	6.28	82.0	89.6
31-Mar-04	5.60	5.95	79.5	84.5
31-Mar-05	6.13	6.33	86.9	89.8
31-Mar-06	7.25	7.36	100.0	101.5
31-Mar-07	7.97	7.83	111.0	109.0
31-Mar-08	12.48	11.92	173.8	166.0
31-Mar-09	9.15	8.50	124.2	115.4
31-Mar-10	9.61	8.78	131.0	119.6
31-Mar-11	13.70	12.17	181.5	161.2

Source: Forestry Commission: Timber Price Indices March 2011

Fisher 5 yearly index corrects distortions in size mix enabling different years to be compared on the basis of a consistent tree size. In order to ensure this base size mix remains relevant over time it is updated every 5 years. The current base year is 2006. *Real Terms* accounts for the effects of general inflation

Hardwoods

The hardwood trade is very complex. Merchants normally assess and value all but the smallest trees on a stem by stem basis. Actual prices fetched can show considerable variation depending on species, size, form, quality and marketing expertise of the seller. Felling usually takes place in the winter months.

Some indicative prices for hardwoods are given below, but it is important to note that actual prices fetched can vary quite widely. Wood quality is particularly important in determining prices.

Harvesting stage	Tree size range (m³)	Price range £ per m³ standing	Possible use
First thinnings	<0.13	0-16	Firewood, board products and pulp wood. Poles for refineries and turnery.
Subsequent Thinnings	0.13-0.3	5-20	Smaller sizes and lower quality
	0.3-0.6	8-25	material may go for fencing or
	0.6 -1.0	10-70	for use in the mining industry.
Clearfellings	1.0-2.0	15-120	Trees over 30 cm in diameter and of better quality may go for planking, furniture or joinery.
	2+	25-250	High quality material may go for veneers and can fetch between £150 and £300 per m³ depending on species and specifications.

Prices for Oak, Sycamore, Cherry and Elm tend to be significantly higher than for Beech, which seldom exceeds about £45 per m³ standing even for stands containing significant volumes of first quality planking. The market for Ash has been historically weak for the past 5-7 years.

TIMBER MARKETING

In-house marketing by the owner or agent can be cost effective but only if they have detailed, up-to-date knowledge of timber buyers in the market place. The alternative is marketing through a forestry manager or management company.

Nationwide electronic sales of timber by auction and tender are now available for all types and quantities of timber.

MARKET VALUE OF ESTABLISHED PLANTATIONS AND WOODS

The value of woods depends on many factors, such as location, access, species, age and soil type. The table on the following page gives an indication of the range of current (2011) market values of commercial woodlands of different ages, based on recent market sales.

From years 20 to 25 onwards prices of commercial woods will also be increasingly influenced by the quantity of merchantable timber they contain. Depending on the time of clear-felling, the timber may be worth between £900 to £6,000 per hectare (£360 to £2,500 per acre).

Woods that are relatively small with high amenity or Ancient Woodland status can often command a premium over prices fetched for commercial woodlands as can those that are freehold and include minerals and sporting rights. This is particularly the case in southern England. Conversely conservation designation can restrict value by potentially preventing economic forest management.

The value of woods containing mature hardwoods will depend on the quality and value of the timber they contain and the quality of access.

Market Value of Commercial Sitka Spruce Woodlands

Age of Commercial Woods and Plantations	Price Range for crop and land	
	£/ha	£/acre
0-5 years...	1,000-2500	(400-1000)
6-10 years..	2,000-2,800	(800-1,200)
11-15 years..	2,500-3,900	(1,000-1,600)
16-20 years..	3,000-4,900	(1,200-2,000)
21-25 years..	3,500-6,000	(1,600-2,600)

WOODLAND GRANTS

Each part of the United Kingdom has its own woodland grant scheme, administered by the Forestry Commission. In England it is called the English Woodland Grant Scheme, in Scotland there are grants for woodlands offered as part of the Rural Development Programme, and in Wales they are offered under the Better Woodlands for Wales (BWW) programme. Details of all the schemes can be obtained via the Forestry Commission's website (www.forestry.gov.uk). Previous grant schemes are now closed to new entrants.

English Woodland Grant Scheme

The English Woodland Grant Scheme (EWGS) is the Forestry Commission's suite of grants designed to develop the co-ordinated delivery of public benefits from England's woods. EWGS is supported via the Rural Development Programme for England (RDPE).

In order to be eligible for the grant scheme, woodlands need to be registered on the Rural Land Register and the owner must hold a Single Business Identifier. There are six components of the scheme as follows:

1. *Woodland Management Planning Grant:* available as a contribution towards the cost of producing plans for existing woodlands, and which meet the UK Woodland Assurance Standard. Rates of grant contribution are £20 per hectare for the first 100 hectares and £10 thereafter. There is a minimum payment of £1,000 for plans covering more than 3 hectares but less than 30 hectares.

2. *Woodland Assessment Grant:* available as a contribution towards the costs of obtaining additional information about the woodland in relation to ecology, landscape, historic and heritage assessments, and to determine stakeholder interests. Grant varies from £2.80 per ha - £5.60 per ha with a minimum payment of £300.

3. *Woodland Management Grant:* aid for providing public benefits and to undertake sustainable woodland management. Potentially eligible activities include public access, maintaining boundaries, protecting archaeological features, management of old wood habitat and open space, soil and ground water protection, controlling non-native species, pest control, woodland health and monitoring sustainability. The rate of grant is in line with ELS payments at £30 per hectare per year.

4. *Woodland Regeneration Grant:* a contribution towards the cost of regenerating woodland after felling. The aim is to promote the replacement of felled woodland whilst changing woodland types for increased public benefit. Grant rates depend on the type of wood being felled and the type of wood which replaces it:

Type of woodland site	Type of woodland being regenerated	Grant (£/ha)
Ancient Woodland Site	Native Woodland....................................	1,750
Ancient Woodland Site	Non-Native Woodland...........................	0

Non-Ancient Woodland Site   Native Woodland.................................   1000

Non-Ancient Woodland Site   Non-Native Woodland.........................   500

These figures are subject to review following the report of the Independent Panel on Forestry in April 2012.

5. *Woodland Improvement Grant:* a contribution towards the cost of work to improve the quality of woodland for social, environmental, and economic benefits. The rate of grant is set between 50% - 80% of standard costs in a five-year plan. The focus is on improving access, biodiversity, and protecting SSSIs. Regions can choose to vary the rate of contributions or priority areas to reflect regional differences.

    A new national *Woodland Improvement Grant* is available which funds mensuration and access works based more on receipted invoices rather than FC standard costs. This will pay 60% towards works in undermanaged and inaccessible woodlands.

6. *Woodland Creation Grants:* aids the establishment of new woodlands. This element of the EWGS is competitive and will be assessed on a points-scoring system with the applications that give the greatest benefits being selected. Woodland creation may be by natural regeneration or by direct seeding/planting. The rates of grant will depend on the type of woodland; Standard (3 ha or more), Small Standard (less than 3 ha), Native Species Only, Community (designed for public access), or Special Broadleaved (species appropriate for growth at wide spacing). Planting density requirements, percentage open space and percentage of shrub element are set for for each woodland type. Rates of grant are as follows:

Woodland category	*Broadleaves* £/ha	*Conifers* £/ha
Standard, Native and Community	1,800	1,200
Special Broadleaved	700	n/a

In addition to the above grant an extra £500 per ha is paid for woodland established within five miles of 100,000 people or within the National Forest Area, or where there is an agreement to provide for public access and there is an identified need. Woodland meeting both of these requirements will be eligible to claim £1000 per ha. An additional £2,000 per ha is also available for woodland planted within target areas located throughout the country.

Payment is made 80% on the completion of the work, with the final 20% payable after 5 years as long as the plantation is maintained. Applications usually have to be made prior to a 30th September deadline prior to the winter/spring when the planting will take place.

Planting on Agricultural Land: Annual payments are available under the Farm Woodland Payment for converting agricultural land to woodland (similar to the old FWPS). Payments will continue for 15 years when new woodlands comprise more than 50% broadleaved species, and 10 years when the percentage broadleaves is less than 50% (or fast growing broadleaved species such as poplar). Payment rates will depend on the agricultural land use category being converted to woodland. Current rates are set out below, although they are subject to revision every 5 years;

Payments available under the Farm Woodland Payment

Agricultural Land Category	Annual payment (£ per ha)
Arable Land in the Lowlands	300
Other improved land in the Lowlands....	200
Unimproved or land in the Uplands	60
None-farmer...	Capped €150 or above rate if lower

More details of the EWGS are available on the Forestry Commission website (www.forestry.gov.uk). There are deadlines for the submission of application forms for the different components of the scheme as funding is limited. Early discussion with one of Forestry Commission England Conservancy offices is advised. Help and advice can also be obtained from the EWGS helpline Tel: 01223 346 004.

WOODLAND SINGLE PAYMENT & CARBON FUNDING

Landowners who are eligible for the Farm Woodland Payment can also continue to claim Single Payment on the same land. The Forestry Commission will not fund applications for new woodland creation that include carbon co-funding if there is any link between the proposals and use of the term 'offsetting'. The Forestry Commission will, however, allow co-funding provided certain criteria are met and appropriate language is used. This is being formalised with the Forestry Commission's Woodland Carbon Code which new plantations can be registered with to verify their CO_2 sequestration and allow it to be marketed (http://www.forestry.gov.uk/carboncode).

WOODLAND TAXATION

Income from commercial woodlands is not subject to income tax, and tax relief cannot be claimed for the cost of establishing new woodlands. In general EWGS grants are tax free but annual Farm Woodland Payments are regarded as compensation for agricultural income forgone and are liable to income tax. The sale of timber does not attract Capital Gains Tax, although the disposal of the underlying land may give rise to an assessment.

Woodlands which are managed commercially or which are ancillary to a farming business may be eligible for either Business Property Relief or Agricultural Relief for Inheritance Tax purposes if owned for more than two years.

Acknowledgement: The above estimates are based on information supplied by Justin Mumford FICFor CEnv of Lockhart Garratt Ltd (Tel: 01536 408 840).

7.   ORGANIC FARMING

The Organic Sector:

The total organic land area fell in the UK from 2008 to 2009 by 1%. Data for 2010 has not yet been published. Others' estimates for 2010 are based on this 2009 data. Throughout 2009, 4.0% of UK agricultural land (excluding common grazing) was in organic production on 4,946 (5,383) holdings. In 2009 the area (in hectares) devoted to organic production was as follows:

	Fully Organic	In conversion	Total	% of Agric. Area	of UK Organic Area	% of UK Organic Producers
England	311,176	67,588	378,764	4.0	51.3	62
Wales	88,566	36,800	125,366	8.4	17.0	20
Scotland	209,256	12,039	221,295	4.0	30.0	12
N. Ireland	10,270	3,015	13,284	1.3	1.8	5
2009	619,268	119,442	738,709	4.2	100	100
2008	594,413	149,103	743,516	4.2		
2007	524,303	157,893	682,196	3.9		
2006	498,646	121,137	619,783	3.6		
2005	533,902	85,951	619,853	3.6		

Following a rise in organic demand and therefore production in recent years, the demand for organic food waned over the last 3 years (12.8% fall in organic demand in 2009, 5.9 in 2010). Not only have shoppers been tightening their belts but the rise of other, sometimes less expensive food brandings have been stealing the 'ethical crown' such as Fairtrade, free range and local produce. Organic products have their share of supermarket promotions to encourage greater consumption. Farm gate organic premiums over conventional foods have fallen over the last 18 months, squeezing organic margins. For example, organic cereal has fallen from a 100% price premium to approximately 50%, and milk which used to have a 9ppl premium has slipped to 3ppl.

There is grant aid to help producers during the required conversion period (see next page). Some organic farmers have reverted to conventional production primarily because of declining premiums. Imports of organic fruit and vegetables, are especially high, indeed, over half of organic produce consumers in the UK is imported.

Many hill and upland livestock farms have converted to organic production – with inputs already low, management changes need only be small. Similar factors have meant that a sizeable number of extensive lowland beef and sheep producers have also embraced organic production. This contributes to the explanation why organic farms are less productive than conventional.

Below are the land use estimates of producers of organic and in conversion crop areas and livestock numbers for the applicable years:

Organic Land Use according to Crop Type (UK)

'000 ha	2005	2006	2007	2008	2009	year on year % change
Cereals	47.7	47.5	51.5	57.2	60.0	4.8
Other crops	10.8	10.2	11.3	11.2	11.2	0.2
Fruit & Nut	1.7	1.8	2.0	1.9	2.2	16.9
Vegetables & Pots	13.7	15.5	16.9	19.8	18.9	-4.4
Herbs & Ornam.s	0.8	0.7	0.6	5.5	5.8	4.5
Temporary pasture	98	102.7	125.1	130	126	-2.8
Permanent pasture	429	422.6	452.0	496	496	0.3
Woodland	6.7	8.2	11.5	5.9	7.2	21.9
Other	12.1	10.6	11.2	17.9	11.6	-35.4
Total area ha	*620*	*619*	*682*	*744*	*739*	*-0.6*

Organic Livestock Numbers (UK)

'000 head	2005	2006	2007	2008	2009	year on year % change
Cattle	214.3	244.8	250.4	*319.6*	*331.2*	*3.6*
Sheep				*n/a*	*884.8*	*n/a*
Pigs	30.0	32.9	50.4	*71.2*	*48.2*	*-32.4*
Poultry	3,439	4,421	4,440	*4,363*	*3,959*	*-9.3*
Goats	0.5	0.6	0.5	*0.4*	*0.1*	*-67.5*
Other Livestock	1.5	4.3	3.4	*4.3*	*3.3*	*-25.2*

The economics to the farmer depend primarily upon the:

- relative yield compared with conventional farming;
- price premium compared with conventional farming.

In the case of cereals both research and experience suggests that yields of organic crops are typically between 60% and 70% of those of conventionally produced crops, but the much higher prices obtained have compensated for this to date, with feed wheat prices having reached £210 per tonne and feed beans £265 per tonne ex-farm, in addition to the obvious saving in fertiliser and spray costs although prices have drifted back since. Hence the gross margin is normally much higher as long as a good yield is achieved. There are also the wider whole farm effects to be considered, e.g., unless the farm already has a substantial percentage of its area down to leys this will probably have to be increased in order to maintain yields and this extra grass has to be utilised profitably – which is far from easy, and the extra capital requirements could be heavy.

There is also a two year 'conversion period' to undergo before full price premiums can be claimed; (though note the aid scheme, below). Also, in the case of vegetable crops, quality (in the sense of appearance) can be badly affected by pests and diseases. Survey data have indicated overall labour requirements to be 10-30% higher than on conventional farms, with machinery costs generally similar.

Aid for Organic Farmers:

In England, support for organic farmers is through the Organic Entry Level Stewardship (OELS) (see Section III). This provides relatively high levels of support per hectare for the two-year conversion period. Rates then drop to a 'stewardship' level thereafter but remain at double the 'mainstream' ELS rates. Similar schemes, but with different categories and payment rates, are available in Wales and in Scotland.

Further Information:

No gross margin data for organic enterprises are included in this section because a specialist publication is available on the subject: the '2011 Organic Farm Management Handbook', (9th Ed - 2011) by Nic Lampkin, Mark Measures and Susanne Padel, Organic Research Centre, Elm Farm, Newbury. Tel: 01488 658 298.

Additional information may be available from the following organisations:

DEFRA (Organic Food and Industrial Crops Division)
Nobel House, 17 Smith Square, London, SW1P 3JR.
http://www.food.gov.uk/foodindustry/farmingfood/organicfood/

Organic Farmers and Growers Limited
The Elim Centre, Lancaster Road, Shrewsbury, Shropshire, SY1 3LE
http://www.organicfarmers.org.uk/   01939 291 800

Soil Association
Bristol House, 40-56 Victoria Street, Bristol, BS1 6BY
http://www.soilassociation.org/   0117 314 5000

Elm Farm Research Centre
Hamstead Marshall, Newbury, Berkshire, RG20 0HR
http://www.organicresearchcentre.com/   01488 658 298

Biodynamic Agricultural Association
The Secretary, Painswick Inn, Stroud, Glos. GL5 1QG
http://www.biodynamic.org.uk/   01453 759 501

Organic Food Federation
1 Turbine Way, EcoTech Business Park, Swaffham, Norfolk, PE37 7XD
http://www.orgfoodfed.com/   01760 720 444

Organic Centre Wales
University of Wales, Aberystwyth, Ceredigion, SY23 3AL
http://www.organiccentrewales.org.uk/   01970 622 248

Tesco Centre for Organic Agriculture
Nafferton Farm, Stocksfield, Northumberland, NE47 7XD
http://research.ncl.ac.uk/nefg/index.php   01661 830 222

8. SUMMARY OF GROSS MARGINS

This page summarises the key figures of the gross margins over the previous pages. There are well in excess of 100 gross margins in the Pocketbook and additional data for other enterprises too. They cannot be directly compared on a like for like basis, as different resources are required in order to produce each one and some offer whole farm benefits beyond the gross margin. Some, for example require higher quality land than others and some will require more overheads in terms of machinery, labour, buildings or working capital than others. Management requirement varies from one enterprise to another. Others are subject to having a supply contract with the processor.

Summary of Arable Crop Gross Margins

Crop (£/Ha)	Price	Yield	Output	Variable Costs	Gross Margin
Winter Feed Wheat	£140	8.35	£1,169	£496	£673
Winter Milling Wheat	£155	7.70	£1,194	£558	£636
Spring Milling Wheat	£153	5.75	£878	£387	£491
Winter Feed Barley	£135	6.90	£932	£400	£532
Winter Malting Barley	£150	6.00	£900	£353	£547
Spring Malting Barley	£155	5.45	£845	£297	£548
Winter Oats	£130	6.30	£819	£299	£520
Spring Oats	£130	5.50	£715	£263	£452
Winter Rape	£340	3.40	£1,156	£442	£714
Spring Rape	£340	2.00	£680	£257	£423
Spring Linseed	£375	1.75	£656	£250	£406
Winter Linseed	£375	2.50	£938	£409	£529
Winter Beans	£187	4.00	£748	£245	£503
Spring Beans	£200	3.70	£740	£218	£522
Blue Peas	£190	3.75	£713	£281	£432
Marofats	£215	3.40	£731	£317	£414
Lupins	£280	3.00	£840	£297	£543
Rye	£160	6.20	£992	£421	£571
Triticale	£135	5.00	£675	£322	£353
Naked Oats	£188	5.50	£1,034	£340	£694
Durum Wheat	£190	6.20	£1,178	£449	£729
Borage	£2,500	0.40	£1,000	£307	£693
Crambe	£250	2.50	£625	£308	£317
Hemp	£160	7.50	£1,200	£493	£707
Grain Maize	£165	7.50	£1,238	£416	£821
Millet	£300	3.00	£900	£302	£598
Poppies		2.00	£850	£329	£521
Soya	£375	2.50	£938	£283	£654
Sunflower	£390	2.00	£780	£276	£504
Vining Peas	£300	4.75	£1,425	£463	£962
Maincrop Potatoes	£154	45.00	£6,930	£3,024	£3,906
Early Potatoes	£210	23.00	£4,830	£2,203	£2,627
Sugarbeet	£31.70	67.00	£2,124	£943	£1,181

Summary of Livestock Gross Margins

Livestock		Output	Variable Costs	Gross Margin /Head	Gross margin £/Ha
Dairy					
Friesian Holsteins	per Cow	£1,723	£818	£905	£1,810
Channel Island	per Cow	£1,330	£685	£645	£1,549
Ayreshire	per Cow	£1,523	£723	£799	£1,919
Friesian Followers	per Head	£1,060	£505	£555	£766
Channel Followers	per Head	£870	£442	£428	£744
Ayreshire Followers	per Head	£770	£434	£336	£585
Beef Cattle					
Bucket Reared Calf 3 month	per Calf	£107	£94	£13	
Bucket Reared Calf 6 month	per Calf	£207	£185	£22	
Spring calving lowland suckler	per Cow	£331	£237	£94	£170
Autumn calving lowland suckle	per Cow	£458	£317	£141	£233
Spring calving upland suckler	per Cow	£302	£226	£76	£121
Autumn calving upland suckler	per Cow	£426	£317	£109	£136
Store Cattle Keeping Summer	per Head	£262	£59	£204	£1,172
Store Cattle Keeping Winter	per Head	£256	£143	£114	
Summer Store Finishers	per Head	£352	£123	£230	£919
Winter Store Finishers	per Head	£358	£265	£93	
Summer finished sucklers	per Head	£591	£151	£440	£1,849
Winter finished sucklers	per Head	£340	£243	£96	
Maize Finishing (dairy)	per Head	£712	£331	£381	
Maize Finishing (suckler)	per Head	£645	£279	£366	
Cereal Bull Beef (continental)	per Head	£639	£573	£66	
Cereal Bull Beef (dairy)	per Head	£733	£573	£160	
Sheep					
Lowland Spring Lamb	per Ewe	£93	£52	£42	£417
Upland Spring Lamb	per Ewe	£72	£48	£23	£197
Gimmering Ewe Lambs	per Ewe	£48	£20	£28	£351
Finishing Store Lambs	per Ewe	£24	£19	£5	£140

Summary of Livestock Gross Margins (Continued)

Livestock		Output	Variable Costs	Gross Margin /Head	Gross margin £/Ha
Pigs					
Weaners	per Sow	£994	£801	£193	
Pork	per Pig	£44	£34	£9.55	
Cutter	per Pig	£59	£45	£13.85	
Bacon	per Pig	£73	£56	£17.05	
Combined Pork	per Pig	£88	£70	£18.22	
Combined Cutter	per Pig	£103	£81	£22.52	
Combined Bacon	per Pig	£118	£92	£25.72	
Poultry					
Caged Eggs	per Bird	£10.60	£13.34	-£2.74	
Free Range Eggs	per Bird	£17.08	£15.15	£1.93	£2,002
Pullets	/Bird Reared	£3.08	£2.38	£0.70	
Broilers	p/Bird	159.40p	152.57p	6.83p	
All year turkey	£/Bird	£36.61	£19.19	£17.42	
Christmas Turkey	£/Bird	£40.47	£23.28	£17.20	
Large Roaster Chickens	£/Bird	£15.52	£6.28	£9.24	
Ducks	£/Bird	£7.42	£5.20	£2.22	
Geese	£/Bird	£48.48	£29.68	£18.80	
Other Livestock					
Breeding & Finishing Deer	/100 Hinds	£19,165	£1,764	£17,401	£957
Deer Calves	/100 Hinds	£10,190	£765	£9,425	£613
Finishing Stag Calves	/200 Hinds	£24,263	£4,215	£20,048	£1,103
Ostriches ~ Laying Trios	per Trio	£1,024	£164	£859	£0
Ostriches ~ Fatteners	per bird	£350	£339	£11	£64
Wild Boar	per Sow	£1,217	£762	£455	
Dairy Sheep	per Ewe	£401	£252	£149	£1,640
Dairy Goats	per Doe	£296	£243	£53	£427
Angora Goats	per Doe	£215	£21	£194	£1,263
Trout	/tonne Fish	£1,930	£1,365	£565	

III.   GOVERNMENT SUPPORT

1.   INTRODUCTION

Agricultural support to farmers and the rural economy is largely provided through the European Union's Common Agricultural Policy (CAP), and delivered in the UK by the devolved Governments of England, Wales, Scotland and Northern Ireland. The World Trade Organisation (WTO) provides a global tier in the hierarchy of agricultural (trade) policy. With the agreements of the WTO Doha Development Round no short term WTO driven trade-policy changes are foreseen. The Doha Round was intended to lead to an agreement that would have meant (amongst other things) the EU reducing barriers to imports (mainly tariffs and tariff quotas) and this could have had the effect of reducing prices (of protected goods) to UK farmers. Now the existing tariff regime largely continues and it is likely to be several years before any changes are agreed and implemented.

The CAP has two main budgets (or pillars). Pillar 1 includes the Single Payment Scheme (SPS) which provides direct aid to farm businesses and also Market Support for agricultural produce – once the mainstay of CAP support, but now much reduced in importance. Pillar 2 is support through Rural Development and provides direct support to farmers and also to rural communities. As an indication of the relative importance of Pillar 1 and Pillar 2 support to English farmers it is estimated that in 2010 Pillar 1 will have amounted to approximately 81% and Pillar 2 19%. Market support (which is not paid direct to farmers) is not included but is now a small proportion of total CAP support. Negotiations are underway on the future of the CAP as the current policy period draws to an end. See section 4 below for initial proposals and timetable for reforms.

Further details of the current main CAP mechanisms are given in the following paragraphs: in individual situations businesses should always check with the latest legislation and their devolved administrations' publications.

2.   SINGLE PAYMENT SCHEME

Major reforms of Pillar 1 of the CAP were implemented for the most part, on the 1st January 2005. Then in November 2005 a major reform of the Sugar Regime was agreed including price cuts and compensation to farmers starting with the 2006 sugar beet crop. In 2007 a reform of the Fruit and Vegetable regime was agreed. These subsequent reforms have now been incorporated into the Single Payment legislation and there have been some significant simplifications. The latest changes were in 2008 when the 'Health Check' of the CAP was agreed. This was not a radical reform.

SINGLE PAYMENT SCHEME BASICS

The major, essential change of the 2005 reforms was **_decoupling_**. This means that farm support is no longer linked to what is being produced on the farm during the year, i.e. to the crops being grown or the livestock kept. In most Member States (and Wales, Scotland and NI), the 'Single Payment' (SP) (also referred to as the 'Single Farm Payment') is made according to what was produced, by each claimant, during the three years 2000-2002 (the reference period). This is known as the 'historic system' of SP allocation. England is in a transition period (2005 to 2012) of allocating the payment from the historic to a 'flat-rate' regional average payment per hectare.

The system may be regarded as a complex method: generally referred to as a 'dynamic hybrid' or 'delayed flat-rate'. It consists of some of each, historic and regional average, with the proportions changing over an eight-year period: starting mainly historic and changing in annual steps to become entirely a flat rate regional average, as follows:

Transitional Percentages from Historic to Regional Component in English SPS

Year	2005	2006	2007	2008	2009	2010	2011	2012
% historic	90	85	70	55	40	25	10	0
% regional	10	15	30	45	60	75	90	100

The regional payments in England differ according to topography, with three types: lowland (or non SDA), non moorland severely disadvantaged areas (SDAs) and moorland SDA. Payments for the second of these are approximately 80% of those in the lowland and those for moorland about 14% (i.e. about a sixth of those in non-moorland SDAs). By 2012, the claimants in each of these regions will receive the same amount as any other recipient in that region.

In order to receive payment, recipients have to be farming 'eligible' land (see below). They must also satisfy 'cross-compliance' rules, which are in two parts: 'Statutory Management Requirements' (directives, largely already in force, on public and plant health, animal welfare and the environment) and keeping the land in 'Good Agricultural and Environmental Condition'. They apply to the entire holding. The rules in England include no cultivating, fertilising or spraying within two metres of the centre line of any hedge or ditch, no hedge cutting between 1st March and 31st July and providing a soil management plan. The area of permanent pasture in each region must be maintained (this is a government responsibility to monitor not an individual farmer responsibility).

A claimant's total reference amount (or historic entitlement) was calculated by multiplying the area and headage claims in the reference period by the 2005 aid rates in euros per hectare, per head or per litre. These were as follows:

2005 Aid Rates used for Calculating Reference Amount

Arable Area: €/ha		Livestock: €/head	
England	371.07	Suckler Cow Premium	237.5
Scotland non-LFA	357.21	Beef Special Premium (steers)	150
Scotland LFA	328.23	Beef Special Premium (bulls)	210
Wales non-LFA	325.71	Slaughter Premium	80
Wales LFA	318.15	Extensification (lower rate)	40
N.Ireland non-LFA	328.86	Extensification (higher rate)	80
N.Ireland LFA	316.89	Sheep Annual Premium (SAP)	21.79
Other Crops:		SAP LFA Supplement	7.00
Hops	480.00	*Dairy: (€/litre)*	
Dried Fodder Aid (€/tonne)	68.83	2005	0.02435
		2006	0.03654

Sugar: Compensation for sugar reform price cuts increased farmers' reference amounts on the basis of their contract tonnage for the 2005 crop. For 2006 the whole amount of £6.58 per tonne was paid separately after receipt of the Single Payment, subject to modulation deductions. Since 2007, compensation has been incorporated into the recipient's reference amount (for the historic component) and has been subject to the increasing deductions under the English regional average scheme.

OTHER SINGLE PAYMENT POINTS

The other important points are as follows:

- As the payments are calculated in euros the pound:euro exchange rate is important. The rate used is that prevailing on 30th September each year. For the first three years the rate was €1 = 68-69p. There was an increase in 2008 to 79p. In 2009 the rate jumped to €1=91p, it reduced in 2010 to €1=86p. For 2011 and 2012 the rate used in the Pocketbook is €1=88p.

- Initial entitlements were awarded to the IACS claimant of agricultural land in 2005. They are transferable/tradable: and can be sold with or without land, or leased only with an equivalent area of land.

- In 2005 only, farmers could opt for the historic payments to which they were entitled to be paid in full on a smaller area of land than that previously farmed. This provision applied in England, and to a much lesser extent elsewhere.

- Most farmland is 'eligible', comprising arable land and permanent pasture but excluding woodland and land in non-agricultural use. Initially 'permanent crops' (essentially orchards and vineyards) were excluded, but new legislation allows this land to be eligible. The land has to be 'at the farmer's disposal', initially for at least ten months (the 10 month rule), but since 2008 the land has to be at the farmer's disposal for just 15th May (the application deadline).

- Since 2008, land growing soft fruit, vegetables and potatoes (fvp crops) can activate any entitlements (this applies to all UK land). This change removed the need for 'FVP Authorised Entitlements' in England.

- Set-aside Entitlements were issued to farmers in 2005, in Scotland and Wales at 10% of the Arable Area Payment claims in the years 2000-02. In England they were based on 8% in English lowland (1.3% in non-moorland SDA) of arable land in 2005. Now that compulsory set-aside has been abandoned by the EU under the Health Check, set-aside entitlements have been converted into 'normal' entitlements. They no longer need to be activated by 'arable land' that is in set-aside although they still retain their existing values (i.e. regional average component only).

- Following the ending of set-aside, English ministers had intended to introduce, as a cross compliance measure under the SPS, a compulsory area of cultivated land in environmental management. This has not been implemented. Instead it was decided to give the voluntary approach, advocated by the CLA and NFU, time to prove it can recapture the environmental benefits of set-aside. The vehicle for this is the 'Campaign for the Farmed Environment' (CFE). Various targets have been set by Defra, for example to double the current uptake of in-field options under ELS to 40,000 Ha, and farmers not in ELS to enter at least 30,000 Ha into voluntary environmental management. Farmers are encouraged to do what they can to help make the CFE a success. They have until 2012 to meet these targets otherwise there is the possibility of a regulatory approach being introduced.

- A Dairy Premium was introduced in 2004 as compensation for intervention price cuts. Details of the payments in 2005 and 2006 are given on the previous page. These were decoupled in 2005 and added to reference amounts based on quota held at 31st March 2005. In England, as with all other payments, the annual historic element is calculated by multiplying the relevant annual percentage, and therefore worth less than in Wales and Scotland.

- There were supplements (euros/ha) for protein crops (€55.57) and energy crops (€45). Following the Health Check, the Energy Crops Premium ended after the 2009 scheme year. The Protein Crop Supplement ends in 2012 at the latest. Member States have the option to end it earlier. In England the Supplement ended in 2011, it will now be included in the regional payments. In Scotland the Supplement finished in 2009, those who grew proteins have had their entitlement values increased. In Wales the payment will continue until 2012.

DEDUCTIONS TO THE SINGLE PAYMENT

Initial deductions: A 'National Ceiling', based on past national subsidy receipts led to a 0.17% reduction in England only. Across the UK 4.2% was deducted for the 'National Reserve', to provide payments for special cases, e.g. new entrants since the end of 2002 and purchasers of extra land. These two deductions were made before issuing the initial entitlements in 2005. Up to 10% of direct payments from each sector can be deducted to set up a 'National Envelope' to support specific types of farming or improve product quality/marketing; in the UK this is only being used in Scotland (for beef).

Modulation: There is compulsory 'Modulation' (for all EU member states) to fund EU-wide Rural Development projects; this was 3% in 2005, 4% in 2006 and 5% in 2007 and initially agreed to be 5% thereafter. But following the Health Check this was increased by 2% in 2009 and then by 1% for the next three years, taking it to 10% in 2012. Additionally, since 2009 there is an extra 4% on top of the normal EU rate for the element of Single Payment exceeding €300,000. From the amount raised through Modulation, Member States get at least 80% of its modulated funds back for use in Rural Development programmes and there is an element of compulsory match-funding by Member States. The first €5,000 of aid on every farm is exempt.

Member States may also levy 'voluntary' (National) modulation, and the UK has levied this at different rates in the devolved administrations since 2005. The Health Check (HC) increased the rates applying from 2009 onwards. Effectively the 'total' modulation rate is now the higher of the pre HC EU rate + national modulation or the new higher EU rate. For the UK the agreed modulation rates for payments under €300,000 are shown below for each devolved administration;

Agreed Total UK and EU Modulation Rates and the New Higher EU Rate

%	2005	2006	2007	2008	2009	2010	2011	2012
Scotland	6.5	8.5	10	13	13.5	14	14	14
Wales	4.5	4.5	5	7.5	9.2	10.8	11.5	11.5
N.Ireland	3	8.5	9.5	11	12	13	14	14
England	5	10	17	18	19	19	19	19

Higher rates of modulation apply in Wales for claims in excess of €300,000; 11% in 2009 rising by 1% per year to 14% in 2012.

Financial Discipline: EU Farm Ministers decide annually what percentage reductions are needed to keep spending within stipulated budget thresholds; as with EU modulation the first €5,000 of aid per farm is exempt. No Financial Discipline has been deducted so far and none is expected for 2011, but for budgeting it may be prudent to allow 1% for 2012.

TOTAL PAYMENTS PER FARM

Every farm has a different total payment per hectare each year up to 2011 because their historic payments are unique. In Wales and Scotland these differences will persist until they change from the wholly historic system which is likely following the next reforms of the CAP. In England the differences have gradually ironed out as a higher and higher proportion becomes a flat-rate per hectare across all 'lowland' (or all non-moorland SDA or all moorland SDA in the case of the other two areas).

The following are estimates of the flat-rate area payments in 2012 and 2013 in the three areas (or sub-regions) of England, with €1 = 88p. 'Lowland' covers all non-SDA (Severely Disadvantaged Area) land, which is more than 84% of farmed land. The estimates are made by The Andersons Centre and include allowance for the inclusion of Dairy Premium and Sugar Beet compensation in the flat-rate area payments.

Estimated 2012 and 2013 Flat Rate Area Payments in England

	Lowland	Non-Moorland SDA	Moorland SDA
	£/ha (acre)	£/ha (acre)	£/ha (acre)
Payments before deductions....	284 (115)	228 (92)	40 (16)
Payments after deductions	231 (93)	186 (75)	35 (14)

SDA = Severely Disadvantaged Area

EXAMPLE FARMS

All policies are about shifting money from one group of people to another so clearly any policy change will have some who gain more than they were previously receiving and others who will receive less, others have to pay.

Arable Example: As a first example, let us take a 100% combinable cropping farm in England. Assuming the same currency conversion and deductions as above, the table below gives actual figures up to 2010 and estimates for 2011 and 2012. Payments increased in 2009 due to currency, then fell in 2010.

Single Payment Calculation for Example Arable Farm

	A. Before Deductions			B. After Deductions
Year	Historic Part £/Ha	Flat-rate Part £/Ha	Total £/Ha	Total £/Ha
2005	215	19	234	222
2006	200	31	231	208
2007	169	66	235	195
2008	151	112	263	216
2009	126	173	299	244
2010	75	207	282	230
2011	32	254	286	233
2012	0	284	284	231

Beef Example: in the next example, a lowland farm has intensive or semi-intensive beef, giving a gross historic payment of approximately £370/ha (at 2005 exchange rate). The example also applies to very intensive dairy farms (i.e. high yield and high stocking rate), except the figures would be higher in 2006 than 2005 (because the dairy premium rises, before levelling off). The rate of the loss compared with pre 2005 increases over time more quickly than the first example, in spite of the currency gain from 2009.

Single Payment Calculation for Example Lowland Beef Farm

	A. Before Deductions			B. After Deductions
Year	Historic Part £/Ha	Flat-rate Part £/Ha	Total £/Ha	Total £/Ha
2005	348	19	367	350
2006	324	31	355	320
2007	274	66	340	284

| | A. Before Deductions | | | B. After Deductions |
| | Historic Part | Flat-rate Part | Total | Total |
Year	£/Ha	£/Ha	£/Ha	£/Ha
2008	245	112	357	294
2009	205	173	378	307
2010	122	207	329	268
2011	51	254	305	249
2012	0	284	284	231

Lowland Sheep Example: Finally, let us examine a lowland sheep farm extensively stocked, giving an historic payment of only £100/ha (at 2005 exchange rate). In this example the farmer gains from the new system increasingly over time, and this is accelerated by the currency gain from 2009.

Single Payment Calculation for Example Lowland Sheep Farm

| | A. Before Deductions | | | B. After Deductions |
| | Historic Part | Flat-rate Part | Total | Total |
Year	£	£	£	£
2005	89	19	108	104
2006	83	31	114	104
2007	71	66	137	115
2008	63	112	175	145
2009	52	173	225	185
2010	31	207	238	195
2011	14	254	268	219
2012	0	284	284	231

3.   MARKET SUPPORT

Market support measures are the other part of Pillar 1 funding, including intervention buying, export subsidies, quotas/set-aside and tariff barriers. The main measures are tariffs which are unlikely to change much in the short term following the lack of WTO change (see the introduction to this section). Milk quotas will end in 2015.   Individual UK producers have seen their quota increase by 0.5% at the end of each of the 2005/06, 2006/07 and 2007/08 milk years.   A further 2% allocation was made at the end of the 2007/08 milk year. As a result of the Health Check individual quotas are increasing by 1% for another five years since 31st March 2009.

Sugar prices are supported within the EU. Following the 2006 reforms, 'institutional' sugar prices have been cut over four years to reach a minimum EU beet price of €26.4 per tonne in 2009 to 2012. For 2012 at €1=88p this would give a price of about £23.23 per tonne before transport and late delivery bonus (LDB). Actual prices paid are determined through the Inter-Professional Agreement (IPA) between British Sugar (BS) and the NFU (refer to page 33).

British Sugar reduced contract offers to growers by 10% in 2008 in anticipation of further EU restructuring and this will be the final 'institutional' led cut of contract tonnage. Compensation was paid for the cut based on contract tonnage held for each of the growing seasons 2005, 2006 and 2007. Payments were made in June 2009 at a rate of €2.18 per tonne converted into sterling on 1st June 2009 giving a sterling price of £1.90 per tonne.

4.   CAP POST 2013

BACKGROUND

Negotiations about reforming the Common Agricultural Policy (CAP) are currently underway.   Previous rounds of reform have been driven by international trade commitments (GATT and WTO) placing limits on farm support or EU Enlargement. The current reform round will be driven by money – specifically the funds available under the next EU Budget period that runs from 2014 to 2020.

This means that there are two separate, but linked, negotiations simultaneously underway; the overall EU budget and the specific CAP policies. Therefore, farm support is a big issue in the wider budget negotiations. Although the proportion of total EU spending going to the CAP has fallen steadily over the decades (from 80% in the 1960's) it still comprises around 40% of the total (with the Single Payment Scheme (SPS) comprising approximately 80% of that).

TIMETABLE

In terms of the EU Budget, the first proposals were published at the end of July 2011. This indicated a slight proportional reduction in CAP funding for the 2014-20 period. However, this was with an overall budget increase of 5% which may be unacceptable to the contributor nations of the EU. Discussions will continue for the remainder of 2011 and through 2012. A final deal is scheduled to be agreed by EU Heads of State in December 2012.

The reformed CAP will have to fit within the budgetary constraints. Negotiations on this are proceeding despite the funding being unknown. The EU Commission published outline reform plans in November 2010. These are vague on many of the important details; more comprehensive 'legislative proposals' will be issued in October 2011.

Negotiations will continue through 2012, and probably into early 2013 pending agreement on the Budget. Any reform needs to be agreed both by EU Farm Ministers and, for the first time with this legislation, the European Parliament.   Once the political agreement has been reached, a further period is required to translate this into implementing regulations.

It is clear that a reformed CAP will be introduced for the 2014 Single Payment Scheme at the earliest. This will mean a roll-over of the current system for the 2013. It may even be the 2015 year before changes are made.

PROPOSALS

The broad outline given below is based on the EU Commission's plans published in November 2010, the Budget proposals of June 2011 and other comments from the Commission.   The CAP is a complex policy with several stakeholders, therefore, substantial compromise is likely before agreement is achieved. The proposals are already unadventurous. Indeed, current indications suggest that this will not be a radical reform of the CAP; primarily the SPS will continue in a recognisable form after 2013. This means a yearly payment to farmers based on the land area they occupy as long as they abide by cross-compliance rules. There will, however, be important 'revisions' to the system;

- There is likely to be a compulsory change from the 'historic' systems currently seen in Wales and Scotland to the flat-rate regional payment scheme as used in England.

- Direct payments in the form of the SPS are to be 'greened'.   Payment of the SPS would be conditional on farmers undertaking certain environmental practices above the current cross-compliance requirements. Details on these are limited at present but are likely to include such measures as fallowing land, crop rotation, permanent pasture, carbon reduction measures etc.

- Single Payments may be subject to 'capping'. This would limit the amount paid to a business above certain defined thresholds. No indications of what the deductions may be have yet been released.

- The rules may be tightened so that the SPS can only go to 'active farmers'. Again, details are lacking on the definition of what constitutes an active farmer but could be meeting cross compliance rules, producing agricultural goods or taking a business risk.

- Under the Rural Development heading optional mechanisms to help farmers to cope with market volatility could be introduced by the reform – a revenue insurance scheme is being mooted. It is not clear whether this would be taken up by the UK Government even if it were available.

- A new set of national Rural Development programmes will be required for 2014 onwards. The UK administrations could use this opportunity to radically alter their agri-environment schemes. However, the future of low-level environmental schemes (such as the ELS) must be in question if the greening of the SPS covers much of what is currently required.

- Although the support systems may not change radically, the amount of funding flowing through them may well do. As well as the overall budget for the CAP discussed above, there is the contentious issue of how this is divided amongst Member States. It seems highly likely that a greater proportion than in the past will go to the 'new' Member States in Central and Eastern Europe. This will leave less for countries such as the UK, and is likely to see a reduction in the level of support.

- A very small decline of CAP funds, a freeze in nominal terms and a shift of payment to Eastern Member States means that in real terms, a farmer could receive 20% - 25% less by 2020.

5.   RURAL DEVELOPMENT

Rural Development or Pillar 2 of the CAP supports environmental protection and improvement of the countryside, and encourages sustainable enterprises and thriving rural communities. A range of support measures are allowed under four 'axes', with a minimum percentage of each Member State's budget in each:

- Axis 1 Competitiveness (min 10%): includes training young farmers, advice, food quality, production groups etc.

- Axis 2 Land Management (min 25%): includes agri-environmental schemes, hill farming (LFA support), forestry and animal welfare.

- Axis 3 Diversification (min 10%): includes grant aid for non-farming business, tourism, rural services etc.

- Axis 4 LEADER schemes (min 5%): funds local partnership programmes to address specific problems in certain areas.

Each country has a 7-year Rural Development programme running from 2007-13. A brief description is given below. For further details contact the relevant agency in England, Wales, Scotland and Northern Ireland. Each devolved administration will have to draw up new Rural Development Programmes for post 2013; these will depend on CAP reform and EU budget negotiations, see 4 above.

ENGLAND

The stated strategy for the Rural Development Programme England (RDPE) is:

- To build profitable, innovative and competitive farming, food and forestry sectors, that meet the need of consumers and make a net positive contribution to the environment.

- To improve the environment and countryside.

- To enhance opportunity in rural areas in a way that harnesses and builds on environmental quality.

The overall budget for the RDPE for the period 2007-2013 is €5,185 million made up of €3,217 million (62%) from EU funds and voluntary modulation and the remainder (38%) from national funds. The total funding split into axes is given below:

	€	%
Axis 1 – Competitiveness	448m	9
Axis 2 – Land Management	4,183m	81
Axis 3 – Diversification	334m	6
Axis 4 – Leader	220m	4
	5,185m	100

Axis 2 Schemes

The vast majority of spending in England is in Axis 2 or the Land Management Schemes. These are being administered by Natural England (NE) and the Forestry Commission. The available schemes are:

- Environmental Stewardship Scheme (ESS)

- England Woodland Grant Scheme (EWGS)

- Energy Crops Scheme (ECS)

Environmental Stewardship Scheme (ESS)

The Environmental Stewardship Scheme was launched in 2005 to replace the Environmental Sensitive Areas, Countryside Stewardship and Organic Farming schemes. The scheme now comprises four elements:

- Entry Level Stewardship (ELS)

- Organic Entry Level Stewardship (OELS)

- Higher Level Stewardship (HLS)

- Uplands Entry Level Scheme (UELS)

A review of the ESS was undertaken in 2009. A few adjustments have been made to the scheme. The latest edition of the Environmental Stewardship Handbooks is the third edition; it includes new ELS options and details of the new Uplands strand of the ELS. It is the basis for all Agreements since 1st February 2010.

ELS: is intended to encourage a large number of farmers across a wide area to adopt simple environmental management practices such as hedgerow management, stone wall maintenance, low input grassland, buffer strips and arable options. The scheme is non-competitive and open to all as long as scheme requirements are met. Points are awarded for each management option adopted. There is a large range of management options including hedgerow management, one side 11 points/100m, both sides 22points/100m; 2m, 4m, 6m buffer strips attracting 300, 400 and 400 points/ha respectively; overwintered stubbles gain 120 points/ha and beetle banks 580 points/ha. Applicants have to achieve a minimum number of 30 points per hectare to be accepted into ELS. An annual payment of £30 per hectare will be made half yearly in arrears. ELS agreements last for five years. Above the moorland line in the LFAs the payment is £8 per hectare for parcels of land over 15ha.

OELS: is open to all organic farmers with land which is registered as organic or in conversion and not currently receiving aid under the Organic Farming Scheme (closed to new applicants). OELS has similar options to those under ELS and participants will receive annual payments of £30 per hectare for carrying out the organic options on the organic land plus an additional £30 per hectare for farming the land organically. There will also be an option to apply for organic conversion with a payment of £600 per hectare per year (for 3 years) for top fruit orchards and £175 per hectare per year (for 2 years) for improved land. To participate in this latter option land must not already have been converted to full organic production and applicants must have registered the land with an organic inspection body. OELS agreements last for five years. Where a business has a mix of organic and conventional land a single OELS must be made and payments will be at £30 per hectare on the ELS eligible land and £60 per hectare on the organic land.

HLS: is targeted towards achieving significant environmental benefits in high priority areas with the objectives being wildlife conservation, protecting historic environments, maintaining and enhancing landscape quality, encouraging public access and resource protection. Applicants have to produce a Farm Environment Plan (FEP) and will usually have to participate in ELS. Only applications that give the best value in meeting the scheme aims will be accepted. Payment will depend on the management options adopted, and can include a mix of capital items and per hectare payments. HLS agreements will normally be for ten years with a break clause for either party after five years. NE is now operating a pre-application screening process so that potential applicants do not get involved in unnecessary work and expenditure. In autumn 2008 NE announced 110 target areas for HLS covering 4.8 million hectares. Farmers in one of these target areas will need to perform one or more of the land management activities specified for that area. Farmers outside these target areas are not excluded from HLS applications, but must contribute to achieving specified themes for their region.

UELS: replaced the Hill Farm Allowance (HFA) scheme in 2010. The UELS is an additional strand to the ELS, with similar rules and principles. The scheme will be open to all farmers who farm within the Severely Disadvantaged Areas (SDAs). Farmers will need to have an ELS agreement over all of their land and enter all their SDA land into the UELS. There are different points targets depending on the classification of the land, see the table below. Producers have to achieve the combined total.

Land Category	ELS Points/ha	UELS Points/ha	Combined Points/ha
SDA Moorland Parcels			
15ha and above	8	15	23
Below 15ha	30	32	62
SDA Land below the Moorland Line	30	32	62

Similar to the ELS, applicants have to achieve the points target. Once achieved the points equate to the level of payment. SDA Moorland parcels 15ha and above will receive £23/ha; all other SDA land will receive £62/ha.

Points are obtained through meeting a number of 'requirements' and also by selecting from a menu of 'options'. There are different requirements for Moorland and Non-Moorland. By meeting the requirements on Moorland parcels above 15ha applicants receive 15 points per ha. By meeting the requirements on Moorland parcels below 15ha and other SDA land the producer receives 11 points per ha. The additional points needed to reach the target must be made up by using the 'options' menu.

The scheme is not available to farmers who have other agri-environmental scheme agreements still running e.g. CSS and ESA schemes. In order that these farmers do not lose out now the HFA has finished, from 2011 there is an Uplands Transitional Payment (UTP). This is similar to the previous HFA scheme. Payments are made to farmers who have an on-going Countryside Stewardship Scheme (CSS) or Environmentally Sensitive Areas (ESA) agreement and who extensively graze eligible land with sheep breeding flocks and suckler cows but not dairy farming or other enterprises such as deer farming.

The 2011 UTP payment was £14.78/ha for Moorland and Common Land, Severely Disadvantaged Land (SDA) received £39.02/ha. The full rate is paid on the first 350ha, half rate on the next 350ha. No payment is made on land in excess of 700ha. No payment is made on Disadvantaged Land (DA). Rates for 2012 to 2014 are expected to be similar but depend on the number of claimants and the eligible area.

England Woodland Grant Scheme (EWGS)

The previous Woodland Grant Scheme (WGS) and the Farm Woodland Premium Scheme (FWPS) have been replaced by the England Woodland Grant Scheme (EWGS), administered jointly by Natural England and the Forestry Commission. Details of the scheme are set out in the Forestry section on page 129.

Energy Crops Scheme (ECS)

The Energy Crops Scheme provides aid for the planting of Short Rotation Coppice (SRC) and Miscanthus (elephant grass). Poplar, willow, ash, alder, hazel, silver birch, sycamore, sweet chestnut and lime have been added to the list of trees that are eligible for the SRC grant. Any land is eligible for the ECS, either agricultural or non-agricultural, but not land already under forestry, energy crops, or common land. There is a minimum application size of 3 hectares. Agreements are normally for five years. Producers must be able to demonstrate that there is an end-use for the crop.

Grant aid is paid at 50% of the actual expenditure. Applicants have to submit invoices showing their actual costs. Applicants will be required to provide estimates of likely costs as part of the application process if these estimates are consistent with an Independent Verification of typical costs then the application can be accepted on a single quote. Where estimated costs are higher than the Independent Verification applicants will be required to provide written evidence to explain the variation – this may also involve getting further quotes. Grant is paid in full on submission of costs.

No English Woodland Grant Scheme payments are available on these crops. Land planted to these crops remains eligible for the Single Payment. See also page 104.

Axes 1, 3 and 4 Schemes

This part of the RDPE used to be administered by the eight Regional Development Agencies (RDAs). Each RDA had its own priorities and schemes. As from 1st July 2011 responsibility for delivery of a' nationally consistent' scheme is transferred to Defra. For the remainder of the programme (2007-2013) key priorities will be skills & knowledge transfer and improving the competitiveness of farming (especially in the uplands).

WALES

The stated strategy for the Wales Rural Development Programme (WRDP) is:

- To stimulate a dynamic and innovative agricultural sector.

- Encourage sustainable production methods with a view to improving the environment.

- Improve the quality of life in rural areas and encourage diversification of the rural economy.

- Build capacity and innovation in rural areas.

The overall budget is a total of €985 million made up of €377 million (38%) from EU funds and voluntary modulation and the remainder (62%) from national funds. The total funding split into axes is given below:

	€	%
Axis 1 – Competitiveness	122m	12
Axis 2 – Land Management	722m	73
Axis 3 – Diversification	94m	10
Axis 4 – Leader	47m	5
	985m	100

Axis 2 Schemes

There have been five environmental schemes in Wales but this is changing to a single scheme in 2010/2011 the current schemes are:

- Tir Gofal, which means 'land in care'. This is an integrated agri-environmental scheme, with 10 year agreements with a 5 year break clause. The whole farm must be entered and there is a combination of mandatory and optional land management payments, and capital grants. This scheme is now closed to new entrants – see below.

- Tir Cynnal, is a whole farm entry level type scheme introduced in 2005. Application is via the Single Application Form (SAF). Applicants enter their whole farm with a 10 year agreement with a 5 year break clause. Payments are made per hectare in bands with the first 20 hectares at £45 per hectare reducing to any area over 200 hectares at £2 per hectare. This scheme is now closed to new entrants – see below.

- There have been schemes to assist organic farming. Applications for the latest scheme; The Organic Farming Conversion Scheme (OFCS) 2011, had to be submitted by 3rd December 2010. Agreements will last for 5 years.

- Better Woodlands for Wales (BWW) helps fund the improved management of existing woodland and funds the creation of new woods in Wales. The scheme is run in conjunction with the Forestry Commission.

- Tir Mynydd makes payments for land in the LFA areas as entered on the previous year's SAF. Under the 2010 scheme, payments per hectare were £24 for DA land and £28 for SDA land. Reduced rates are paid above 140 hectares but there is no upper limit. Above 640 hectares the percentage paid is 30% of the full payment. (see below)

A new scheme is being introduced called Glastir, rationalising the current suite of schemes into one. The Tir Gofal and Tir Cynnal schemes (see above) are now closed to new entrants. All existing scheme agreements will end on 31st December 2013 unless they expire earlier. Transitional arrangements will be put in place for those who are still in these schemes in 2012 and 2013.

The last payment under Tir Mynydd will be made in March 2012. Under transitional arrangements farmers were able to claim for the 2012 payment capped at the 2011 payable area on their 2011 SAF application. After this there will no longer be a dedicated measure for the Less Favoured Areas, but the payment (see below) for all LFA farmers entering the all-Wales part of Glastir will be increased by 20%, including dairy farmers who are currently not included under Tir Mynydd.

Funds for organic farmers will be available through Glastir. Interim funds will be available under the OFS for those converting to organic in the period 2010 – 2012 subject to a formal offer. Better Woodlands for Wales (BWW) is also closed to new applications. A new woodland creation grant is now being delivered by the Forestry Commission Wales until 1st January 2013. After this the scheme will be fully integrated into Glastir. Establishment Grants, Fencing Grants and Income Foregone Payments are available to those with eligible land greater than 0.25ha.

Glastir

Glastir will have two main elements; The All-Wales Element and the Targeted Element. The first will be open to all farmers in Wales and the second element will be targeted at those areas that can deliver important environmental benefits. The new scheme will commence in 2012 with transitional arrangements in place until 2014. The first application packs were sent out in September 2010 to those wishing to enter in 2012 and who expressed an interest on their 2010 Single Application Form (SAF). The second window for applications will run from 1st December 2011 to 29th February 2012, with a 2013 start date for those who expressed an interest on their 2011 SAF.

The All-Wales Element is a whole farm entry level management scheme. Contracts will be for five years and applicants must enter all the eligible land they will have full management control of for the full five years. Applicants have to obtain a points threshold for their farm which is either 28 x total hectarage or 14 x total hectarage. To reach the threshold applicants choose from a number of management options. Each option is allocated a set number of points. Producers can also opt to choose from a list of options in the Regional Package. These are considered to offer the greatest environmental value for their area. If the regional options are chosen the applicant will receive 10% more points per option.

Payment for the All-Wales Element will be a flat rate of £28 per hectare for all land entered into the scheme or £14 per hectare for reaching the reduced threshold. Land within the LFA will receive £33.60 per hectare. Claim for payment will be made annually on the SAF. The first claim will be in 2012.

The All-Wales Element will also include:

- A Common Land Element – for those who hold rights on Common Land and who have joined together to establish a Grazing Association

- An Organic conversion fund and maintenance payment (details not yet available but should be available before the 2nd application window opens).

- Agricultural Carbon Reduction and Efficiency Scheme (ACRES). This will provide capital grants aimed at reducing the carbon emissions of agricultural and horticultural holdings.

To be eligible for the scheme, producers also need to comply with the Whole Farm Code - 13 standards of environmental practice. This attracts an additional payment of:

0 – 20 hectares	£15/ha
21 – 50 hectares	£8/ha
51 - 100 hectares	£2.75/ha

The Targeted Element aims to address concerns over soil carbon management, water quality, water quantity management, biodiversity, the historic environment and improving access. Land will be assessed against target maps. At this level management will be of a prescribed nature, payments will vary consisting of both capital and non-capital items.

Note: Due to the poor uptake of Glastir during the first round of applications a review of the scheme was undertaken. Some of the recommendations were put into place immediately and have been included in the above scheme summary whilst others are still being worked through, further scheme details should be available before the next window for applications opens in December 2011.

Axes 1, 3 and 4 Schemes

The WRDP covering these three axes has an emphasis on collaboration and co-operation in the whole food chain. At the centre of the strategy is the processing and marketing grant scheme (PMGS) which covers food and forestry. Grant is available for adding value to agricultural products and for marketing. The rate of Grant is 40% of eligible costs (50% in some designated areas). Eligible expenditure includes erection of buildings as well as product development, market research etc. There will also be assistance for diversification and tourism and farm business advice through Farming Connect.

In 2010 a revised new entrants scheme started called The Young Entrants Support Scheme (YESS). It will run for five years or until funds are exhausted. It is available to young farmers (less than 40 years) who are setting up as head of a holding for the first time or have set-up as head of a holding for the first time within the last 12 months. It will provide grant aid of 50% of agreed eligible expenditure up to a maximum of £15,000 whichever is less. It will also provide sign posted access to funded mentoring services from established farmers and or processors.

The other main support for farmers in Wales is through Farming Connect. This offers one-to-one support, guidance, advice and training. Up to five days subsidised support is available to produce a Whole Farm Plan. A subsidised Skills Development Programme is delivered by Lantra to provide access to practical and regulation linked courses. Through the Farm Advisory Service, help is provided to meet cross compliance measures.

SCOTLAND

The overall strategy for the Scotland Rural Development Programme (SRDP) is to:

* support business viability

* add value to the rural economy and facilitate increased market orientation.

* Support a coherent and integrated approach to meet environmental objectives.

* Encourage private enterprise and entrepreneurship, improve services and infrastructure at local level and support Scotland's cultural opportunities.

* Support capacity building and innovation.

The overall budget from the SRDP is €2,131million of which €676 million (32%) is from European funds and voluntary modulation and the remainder (68%) from national funds. The total funding split into axes is given below:-

	€	%
Axis 1 – Competitiveness	306m	14
Axis 2 – Land Management	1,469m	69
Axis 3 – Diversification	248m	12
Axis 4 – Leader	108m	5
	2,131m	100

Rural Development Contracts

The SRDP is delivered through a single mechanism known as Rural Development Contracts (RDCs), and is divided into three tiers:-

Tier I: The Single Payment Scheme – through the cross-compliance requirements a basic level of environmental protection, food safety and animal welfare is provided.

Tier II: Land Manager's Options - Farmers choose from a menu of options with application at the same time as the Single Application Form (SAF).

Tier III: Rural Priorities – This element is discretionary and competitive and it covers the areas that were previously aided under schemes such as the Rural Stewardship Scheme (RSS), Organic Aid Scheme (OAS), Farm Business Development Scheme (FBDS) and Forestry Support. Now a New Entrants scheme has been added, there is also aid for processing and marketing which is available at the farm level through the SRDP, but larger scale projects are funded directly by Scottish Government.

A review of the workings of the SRDP took place in 2009 and some changes were announced. There are two new Land Managers Options (LMOs) for 2011. There have been changes to the Rural Priorities (RP) scheme. These include streamlining the application process, but also providing additional support to New Entrants, renewable energy projects, and slurry handling facilities.

Less Favoured Area Support Scheme (LFASS) 2010 - 13

Hill Farming Support (LFASS) is outside the RDCs. It is recognised that there is a problem with destocking in the remotest hill areas. Various policy options have been looked into but the decision has been made to continue the LFASS on a similar basis to 2008 but with a few changes which will apply from 2011. These include an increase in the payment rates for the Standard Areas (other areas received an increase in previous years) and an update of the historic reference on which payments are based. At the same time a new grazing category will be introduced for land not currently designated together with a new variable minimum stocking rate to ensure payments are targeted towards active producers.

The LFASS is applied for on the annual SAF application. Eligible hectares are adjusted for non-ring fenced dairy land, variable minimum or maximum stocking density restrictions, grazing category and an enterprise mix multiplier. The adjusted hectares are then paid at the payment rates below depending on the grazing category and location of the land.

£ per adjusted Hectare	2010		2011	
Grazing Category	A & B	C & D	A & B	C & D
Very Fragile	71.35	63.00	71.35	63.00
Fragile	62.10	54.51	62.10	54.51
Standard	37.80	32.50	52.16	34.12

There is a minimum payment of £385

Whole Farm Review

The other main support for farmers in Scotland outside the RDCs is the Whole Farm Review, which grant aids a business review, action plan and implementation up to a maximum of £2,400.

NORTHERN IRELAND

The strategy for the Northern Ireland Rural Development Programme (NIRDP) is to:

- Focus on vocational training, farm modernisation and supply chain improvements
- Support for less favoured areas and agri-environment and forest environment measures
- Diversification of rural economy, cultural heritage and promotion of tourism, to be supported by the local communities through a bottom up approach.

The overall budget from the NIRDP is €647million of which €328 million (51%) is from European funds and voluntary modulation and the remainder (49%) from national funds. The total funding split into axes is given below:-

	€	%
Axis 1 – Competitiveness	61m	10
Axis 2 – Land Management	456m	70
Axis 3+4 – Diversification/Leader	130m	20
	647m	100

CLOSED ENVIRONMENTAL SCHEME PAYMENTS

There are many schemes across the UK that are now closed to new applicants but are still providing annual payments to some farmers. Some were available across all the devolved regions such as the Environmentally Sensitive Areas (ESA) schemes and support for farmers in the LFAs. The other major agri-environmental schemes include the Countryside Stewardship (CSS) in England, Tir Gofal and Tir Cynnal in Wales, and Rural Stewardship (RSS) in Scotland. The table below summarises the latest payments made for these closed schemes and for the schemes that are still open.

Environment Schemes Payments, 2009 (provisional)

		£ million
England:	Organic Farming Scheme (c)	0.0
	Environmentally Sensitive Areas (c)	41.7
	Countryside Stewardship (c)	82.8
	Hill Farm Allowance(c)	27.2
	Environmental Stewardship Scheme	226.6
Wales:	Organic Farming Scheme (c)	4.2
	Environmentally Sensitive Areas(c)	2.2
	Tir Mynydd	25.2
	Tir Gofal (c)	30.7
	Tir Cynnal (c)	8.6
Scotland:	Organic Aid Scheme	2.6
	Environmentally Sensitive Areas (c)	2.7
	Rural Stewardship (c)	13.0
	Less Favoured Area Support Scheme	64.0
	Land Management Contract Scheme	18.5
N. Ireland	Organic Farming Scheme	0.1
	New Environmentally Sensitive Areas	6.5
	Countryside Management Scheme	16.2
	Less Favoured Area Compensatory Allowances	22.5

Source: DEFRA, SGRPID, DARD, WAGDEPC. Agriculture in the UK 2010.
  (c) Schemes that are now closed to new entrants.

IV. LABOUR

1. LABOUR COST

Note, 2012 is a leap year and there are 9 Bank Holidays; New Year's Day January 2, Good Friday April 6, Easter Monday April 9, May Bank Holiday May 7, Spring Bank Holiday June 4, Diamond Jubilee June 5, Summer Bank Holiday August 27, Christmas and Boxing Days December 25 - 26.

STATUTORY MINIMUM WAGE RATES

The following rates are taken from the proposed Agricultural Wages Board (AWB) Order for the year from 1st October 2011. They are subject to ratification. The minimum weekly rates relate to a 39-hour standard week of normal hours worked on any five days between Monday and Saturday. The abolition of the AWB will lead to changes in 2012.

Normal Hours (Standard Rates)

Grade		39 Hr Weekly Rate	Hourly Rate	Overtime per Hour
		£	£	£
1.	Initial Grade Over 16 years	237.90	6.10	9.15
	Under 16 years	-	3.05	4.58
2.	***Standard Worker***	***264.03***	***6.77***	***10.16***
3.	Lead Worker	290.55	7.45	11.18
4.	Craft Grade	311.61	7.99	11.99
5.	Supervisory Grade	329.94	8.46	12.69
6.	Farm Management Grade	356.46	9.14	13.71
Apprentice:	Year 1	139.23	3.57	5.36
	Year 2 ~ 16-17 years	143.52	3.68	5.52
	Year 2 ~ 18-20 years	194.22	4.98	7.47
	Year 2 ~ 21 years and over	237.12	6.08	9.12

Night work rates are £1.33 per hour; dog rates £7.42 per week.

Flexible Working

Grade		Number of days basic hours worked	Weekly Rate	Hourly Rate	Overtime per Hour
			£	£	£
1	Initial Grade (16+ only)	4 to 5	249.99	6.41	9.15
		6	254.67	6.53	9.15
2.	Standard Worker	4 to 5	277.67	7.11	10.16
		6	282.36	7.24	10.16
3.	Lead Worker	4 to 5	304.98	7.82	11.18
		6	310.83	7.97	11.18
4	Craft Grade	4 to 5	327.21	8.39	11.99
		6	333.45	8.55	11.99
5	Supervisory Grade	4 to 5	348.32	8.88	12.69
		6	352.95	9.05	12.69
6	Farm Management Grade	4 to 5	374.40	9.60	13.71
		6	381.42	9.78	13.71

1. There are no age differentials apart from the under 16 category in the Initial Grade.

2. *Standby duty days* are referred to as *'on call'* so the payment is called *'on call allowance'*. It is calculated as 2 hours overtime pay. If a worker is called to work, he is paid overtime rate (with a minimum of 2 hours)

3. *A deduction* up to £33.11 a week or £4.73 a day for non-house accommodation can be made. There are specified provisions for sick pay, paid bereavement leave and paid paternity leave.

4. *Full details* are available from the Agricultural Wages Board for England and Wales (Pay and Work Rights helpline 0800 917 2368 or AWB 020 7238 6523).

Holiday Pay

Holidays with pay. The number of days holiday that workers are entitled to in a year depends on the number of days worked each week. Those working full-time, 5 days a week, have 23 days per year. There are rules as to timing. For part-time workers the number of days worked per week is based on the total hours worked over the 12 months ending on the last 5th April.

TYPICAL ANNUAL LABOUR COST
Estimated for the 2011/12 year (from 1st October), based on a Standard Worker.

Average Labour Costs	Weekly	Annual	Hourly
	£		£
Minimum Wage (basic standard worker rate) (1)	264.03	13,730	7.82
National Insurance Contribution and Employers Liability Insurance (2, 3)	39.08	2,032	1.16
Minimum Cost (4)	**303.11**	**15,762**	**8.98**
Overtime, average 10 hrs per working week *(45)* @ £10.16 (+ NIC, ELI)	100.89	5246	
Typical cost inc. Overtime (5, 6)	**404.00**	**21,008**	**9.53**

1. *Hours work, excluding overtime*, based on 45 weeks (of 39 hours) per year = 1,755 hours, i.e. statutory holidays (23 days), public holidays (9 days) and illness (3 days), have been deducted.

2. NIC = National Insurance Employer Contribution = 13.8%

3. ELI = Employer's Liability Insurance = 1.0%

4. *Annual cost of cottages* (or net value), value of perquisites, contribution towards payment of the council tax, etc., would have to be added where appropriate.

5. *Hours including overtime;* based on 1755 + 450 (10 hours/week) = 2,205 hours per year

6. *Total average worker's gross earnings* on the above assumptions = £18,299 a year.

2. LABOUR HOURS AVAILABLE FOR FIELD WORK

This section calculates the theoretical maximum time a single worker could spend on field work per month in 2012.

Hours available for field-work per worker per month in 2012

	Total Ordinary Hours (1)	Adjusted Ordinary Hours (2)	% workable (3)	Available Hours (4,5)			Total Available Hours (6)		percent o/t at w-ends (7)
				Ordinary	Overtime				
Jan	168	141	50%	70	27	(63)	97	(133)	100%
Feb	168	141	50%	70	29	(63)	99	(133)	75%
Mar	176	152	60%	91	60	(66)	152	(157)	50%
Apr	152	131	65%	85	74	(57)	159	(142)	54%
May	168	149	70%	104	102	(84)	207	(188)	45%
Jun	160	142	75%	107	107	(80)	213	(187)	47%
Jul	176	156	75%	117	108	(88)	225	(205)	42%
Aug	176	156	75%	117	108	(88)	225	(205)	42%
Sep	160	142	70%	99	100	(80)	199	(179)	47%
Oct	184	159	65%	103	70	(69)	174	(172)	41%
Nov	176	147	50%	74	32	(66)	105	(140)	69%
Dec	152	127	50%	64	32	(57)	96	(121)	100%

1. *Ordinary Hours:* 8 hours per work day (less 9 Bank Hols). No deductions have been made for other holidays because they may be taken at various times of the year.

2. *After deducting* for illness (10% Nov. to Feb., 7½% March, April and Oct., 5% May to Sept.), and for contingencies and non-delayable maintenance (½ hour/day).

3. *Per cent Workable:* accounts for severe weather, soil conditions e.g. waterlogging etc.

4. *Available Ordinary Hours:* Adjusted Ordinary Hours x Percentage Workable.

5. *Available Overtime Hours: Daylight hours above working day (8 hrs) to a* maximum of 4 hours per day and 12 to 14 hours at weekends according to season. Same adjustments for illness and percentage workable. Figures in brackets indicate hours available if headlights used, up to 4 hours/day (summer) and 3 hours/day (winter).

6. *Total Available Hours:* Percentage overtime without headlights available from weekend work as opposed to evenings.

Additional Notes

7. *Figures relate to medium land.* The percentage workability will be higher with light soils, less with heavy soils. On heavy soils, land may be almost 100% unworkable from late November to early March (or later, according to the season), particularly if un-drained. A rough estimate of variations in workability according to soil type (compared with the figures above) is as follows.

   Heavy land - March, October, November: 30% less; April: 20% less; September: 10% less; May to August: no difference. Light land — October to April: 15% more; May and September: 10% more; June to August: no difference.

8. *It must be remembered that indoor work*, e.g. livestock tending or potato riddling, can be continued over the full working week, i.e. the hours available are the Adjusted Ordinary Hours, plus overtime adjusted back for workability. Also, some handwork in the field has to continue even in rain, e.g. sprout picking.

9. *Percentage workability* varies according to the particular operation, e.g. compare ploughing and harvesting.

3.   SEASONAL LABOUR REQUIREMENTS

CROPS AND GRASS

On the following pages, data on labour requirements for various crops and types of livestock are given. Two levels are shown: average and premium. The average figures relate to the whole range of conditions and farm size, i.e. small and medium-sized farms as well as large; the figures give all farms equal weight. The premium rates do not denote the maximum rates possible, for instance by the use of especially high-powered tractors under ideal conditions, but relate to rates of work estimated to be obtainable over the whole season, averaging good and bad conditions, with the use of wide implements, relatively large tractors (120 kW to over 150 hp) and high capacity equipment in 8 hectare fields and over, where no time is wasted. Most farmers with more than 200 hectares (500 acres) of arable land ought to achieve at least the premium levels shown. Those with over 400 hectares (1,000 acres) will have still bigger machines and therefore faster work rates, and thus require 15 to 25% less labour than even the premium levels given.

The rates of work include preparation, travelling to fields, allow for minor breakdowns and other stoppages. They relate broadly to medium and medium-heavy land; some jobs, such as ploughing, may be done more quickly on light soils. Operations such as combine harvesting can obviously vary according to many factors to do with the topography and other natural features of the farm.

The usual times of year when each operation takes place are shown; these relate to lowland conditions. They will obviously vary between seasons, soil types, latitude and altitude. In particular, light land can be ploughed over a longer winter period and a high proportion of cultivations for spring crops may be completed in February in many seasons. All such factors must be allowed for in individual farm planning. Conditions in different seasons will also affect, for instance, the number and type of cultivations required in seedbed preparation. Typical monthly breakdowns of requirements are given for various crops.

To illustrate the type of questions that need to be asked for full details of seasonal labour requirements on the individual farm, critical questions affecting timing are listed for cereals.

Winter Cereals

Operations	Labour-hours per hectare		Time of Year
	Average	Premium	
Plough (1)	1.4	1.0	July to October (according to previous crop)
Cultivate (often power harrow)	1.0	0.7	September to October (according to previous crop) (½ Aug if ploughed in July)
Drill (often with power harrows) followed by roll	1.1	0.7	Mid-September to 3rd week October (according to previous crop and soil)
Apply Fertiliser	0.3	0.2	
Spray	0.3	0.2	October-November
Top Dress (three times [2])	0.9	0.6	March and April
Spray (three or four [2])	1.0	0.5	Spring/early summer
Combine, Cart Grain, Barn Work	2.5	1.9	Mid-Aug to approx. 10th Sept
Later Barn Work (3)	0.7	0.4	September to June
Total	**9.2**	**6.2**	
Straw: Bale	1.3	0.8	Mid-August to end
Cart	3.5	2.6	September

Typical Monthly Breakdown

Month	Average	Premium	Notes
October	2.4	1.7	Approx. 60% of Ploughing,
November	—	—	Cults., Drill, Harrow
December	—	—	
January	—	—	
February	—	—	
March	0.4	0.2	Part Top Dress
April	0.8	0.5	Part Top Dress, Spraying
May	0.3	0.2	Spraying
June	0.3	0.2	Spraying
July	—	—	
August	1.7	1.3	⅔ of harvesting (4)
	(+2.4 Straw)	(+1.7 Straw)	
September (harvest)	0.9	0.6	⅓ of harvesting (4)
	(+2.4 Straw)	(+1.7 Straw)	
September (prepn. drill)	1.7	1.1	40% of Ploughing, Cults., Drill, Harrow

1. *Some cereal crops* are direct drilled or drilled after reduced, or minimal, cultivations, i.e. without traditional ploughing. Direct drilling reduces man-hours per hectare by about 2.5 (average) or 1.8 (premium), and minimal cultivations by about 1.2 (average) and 0.9 (premium).

2. *This is for winter wheat;* winter barley will often have one less top dressing and spraying and oats two less. Also see next page for harvest times for winter barley and oats.

3. *Later barn work* is excluded from monthly breakdown.

Spring Cereals

Operations	Labour-Hours per hectare		Time of Year
	Average	Premium	
Plough (1).....................................	1.4	1.0	July to October (according to previous crop and soil type)
Cultivate (often power harrow) ..	1.0	0.7	March (½ in second half February on light land)
Apply Fertiliser............................	0.3	0.2	
Drill (often with power harrow), plus roll	1.2	0.8	March (½ at end February on light land)
Top Dress (once, some possibly twice)..	0.4	0.2	
Spray (two or three).....................	0.7	0.3	May
Combine, Cart Grain, Barn Work	2.4	1.8	Last ¾ of August (affected by variety and season)
Later Barn Work (2)	0.6	0.4	September to June
Total...	**8.0**	**5.4**	
Straw: Bale (unmanned sledge)	1.3	0.8	Mid-August to end
Cart..	3.5	2.6	September

Typical Monthly Breakdown

Month	Average	Premium	Notes
October..	0.4	0.3	Ploughing. How much in
November.....................................	0.8	0.5	October depends on area
December.....................................	0.2	0.2	W. Wheat, Potatoes, etc.
January	—	—	
February	—	—	
March	2.4	1.6	All Cults. Drilling, Rolling, (nearly half in February on light land)
April	—	—	
May	1.1	0.6	Spray and Top dress
June	—	—	
July..	—	—	
August (3)	2.4 (+2.6 Straw)	1.8 (+1.8 Straw)	Harvesting
September	— (+2.2 Straw)	— (+1.6 Straw)	

1. *Autumn drilling* preferable if possible to allow frost to crumble soils

2. *Later barn work* excluded.

3. *This is for spring barley*; spring wheat and oats partly September.

Crop Timings in a Normal Season:

Winter Wheat

Drilling mid-September to 3rd week October.
Harvesting mid-August to approx. 10th September.

Winter Barley

As for winter wheat, except that:
- Ploughing unlikely to start before cereal harvest, as usually follows a cereal crop.
- Harvesting some weeks earlier: mid July to approx. 10th August.

Winter Oats

As for winter wheat, except that:
- Drilling usually first full half of October.
- Harvesting earlier (late July or first half of August).

Spring Barley

Drilling end of February to very early April
Harvesting last half of August to early September

Spring Wheat

As for spring barley, except that:
- Drilling on average 1-2 weeks earlier (should finish in March) - lose more if later than barley.
- Harvesting, on average, 2 weeks later: last week August/first half of September (two-thirds in September).

Spring Oats

As for spring barley, except that:
- Drilling usually a little earlier.
- Harvesting is later than spring barley, earlier than spring wheat: end of August/beginning of September.

Critical Questions affecting Timing for Spring-sown Cereals

1. Previous crops.
2. Will the crop be ploughed traditionally, chisel ploughed, subsoiled, minimally cultivated, or direct drilled?
3. Months when winter ploughing is possible, on average (where relevant).
4. Is spring ploughing satisfactory (where relevant)?
5. Average period of cultivations and drilling.
6. Earliest dates for starting and finishing spring cultivations/drilling and latest dates for starting and finishing cultivations/drilling, ignoring extreme seasons (1 year in 10).
7. Effect on yield if drilling is delayed.
8. Is the crop rolled (a) within a few days of drilling or (b) later?
9. (a) Average period of harvesting.
   (b) Earliest dates for starting and finishing harvest, and latest dates for starting and finishing harvest, ignoring extreme seasons (one year in ten).

Critical Questions affecting Timing for Autumn-sown Cereals

1. Previous crops (affects time available and need for ploughing and cultivations).

2. Will the crop be ploughed traditionally, chisel ploughed, subsoiled, minimally cultivated, or direct drilled?

3. Earliest and latest drilling date, by choice.

4. Effect on yield if drilling is delayed.

5. Autumn weed control?

6. In the spring: (a) whether crop is rolled, and when,
                      (b) whether crop is harrowed, and when,
                      (c) time of top dressings,
                      (d) number of spray applications.

7.   (a) Average period for harvesting.

    (b) Earliest dates for starting and finishing harvest, and latest dates for starting and finishing harvest, ignoring extreme seasons (1 year in 10).

Maincrop Potatoes

Operations	Labour-Hours per hectare		Time of Year
	Average	Premium	
Plough	1.4	1.0	September to December
Cultivating, Ridging, De-stoning/ Clod sep. (as required)	6.5	5.0	March, early April
Plant and Apply Fertiliser (1)	4.5	3.5	Last quarter of March, first
Apply Herbicide	0.3	0.2	three-quarters of April
Spray for Blight (av. 6 times)	1.2	0.9	July, first half August
Burn off Haulm	0.3	0.2	End September, early October
Harvest, Cart, Clamp (2)	15.0	10.0	End September, October
Work on Indoor Clamp	4.8	3.2	November
Riddle, Bag, Load	40.0	30.0	October to May
Total	**74.0**	**54.0**	

1. *Automatic planter.* Hand-fed planters: approx. 12 hrs plus 8 (could be casual labour).

2. *Mechanical harvester,* excluding up to 25 hours for picking off on harvester - usually casual labour. None may be needed on clod and stone-free soils. Hand harvesting: additional approx. 80 hours of casual labour.

Typical Monthly Breakdown

Month	Average	Premium	Notes
October	12.2	8.2	80% of harvest, ½ burn off
November	5.9	4.0	Clamp work and ¾ plough
December	0.3	0.2	¼ plough
January	—	—	
February	—	—	
March	7.8	6.0	All fert', ½ cults', ¼ plant
April	3.5	2.7	½ cult's, ¾ plant
May	—	—	
June	—	—	
July	0.9	0.7	3 blight sprays
August	0.3	0.2	1 blight spray
September	3.1	2.0	20% harvest, ½ burn off

These figures exclude casual labour and riddling.

Early Potatoes

Operations	Labour-Hours per hectare		Time of Year
	Average	Premium	
Plough	1.4 (1)	1.0 (1)	September to December
Cultivating, etc	6.5 (1)	5.0 (1)	Late February, early March
Plant and Apply Fertiliser	4.5 (1)	3.5 (1)	Late February, early March
Apply Herbicide	0.3 (1)	0.2 (1)	1st half March (some in February on light land or in early season)
Further Spraying	0.3 (1)	0.2 (1)	
After-Cultivation/Spray	0.3 (1)	0.2 (1)	April, early May
Harvest, bag, load	30.0 (1)	25.0 (2)	2nd week June onwards. All June or till mid-July

1. Excluding 80 hours picking—usually casuals.
2. Excluding 60 hours picking—usually casuals.

Second Early Potatoes

Operations	Labour-Hours per hectare		Time of Year
	Average	Premium	
Plough	1.4 (1)	1.0 (1)	September to December
Cultivating, etc	6.5 (1)	5.0 (1)	March
Plant and Apply Fertiliser	4.5 (1)	3.5 (1)	March
Apply Herbicide	0.3 (1)	0.2 (1)	Half 2nd half March, half 1st half April
Further Spraying	0.9 (1)	0.7 (1)	End April, May, early June
Harvest	15.0 (1)	10.0 (2)	Mid-July to end August

1. *Spinner or elevator-digger*, excluding picking and riddling—usually casual labour.
2. *Mechanical harvester*, excluding picking off on harvester/riddling - usually casual.

Sugar Beet

Operations	Labour-Hours per hectare		Time of Year
	Average	Premium	
Plough	1.4	1.0	September to December
Seedbed Cults	3.2	2.2	Mainly March (some early April. Some late February
Load, Cart, Apply Fertiliser	0.7	0.4	in good seasons)
Drill (and Flat Roll)	1.8	1.1	Between mid-March and mid-April
Spray (herbicide: pre- and post-emergence)	0.6	0.3	Late March/April
Spray (x 2)	0.6	0.3	May/June
Spray (aphis)	0.3	0.2	July
Harvest (machine)	14.0	9.0	End September, October, November
Load	3.4	2.5	End September to early January
Total	**26.0**	**17.0**	

Typical Monthly Breakdown

Month	Average	Premium	Notes
October............................	7.2	4.6	45% harvest; + loading
November	8.2	5.3	45% harvest; ¾ ploughing; + loading
December.........................	1.0	0.8	¼ ploughing; + loading
January............................	0.5	0.4	Loading
February..........................	—	—	
March	3.8	2.3	Fert., most cults., some drilling
April	2.5	1.7	Some cults., most of drilling
May	0.3	0.2	Spray
June	0.3	0.15	Spray
July..................................	0.2	0.15	Spray
August.............................	—	—	
September	2.0	1.4	10% harvesting; + loading

Vining Peas

Operations	Labour-Hours per hectare		Time of Year
	Average	Premium	
Plough	1.4	1.0	September to December
Cults, Fert. and Drill	2.3	1.6	Mid-Feb. to April
Post Drilling and Spraying..........	1.5	0.8	
Harvesting....................................	19.0	14.0	July and early August
Total...	**24.2**	**17.4**	

Drilling is staggered in small areas through the season, ranging from early varieties to late varieties.

Dried Peas

Month	Labour-Hours per hectare		Notes
	Average	Premium	
October..	1.2	0.8	
November.....................................	0.8	0.5	Stubble cult., Plough
December	—	—	
January	—	—	
February	0.2	0.1	Cult. x 2, harrow; drill & fert.
March	2.8	1.9	(80% March); light harrow
April	0.6	0.4	roll; and spray
May	2.5	1.2	
June	0.2	0.2	Scare pigeons; spray
July..	1.8	1.1	Possible spray desiccant;
August..	2.2	1.3	combine and cart, dry
September	0.5	0.3	Stubble cult.

Assumes direct combining.

Field Beans

Winter Beans

Operations	Labour-Hours per hectare		Time of Year
	Average	Premium	
Broadcast Seed...........................	0.6	0.4	
Apply Fertiliser...........................	0.3	0.2	
Plough	1.4	1.0	September/October
Power Harrow............................	1.0	0.8	
Spray (pre-emergence)...............	0.3	0.15	
Spraying (two or three times).....	0.8	0.35	Spring
Combine and cart and			
Barn-work	3.0	2.4	August

Spring Beans

Operations	Labour-Hours per hectare		Time of Year
	Average	Premium	
Plough	1.4	1.0	September to December
Cultivate (often power harrow) ..	1.0	0.7	
Apply Fertiliser...........................	0.3	0.2	
Drill, Roll	1.2	0.8	End Feb, early March
Spray (two or three times)	0.8	0.4	
Combine and cart and			
Barn-work	3.0	2.4	September

Winter Oilseed Rape (*Desiccated*)

Month	Labour-Hours per hectare		Notes
	Average	Premium	
October............................			
November........................	0.6	0.3	Spray herbicide and
December			insecticide if necessary
January	—	—	
February	—	—	
March			
April	0.8	0.4	Top dress twice
May	—	—	
June	—	—	Desiccate (1st half July);
July	2.4	1.7	combine ($\frac{1}{2}$ 2nd half July
August	2.0	1.4	$\frac{1}{2}$ 1st half Aug.); dry
August	1.6	0.9	Cults. (x 2), spray, drill, fert.;
September	1.6	0.9	harrow, roll, barn work (0.5)

Herbage Seed *(first production year)*

Undersown

Operations	Labour-Hours per hectare		Time of Year
	Average	Premium	
Undersown	0.6	0.4	March, April
Roll... {	(0.6	0.4)	Straight after drilling
	0.4	0.3	September
	0.4	0.3	Late February, March
Harvest (by Combine): Mow......	1.4	0.9	3 to 4 days before combining
Combine and Cart	4.5	3.5	Ital. Ryegrasses and Early *Perennials: late July.* *Intermed. Perennials: late July/early August.* *Late Perennials/White Clover: mid-August*
	6.0	4.5	Meadow Fescue: early July
	7.0	5.0	Cocksfoot: early July
	10.0	7.0	Timothy: mid-August Red Clover: late September

Direct Drilled in Autumn

Operations	Labour-Hours per hectare		Time of Year
	Average	Premium	
Plough	1.4	1.0	
Seedbed Cults	2.2	1.6	Depends on previous crop—
Load, Cart, Apply Fertiliser........	0.3	0.2	Usually July or August
Drill (with harrows behind)........	0.8	0.6	As early as previous crop allows. This may be up to mid-Sept for ryegrass without detriment to the yield.
Roll (soon after drilling)	0.6	0.4	Meadow fescue and cocksfoot are best sown no later than July and it is risky to sow Timothy much later than this.

Grass

Production

Operations	Labour-Hours per hectare		Time of Year
	Average	Premium	
Plough	1.4	1.0	Autumn drilling: may not
Seedbed Cults	2.2	1.6	
Load, Cart, Apply Fertiliser........	0.3	0.2	
Drill*	0.7	0.5	Mid-March to mid-April (1) or end July to mid-Sept.
Roll...	0.6	0.4	Soon after drilling
Load, Cart, Apply Fertiliser* (three lots)...................................	0.9	0.6	March to mid-August (2)
Top*	1.3	0.8	Mid-June to mid-July; if grazed only.

1.   * These operations apply only where the seeds are undersown in a spring cereal crop soon after drilling. One extra harrowing and rolling is needed if undersown in an autumn-sown cereal crop.

2.   *Spring drilling* may continue to mid-May to enable extra cleaning cultivations or the application of farmyard manure.

3.   *P. and K.* may be applied in September - especially on undersown ley in year sown.

Conservation

Operations	Labour-Hours per hectare		Time of Year
	Average	Premium	
Plough	1.4	1.0	Autumn drilling: may not
Hay (5.5 tonnes per hectare)			
Mow	1.2	0.9	
Turn, etc	2.6	1.9	Two-thirds June, one-third
Bale	1.3	0.9	July
Cart	6.0	4.5	
Total per hectare	11.1	8.2	
Total per tonne	2.0	1.5	
Silage (17 tonnes per hectare)			
Mow	1.2	0.9	
Turn, etc	0.7	0.5	Two-thirds May, one-third
Load	2.3	1.7	June
Cart	3.0	2.3	
Clamp	2.3	1.7	
Total per hectare	9.5	7.1	
Total per tonne	0.56	0.42	

Specialised Equipment Prices for Grass Conservation: see page 163.

Typical Monthly Breakdown

Production (figures averaged over the life of the ley)

	1-year ley undersown in spring		3-year ley undersown in autumn (1)		1-year ley drilled		3-year ley drilled	
	Ave.	Prem.	Ave.	Prem.	Ave.	Prem.	Ave.	Prem.
March	0.9	0.5	0.7	0.5	0.6	0.3	0.6	0.3
April	0.9	0.5	0.7	0.5	0.6	0.3	0.6	0.3
May	0.6	0.3	0.6	0.3	0.6	0.3	0.6	0.3
June	0.6	0.3	0.6	0.3	0.6	0.3	0.6	0.3
July	0.6	0.3	0.6	0.3	0.6	0.3	0.6	0.3
August	0.3	0.2	0.3	0.2	5.0	3.4	1.9	1.4
September	0.6	0.3	0.3	0.2	3.2	2.2	1.4	1.0

1.   *If ploughed after a cereal crop,* drilled early August to mid-September.

	1-year ley drilled in autumn (1)		3-year ley drilled in spring		Permanent Pasture	
	Ave.	Prem.	Ave.	Prem.	Ave.	Prem.
March	3.0	2.1	1.4	1.0	0.6	0.3
April	1.8	1.2	0.9	0.7	0.6	0.3
May	0.3	0.3	0.6	0.3	0.6	0.3
June	0.6	0.3	0.6	0.3	0.6	0.3
July.....................	0.6	0.3	0.6	0.3	0.6	0.3
August................	0.3	0.2	0.2	0.2	0.3	0.2
September	—	—	—	0.2	0.2	0.2
October..............	0.9	0.5	0.6	0.3	—	—
November...........	1.4	1.0	1.0	0.3	—	—
December...........	0.7	0.5	0.6	0.2	—	—

Conservation

	Hay				Silage			
	per hectare		per tonne		per hectare		per tonne	
	Av.	Prem.	Av.	Prem.	Av.	Prem.	Av.	Prem.
May	—	—	—	—	6.3	4.7	0.37	0.28
June	7.4	5.6	1.3	1.0	3.2	2.4	0.19	0.14
July................	3.7	2.6	0.7	0.5	—	—	—	—

Kale

Production

Operations	Labour-Hours per hectare		Time of Year
	Average	Premium	
Plough	1.4	1.0	September onwards
Seedbed Cults	2.2	1.6	March, April, early May
Fertiliser......................................	0.3	0.2	April, early May
Drill...	1.3	1.0	May
Roll..	0.6	0.4	Straight after drilling
Spray (weed killer)......................	0.3	0.2	6 weeks after drilling

Catch Crop

Kale may be drilled up to the first week of July; the crop will be smaller but either an early bite or silage crop may have been taken from a ley earlier in the year, or the ground may have been fallowed and thoroughly cleaned during the spring and early summer. The smaller crop is also easier to graze using an electric fence.

The above operations will still apply although the times of the year will obviously be different, but there may be an additional three or so rotavations and two or three heavy cultivations if fallowed for the first half of the year or ploughed after an early bite. This means approximately an extra 10 (average) or 8 (premium) man-hours per hectare in April, May, June.

FIELD SCALE VEGETABLES

(Labour hours per hectare unless otherwise stated)

Cabbage Transplanting	Hand 150-160. Spring cabbage, Sept.-Oct.; summer, April; autumn, May-June Machine (3.5 gang). Spring cabbage 75, summer 85, autumn 100. Pulling and dipping plants. 20 per hectare transplanted.
Cabbage Harvesting	Early spring cabbage, 210, Feb.-April; hearted spring, 250, April-June; summer, 220, June-July; autumn, 220, Oct.-Dec.
Brussels Sprouts Transplanting	45 (machine) to 55 (hand), May-June.
Brussels Sprouts Picking	320-400: picked over 3-5 times, maximum approx. 3 hectares per picker per season. Early sprouts, Aug.-Dec.; late, Nov.-Mar.
Peas Hand Pulling	475-525 (150 per tonne). Early, June; maincrop, July-Aug.
Runner Beans (Picked)	Harvesting. 625 (175 per tonne), July-Sept.
Runner Beans (Stick)	Harvesting. 675, July-Sept.
Runner Beans (Stick)	Erecting Canes and String. 100-150, May-June.
Carrot Harvesting.	Elevator-digger: 260 (1 man + 12 casuals, 20 hours per hectare). Earlies, July-Aug.; maincrop, Sept.-Feb. Harvester: 30 (3 men, 10 hours per hectare). Riddle and Grade: (1° per tonne), Dec.-Feb.
Beetroot Harvest and Clamp.	25, Oct.-Dec. 12-15 man-hours per tonne to wash and pack.

Source: The Farm as a Business, Aids to Management, Section 6: Labour and Machinery (M.A.F.F.). (N.B. This data is now very dated, but it is still the latest known to the author.)

LABOUR FOR LIVESTOCK

Dairy Cows

Time Required per Cow Depending on Yield.

Yield of Cow	5,500	7,000	8,000	9,000
	hours per cow per month			
January	2.0	2.5	3.1	3.8
February	1.9	2.5	3.1	3.8
March	1.8	2.5	3.1	3.8
April	1.6	2.4	3.0	3.8
May	1.6	2.1	2.7	3.5
June	1.6	2.1	2.6	3.2
July	1.6	2.1	2.6	3.2
August	1.6	2.1	2.6	3.2
September	1.6	2.2	2.8	3.5
October	1.8	2.4	3.1	3.8
November	1.9	2.5	3.1	3.8
December	2.0	2.5	3.1	3.8
Total per Cow per Year	21	27.9	34.9	43.2
Average Seconds per Litre	*13.7*	*14.3*	*15.7*	*17.3*

No time is allocated here for dairy young stock. This schedule is based on a 100-cow herd. Low yielding cows tend to spend more time at grass and less housed. High milk yielders take more management time.

13.7 seconds per litre = 1 man per 725,000L

17.3 seconds per litre = 1 man per 575,000L

The most labour efficient milk producing operations in the UK achieve over 800,000 litres per employed man.

Hours staff Requirement per Cow per Year.

	Cow Annual Milk Yield (L)			
	5,500	7,000	8,000	9,000
Cows per Herd				
60	21.9	29.1	36.4	45.0
100	21.0	27.9	34.9	43.2
150	20.0	26.6	33.2	41.1
300	17.5	23.3	29.1	36.0
500	15.0	19.9	24.9	30.9

Labour Cost per Litre

	Cow Annual Milk Yield (L)			
ppl	5,500	7,000	8,000	9,000
Cows per Herd				
60	3.96	4.14	4.53	4.98
100	3.80	3.97	4.35	4.78
150	3.62	3.78	4.14	4.55
300	3.17	3.31	3.62	3.98
500	2.72	2.84	3.10	3.42

Earnings. The average earnings of 'dairy herdsmen' in 2011/12 is estimated to be £27,594 a year and working 2,770 hours (10 hours for 277 days). This includes relief milking etc but no cover for young stock or fieldwork, such as hay and silage making.

Dairy Followers and Beef

No recent survey work has been published on labour requirements for beef animals and dairy followers. The following data is therefore only 'best estimates'. They are for average performance and average conditions, excluding fieldwork. Substantial variations occur, e.g. through differing management styles or economies of scale with differing herd sizes.

Calves (per head, early weaning)

Age Group	Labour hours per month	
	Average	Premium
0-3 months...	2.3	1.6
3-6 months...	0.9	0.6
(av. 0-6 months.......................................	1.6	1.1)
6-12 months, yarded....................................	1.1	0.8
6-12 months, summer grazed...........................	0.3	0.2
(av. 0-12 months, during winter (1).................	1.3	0.9)
(av. 0-12 months, during summer (1).................	0.9	0.6)

1. Assuming 6 to 12-month olds housed in winter and grazed in summer, and calvings or calf purchases fairly evenly spaced throughout the year.

Stores (per head)

Yearling, housed....................................	1.0	0.7
2 year olds and over, housed......................	1.4	0.8
Out-wintered store.................................	0.7	0.5
12 months and over, summer grazed.............	0.2	0.1

Dairy Followers

(Per 'replacement unit', i.e. calf + yearling + in-calf heifer.) (1)		
During winter......................................	2.9	2.0
During summer....................................	1.2	0.8

1. Assuming calvings fairly evenly spaced throughout the year and heifers calving at 2 to 2.5 years old.

Beef Finishing (per head)

Housed...	1.8	1.2
Summer Grazed..................................	0.2	0.1
Intensive Beef (0-12 months)....................	1.3	1.0

Suckler Herds (per cow)

Lowland Single suckling (av. whole year)....... .	0.9	0.6
Lowland Multiple suckling (av. whole year)...	2.9	2.1
Upland/Hill Single suckling (av. whole year)...	1.1	0.7

Sheep (per Ewe)

	Labour hours per month	
	Average	Premium (4)
January	0.3	0.2
February	0.3	0.2
March	1.0 (1)	0.7
April	0.4	0.25
May	0.3	0.2
June	0.4 (2)	0.3
July	0.2	0.15
August	0.2	0.15
September	0.25	0.15
October	0.25	0.15
November	0.2	0.15
December	0.2	0.15
Total	4.0 (3)	2.75

1. Assuming mainly March lambing.
2. 0.3 if shearing is by contract.
3. A full-time shepherd, i.e. one who did no other work on the farm, would have to have a flock of at least 600 ewes for the average 4 hours per ewe per year to be achieved, assuming full-time assistance during lambing time.
4. In a national survey conducted in 1999 the average annual requirement for flocks exceeding 500 ewes was 2.9 hours.

Pigs

	Labour hours per month	
Age Group	Average	Premium
Breeding and Rearing, per sow	1.5	1.20
(Average 130 sows per worker, Premium 160)		
Feeding only, per 10 pigs	1.6	1.25
No. at a time, per worker:		
Average 1,200 per man, Premium 1,600		
No. per year, per worker:		
Average: 6,000 porkers, 4,800 cutters, 4,450 baconers		
Premium: 8,000 porkers, 6,400 cutters, 5,750 baconers		
Breeding, Rearing and Feeding, per sow (with progeny)		
Porkers, average 90 sows per worker, premium 110	2.4	2.0
Cutters, average 80-85 sows per worker, premium 100-105	2.6	2.1
Baconers, average 75-80 sows per worker, premium 95-100	2.8	2.2

Poultry (large scale, automated)

	Labour hours per month
Laying hens: battery cages (18,000 per full-time worker)	1.1 per 100
free range	4 per 100
Broilers: 32,500 at a time per full-time worker*	
(225,000 a year)	1.0 per 100

* additional help needed for catching and cleaning out (included in labour hours/ month)

4.   STANDARD MAN DAYS

The Standard Man Day (SMD) estimates are drawn from the labour use figures above, and are based on a standard 8-hour day. Most of these SMD figures are based on limited data only - though all that is available; these are subject to substantial variations with scale and production methods. Little research has been done recently to update these figures.

Crops (per hectare)	S.M.D.s
Winter Feed Wheat	
Winter Milling Wheat	
Spring Wheat	
Winter Feed Barley	1.15 /
Winter Malting Barley	1.75 (1)
Spring Malting Barley	
Winter Oats	
Spring Oats	
Winter Oilseed Rape	1.10
Spring Oilseed Rape	1.00
Linseed	1.00
Winter Field Beans	0.90
Spring Field Beans	0.95
Dried Peas	1.60
Lupins	1.50
Vining Peas	3.00
Maincrop Potatoes	9.25 (2)
Early Potatoes	5.50 (2)
Sugar Beet	3.00
Herbage Seed (Ryegrass)	1.40
Hops	9.50 (2)
Kale (grazed)	1.40
Silage:~ one cut	1.60 (3)
two cuts	2.80 (3)
Grazing only	0.40 (3)
Hay for sale	1.80 (3)
Let Keep	0.40 (3)
Bare fallow / set-aside	0.20
Rough Grazing	0.20

Notes Overleaf

Livestock *(per head)* *(4)*

Dairy Cows	4.00
Bulls	3.50
Beef Cows (single suckler including calf):	
lowland	1.35
upland/hill	1.68
Cereal Beef (0-12 months) (5)	1.90
18-month Beef (5)	1.60
Grass Silage Beef (5)	1.90
Finishing Suckler bred stores:	
Grass	1.10
Winter	1.10
Calves; to 6 months (5)	1.20
Ewes:lowland	0.50
upland	0.45
hill	0.40
Rams	0.50
Winter Finishing Store Lambs	0.30
Sows (including weaners to 30kg)	2.25
Boars	2.00
Other Bacon Pigs	0.25
Laying Birds:battery cages	0.017
free range	0.06
Pullets reared (5)	0.005
Broilers (5)	0.002

1. 1.15 if straw ploughed in; 1.75 if straw harvested. Highly mechanised larger farms will require no more than 0.75 S.M.D./ha of direct labour for cereals and other combinable crops (assuming straw ploughed in).

2. Excludes casual labour for harvesting.

3. Excludes any reseeding carried out – this is likley to be around 0.6 S.M.D./ha in the year reseeding is carried out.

4. Note that for grazing livestock, the S.M.D.s per head exclude field work, e.g. grass production and silage making, i.e. the labour for these has to be added to give total labour for these enterprises.

5. For these livestock, S.M.D. per annum should be based on numbers produced (sold) during the year. For all other livestock, average numbers on the farm at any one time during the year should be used (i.e. average of numbers at end of each month).

7. 'Other Cattle' can refer to both beef animals and dairy followers (ref. detail on page 170).

V.   MACHINERY

1.   AGRICULTURAL MACHINERY PRICES

This price schedule is for spring 2012 purchase of new machinery, net of discounts and ex. V.A.T. Machinery inflation has been subdued over much of the last decade compared with most other benchmark inflation indicators (mainstream and agricultural). Between 1997 and 2003, machinery inflation totalled only 1.1 per cent. Since then, inflation has affected machinery prices by much more, with rises in 2006 of 4.5%, 2007 of 5.6%, 2008 of 6.5%, 2009 of 3.9% and 2010 of 2.6%. Over 2012, it is expected that machinery costs will rise by 3-5% (this is assumed in the schedule below - prices shown are a range). Machines with a star '*' denote those used in subsequent 'farmer' cost' calculations.

Tractors		*£ Range*	
(a) Two-Wheel Drive			
80-90 hp	....	29,120	34,320
90-100 hp	....	29,120	35,360
(b) Four- Wheel Drive			
* 100-120 hp	....	41,600	57,200
* 125-140 hp	....	46,800	62,400
* 150-180 hp	....	62,400	78,000
180-220 hp	....	72,800	93,600
225-270 hp	....	83,200	119,600
(c) High Road Speed (50 Km /hour)			
155-175 hp	....	69,680	88,400
190-220 hp	....	81,120	104,000
(d) Crawlers - rubber tracks			
* 230-300 hp	....	150,800	166,400
340-400 hp	....	166,400	187,200
450-550 hp	....	197,600	239,200

Cultivating Equipment

(a) Ploughs				*Variable width*	
		Mechanical		Hydraulic	
Reversible:		Adjustment		Adjustment	
3-furrow	....	9,880	11,960	—	
4-furrow	....	11,960	14,040	14,352	16,640
* 5-furrow	....	15,080	17,160	17,680	20,280
6-furrow	....	16,640	19,760	19,344	22,880
7-furrow (mounted)	....	27,040	30,160	31,200	34,840
8-furrow (mounted)	....	29,640	31,720	34,320	36,400
(b) Furrow Presses					
1.6-1.8 m double row	....			3,640	4,160
2.0-2.4 m double row	....			3,952	4,992
* 2.6-3.0 m double row	....			5,720	7,800
3.2-3.6 m double row	....			8,320	9,672
3.8-4.0 m double row	....			9,880	11,024

(c)	*Front Presses (excluding linkage)*		
	1.5 m single row	2,600	3,120
	3.0 m single row	3,640	5,720
*	4.0 m single row — hydraulic folding	6,240	8,320
(d)	*Front Press Linkage*		
	1.5 to 2.0 tonne	2,392	2,704
	3.5 to 5.5 tonne	2,912	3,640
(e)	*Other Cultivating Equipment*		
*	Sub Soiler 2-3 leg	3,120	4,160
	Shakarator (3m)	9,360	12,480
	Stubble Cultivator (3m)	6,240	10,400
*	(heavy duty) (4m) hydraulic folding	12,480	16,640
	(6 m): hydraulic folding	15,600	19,760
*	Spring-tine Cultivator (3-4 m):	2,600	3,640
	(5-6 m): hydraulic folding	6,240	8,840
	Tine / Disc Cultivator Combinations		
	(3-4 m) mounted	12,480	22,880
*	(5-6 m) trailed	26,000	46,800
*	Disc Harrows (3.6 - 4.4 m): trailed	12,480	20,800
	(4.4-6.0 m): trailed folding	26,000	41,600
*	Harrows (5-6 m): light-medium, hydraulic folding	2,600	4,160
*	Rotovator (up to 135 hp tractor)	7,800	9,360
	(200 hp tractor)	13,000	15,600
	Power Harrow (with packer roller)		
	(3 m)	7,280	8,840
*	(4m)	11,960	13,520
	(4-6m): folding	24,960	27,040
*	Rolls: Triple gang, hydraulic folding (6 m)	7,280	10,400
	Five gang, hydraulic folding (12m)	16,640	21,840

Fertiliser Distributors, Seed Drills, Sprayers

(a)	*Fertiliser Distributors*		
	Mounted Spinners		
	(700-1,200 litre): twin disc, hydraulic control	3,120	6,760
	(1,300-1,700 litre): twin disc, hydraulic control	5,200	8,320
*	(1,650-2,300 litre): twin disc, electronic control	8,320	10,400
	(3,200 litre): twin disc, electronic control	10,400	14,560
	Bag lifter (850-1,000kg)	1,872	2,600
(b)	*Seed Drills*		
	Grain: 3 m, gravity fed	7,280	9,360
*	3-4 m, pneumatic	13,520	16,120
	6 m, pneumatic	16,640	24,960
(c)	*Combined Cultivator and Pneumatic Drill*		
	3-4 m	17,680	23,920
	6 m	36,400	46,800

(d) Combined Power Harrow and Pneumatic Drill
*	3-4 m	18,720	28,080
	6 m	39,520	57,200
(e)	*Direct Drill (6m)*	31,200	52,000
(f)	*Sprayers*		
	Mounted, 600-800 litre tank, 12 m boom	3,120	5,200
	Mounted, 1,000-1,800 l, 20-24 m hydraulic boom	14,560	18,720
*	Trailed, 2,500-3,000l tank 18-24 m boom	24,960	35,360
	Trailed, 3,000-4,500l tank 24-36 m boom	31,200	41,600
	Self-propelled sprayers,		
	2,500-4,000l, 24-36 m boom	83,200	119,600
	5,000-6,000l tank, 24 - 36m boom	104,000	156,000

Grass Conservation and Handling Equipment

(a) Silage Equipment
*	Forage Harvester: trailed, precision chop	28,080	37,440
	Self-propelled (3 m pick-up 400-600 hp)	145,600	208,000
	Maize attachment, 8 row	31,200	36,400
	Silage Trailer, 12 tonne, tandem axle	9,880	13,000
	Silage Trailer, 14 - 16 tonne, tandem axle	11,752	14,040
	Buckrake (push off)	3,640	6,240

(b) Haymaking Equipment
	Mowers 1.5-1.8 m, 1-2 drum	2,704	3,536
*	Disc Conditioner, mounted (2.4-3.2 m)	8,320	13,520
	trailed (3.2 - 3.8 m)	15,600	19,760
*	Rake: single/double rotor, 3.2m-4.5m range	3,640	7,280
	multiple rotors 8-10m range	14,560	26,000
	Tedder/swather		
*	5-7 m, 4-6 rotors	5,720	9,360
	8-11m multiple rotors	12,480	22,880
	Balers and Bale Handling: see 5(c) and (d) below		

(c) Silage Handling Equipment
	Silage shear bucket	2,080	3,120
	Silage grab	1,820	2,600
	Big Bale Silage Feeder, mounte	8,320	12,480
	Diet-feeder Wagon (6 tonne)	18,720	22,880
	Clamp Silage Mixer (10 tonne)	23,920	29,120

Grain and Straw Harvesting and Handling Equipment

(a) Combines

Engine size hp	Cutterbar width metres (feet)		
220-249	4.5-5.5 (14-18)	114,400	166,400
250-299	5.4-6.1 (18-20)	145,600	208,000
300-399	6.0-7.7 (20-25)	187,200	254,800
400+	9.0-9.15 (25-30)	239,200	374,400

(b)	Yield monitoring/mapping	7,800	9,880
(c)	Balers		
*	Conventional Balers	10,400	12,480
*	Round balers, twine tying and net wrap	20,800	26,000
*	Big Square Balers	72,800	83,200
(d)	Bale Wrappers		
	Big Bale Wrapper: trailed	9,360	13,520
	Big Square Bale Wrapper: trailed	20,800	26,000
	Combined Baler and Wrapper	43,680	49,920
	Bale Trailers, 30 ft - 35 ft long	3,640	4,680
	Accumulator, flat 8, mechanical	2,496	3,120
	Big bale accumulator	10,400	12,480
	Big Bale Shredder, silage or straw	6,240	8,320
(e)	Drying, Handling, Feed Processing Equipment		
	Grain driers and Grain storage:		
	Cleaner/grader, 10-20 tonnes/hour	10,660	14,820
	Grain augers 150 mm, 6-8.5 m, with trolley	2,080	2,600
	Grain conveyors, (25-50t/hour)	1,560	2,080
	Hammer mill, 7.5-15 kW	3,952	4,368
	Roller mill, 4-5.5 kW	3,380	3,952
	Mixer, 750-1000 kg	4,680	5,200
	Mill and mixer, 1,000-1,300kg, 3.7-5.5 kW	6,760	8,320

Potato, Sugar Beet and Vegetable Machinery

(a)	Potato Machinery		
*	De-stoner	46,800	52,000
*	Bedformer, 1 bed	5,200	7,280
	Bed tiller (1 bed)	8,840	9,880
*	Planter: 2 row mounted	12,480	15,600
	6 row	36,400	39,520
	Haulm pulveriser (2 row):	6,760	8,320
*	Harvesters trailed: 2 row elevator manned/unmanned	78,000	88,400
	2 row, self-propelled	145,600	197,600
	Store loader (heavy duty)	26,000	31,200
	Self-unloading hopper, 3-5 tonnes	11,440	13,000
	Clod separator	11,440	13,520
	Sizer, 5-30 tonnes/hour	11,440	14,560
	Barrel washer, 8-10 tonnes/hour	26,000	31,200
	Roller inspection table, 1.2 x 2.4 m	3,120	5,200
	Weigher, automatic, 8-10 tonnes/hour	7,280	8,320
	Box tipper with cross conveyor	18,720	21,840
	Box filler, automatic	16,640	17,680
	Bag stitcher (hand held)	1,040	1,560
	Complete out of store grading line: 20 tonnes/hour	44,720	52,000
	30 tonnes/hour	88,400	104,000

(b) Sugar Beet Machinery

*	Precision Drill 6 row (pneumatic)		11,440	13,520
		12 row-18 row (pneumatic)	22,880	36,400
*	Hoe:	6 row-12 row (heavy duty)	8,320	13,520
	Harvesters:	Trailed, 2 row, tanker	72,800	79,040
		Trailed, 3 row, tanker	87,360	94,640
		Trailed, 4 row, tanker	98,800	109,200
*	Self-propelled, 6 row, 18 tonne tank		332,800	395,200
	Cleaner-loader, with engine, 1-3 tonnes per minute		26,000	31,200
	Fodder beet harvester		7,280	93,600

(c) Vegetable Machinery

Onion windrower		10,920	11,960
Root crop digger: 1 webb		7,800	8,320
2 webbs		8,840	10,400
Top lifting veg single row, bunker		57,200	65,520
twin row, bunker/elevator		98,800	119,600
four row, elevator		130,000	150,800
four row, self-propelled		343,200	374,400
Leek harvester (mounted)		22,880	36,400

General

	Trailer, 12 tonne tipping; grain/silage	8,840	11,440
*	Trailer, 14t tipping, tandem axle; grain/silage	10,400	12,480
*	F.Y.M. Spreader, (10 - 12 tonne)	10,400	15,600
	(12 - 14 tonne)	14,560	18,720
*	Loaders, front mounted	5,200	7,280
*	Materials Handler, telescopic boom (2.5-3.0 tonne)	41,600	52,000
	Skid steer loader (500-600 kg)	15,600	20,800
	Quad Bikes	3,640	5,200
	Slurry Stores (metal), including base for 180 day storage period for:		
	100 cows	410	per cow
	200 cows	379	per cow
	400 cows	331	per cow
	Vacuum Tankers (5,000-6,000 litre)	5,720	6,240
*	Low Ground Pressure Tankers (9,000-11,000 litre)	11,440	13,520
	Slurry pump	4,160	4,680
	Cattle crush	1,040	1,560
	Cattle crush with weigher	2,080	2,600
	Cattle trailer (twin-axle)	2,600	3,640
	Yard scrapers	676	936
	Rotary brush (2-2.5 m)	1,872	2,496
*	Flat roll, ballastable (2.5-3 m)	1,248	1,560
*	Pasture topper (2.0-3.0 m)	1,560	2,600

Hedge cutter:

* hydraulic angling; flail head	12,480	15,600
7.6m reach, 1.3m flail head, double sided	28,080	35,360
Ditcher: fully slewing	9,880	11,440
Post hole digger	1,300	1,820
Post hole driver	1,560	3,120
Saw bench	2,080	2,340
Log splitter	832	1,144

2. CONTRACTORS' CHARGES, AVERAGE FARMERS' COSTS, AND RATES OF WORK

This section has under-gone considerable review in this edition and consequently there are differences in the layout and assumptions to previous years. The changes are to ensure the section is up-to-date, accurate and representative.

Contractors' charges vary widely according to many factors: these are estimates for 2012. Farmer-contractors often charge less than dedicated contractors, since their overheads and machinery fixed costs are largely *considered* covered by their own farming operations, but the service may not always be so complete, including specialist advice.

Farmers' own costs (including the value of the farmers' own manual labour) vary even more widely; those given (for 2012) are averages in every respect - different types of soil, size of farm, and so on; they are based on accounting cost procedures in that labour, tractor and machinery fuel, repairs and depreciation are included - no allowance has been added for general farm overheads, interest on capital, supervision/management or under-occupied labour during slack times. They assume four-wheel drive 130 hp tractors for heavy work such as ploughing, cultivations and drilling and 165 hp tractors are assumed for work with a very high power requirement such as heavy discing, sub-soiling and deep ploughing. Four-wheel drive 110 hp tractors are assumed to be used for most other operations (these individual tractor costs are shown in the tractor costs schedule on page 187). The figures should not be used for partial budgeting. The machinery used in the calculations for farmers' costs is identified by a 'star' adjacent to specific items of equipment in the machinery list in the previous section. Where a range in prices exists, an average has been used for the purchase price.

The contract charges and average farmers' costs are put side-by-side for tabular convenience, not to facilitate comparisons. Apart from the fact that contractors' charges must cover expenses omitted from the farmers' cost, the advisability or otherwise of hiring a contractor for a particular job depends on many factors, varying widely according to farm circumstances; therefore, there are advantages and disadvantages not reflected in a cost comparison alone.

Assumptions: Contractors' costs are particularly sensitive to many factors. These include fuel costs, capital machinery prices, and demand versus local competition. Of these, fuel has risen by a quarter in the preceding 12 months and at the time the data was struck, was at 66ppl for tractor diesel. Many contractors are now making individual arrangements with customers regarding fuel (i.e. prices quoted before fuel – therefore using the farmer's fuel when on site). The contractor charges shown below are inclusive of fuel and do not reflect this trend.

Machinery rings. Prices charged by farmers offering services through machinery rings are extremely variable but are generally between average farmers' costs and contractors' charges. There are exceptions, which mainly relate to relatively expensive items of machinery (e.g. precision drills, destoners and combine harvesters), where the charges for services offered through machinery rings are close to and often less than average farmers' costs.

The rates of work include preparation, travelling to and from the fields and allow for minor breakdowns and other stoppages. All charges and costs below are per hectare unless otherwise stated.

* *Figures in the first two columns overleaf are £/ha unless otherwise stated and represent a national average.*

Average Contractors Charges & Farmers Costs of Performing Mechanical Operations.

Operation	Contract Charge £/ha *	Farmer's Average Cost £/ha *	Days Use Per Year	Average Rate of Work (Ha per 8 hr day)
Cultivations				
Ploughing – light land	56.50	55	30	7
– heavy land	62.75	59	30	6.5
-- with furrow press	8.20	9	30	6
Deep ploughing (over 30cm)	62.50	84	25	5.5
Rotovating - ploughed land	64.25	83	18	5
- grass		104	18	4
Sub-soiling/Flat Lifting	62.50	61	10	6
Mole-ploughing – single leg	88.20			
Stubble cultivating	37.00	33	20	12
Discing: Shallow	33.85			
Deep	40.50	45	20	10
Power harrowing – Deep/on ploughing	56.00	44	20	9
Shallow/seedbed prep	54.35			
Spring-tine Harrowing	28.40	23	20	12
Pressing	32.10	26	10	
One-pass tillage train (solo/discordon etc)	56.85	59	20	15
Rolling – flat (grassland)	22.25	21	10	12
– ring (seedbeds)	17.30	15	10	20
Drilling				
Rape drilling with flatlift/subsoiler	58.00	61	10	6
Cereal drilling – conventional	46.00	30	12	14
combi-drilling	61.75	51	12	10
direct drilling	51.90			
Sugar beet drilling	47.00	49	5	10
Grass seed (broadcast)	25.70	26	2	11
Grass seeding with harrow (e.g. Opico)	31.90			
Cross drilling grass	24.70			
Chain Harrowing	21.65			
Maize Precision Drilling	44.00			
Maize Drilling Under Plastic	115.75			
Fertilising & Spraying				
Fertiliser distribution	14.20	9	15	45
Extra for variable rate application	2.35			
Lime spreading (per tonne)	5.25/tonne			
Spraying (based on 200 l/ha & 24m boom)	13.10	12	20	40
Extra if less than 50 acres (20 ha)	6.70			
Liquid Fertiliser	12.60			
ATV spraying (£/hr)	30.00/hr			
Slug-pelleting	11.10			
Avadex Spreading	12.85			

Operation	Contract Charge £/ha *	Farmer's Average Cost £/ha *	Days Use Per Year	Average Rate of Work (Ha per 8 hour day)
Combining				
Combining cereals	85.25	83	14	21.6
Extra for straw chopper on combine	7.65	*Farmer's cost assumes*		
Extra for seeding (Autocast)	14.85	*300 ha per year harvested*		
Extra for yield mapping	2.50			
OSR harvesting – out of windrow	86.25			
– direct combining	85.75	83	14	21.6
Combining peas/beans	88.70	83	14	21.6
Combining grain maize	96.00			
Swathing OSR	40.75			
Grain carting to barn (per hour)	36.85/hr	33.86 /hr		
Grass & Forage				
Set-aside topping	30.40			
Grass topping	29.30	26	3	12
Grass mowing	30.90	32	10	12
Tedding	16.30	15	10	20
Raking	16.70	22	3	20
Forage harvesting only – first cut	58.00	53	6	16
- other cuts	53.10	42	6	20
Forage harvesting, cart (3 trailers) and clamping	124.75			
Whole Crop forage harvesting, cart (3 trailers) and clamping	166.50			
Complete service – mow, rake, forage harvest, cart (3 trailers) and clamp	146.40			
Maize harvesting incl carting (3 trailers) and clamping	175.50			
Extra forage trailer	13.60			
Forage box	100.00/hr			
Baling				
Baling (per bale) - 'small'	0.50/bale	0.29 / bale	10	6.4
- 80cm × 70cm	3.80/bale			
- 120cm × 70cm	4.60/bale	4.01 / bale	25	20
- 120cm × 130cm	6.30/bale			
- Round 120cm	2.60/bale			
- Round 150cm	2.80/bale	2.23 / bale	25	13.6
Bale-wrapping – Round 120cm (6 layers)	5.20/bale			
- Round 120cm (with 4 layers)	4.30/bale			
- Round 120cm (without plastic)	1.70/bale			
- Square 120cm × 70cm (6 layers)	5.15/bale			
- Square 120cm × 70cm (4 layers)	4.15/bale			
- Square120cm × 70cm (without plastic)	1.95/bale			

Operation	Contract Charge £/ha *	Farmer's Average Cost £/ha *	Days Use Per Year	Average Rate of Work (Ha per 8 hour day)
Root Crop Operations				
Potato harvesting – harvesting only	638.75	424	20	2
- Harvesting and carting	1,073.60	695		
De-stoning potato land	210.00	279	16	2.5
Potato ridging	55.60	44	4	9
Potato Planting	106.25	141	16	2.5
Sugar beet harvesting	247.00	302	20	8
Irrigation (25 mm application / ha)	98.00			

Manure Handling - *see below for telehandler costs for loading*			
FYM spreading – tractor and rear discharge :	41.75/hr	49	
- tractor and side discharge spreader	35.50/hr		
Slurry spreading – tanker	43.25/hr	48	
- umbilical	76.70/hr		
- extra pump	37.40/hr		
Slurry injection	68.50/hr		

General / Rural Maintenance		
Hedge cutting - flail	31.40/hr	39
- saw-blade	44.50/hr	46
Hedge laying	12.50/metre	
Fence erection (with materials)		
– post and 4 Barb	4.05/metre	
– post, stock net & 2 Barb	4.90/metre	
– post and 3 rails	13.00/metre	
Tractor + Post Knocker + Man	41.00/hr	
Ditching using 360 deg digger	34.70/hr	
Tractor + trailer + man	37.80/hr	34
100 – 150 hp Tractor + man	29.35/hr	
150 – 220 hp Tractor + man	36.50/hr	*See tractor costs schedule*
220 – 300 hp Tractor + man	54.00/hr	*for farmer's average cost*
300 hp + Tractor + man	65.75/hr	
Forklift/Telehandler + Man	36.20/hr	31

Livestock Husbandry	
Sheep dipping	0.95/head
Sheep jetting / showering	0.75/head
Sheep – shearing	1.45/head
-- rams	2.90/head
-- crutching	0.68/head
Sheep ultrasound scanning	0.50/head
Cattle ultrasound scanning	2.00/head
Foot trimming – sheep	0.65/head
Livestock husbandry	14.00/hr

Acknowledgement. The above estimates for contractors' charges are kindly supplied by the National Association of Agricultural Contractors.

Contract Charge for All Operations

Cereals and Combinable Break Crops, 'stubble to stubble' (i.e. up to and including combine harvesting and carting the grain to store): £240 to £320/ha (£100-130/acre). Variations depend upon such factors as distance away, area contracted, size of fields, type of terrain, quality of soil, level of inputs (as affecting weight of crop to be harvested and carted) and local competition.

Management Agreements.

Generally these are formalised with a written agreement which sets out the terms for the "Farmer" (who can be a landowner or tenant) and a "Contractor". The "Contractor" can be a neighbouring farmer or traditional contractor. "Contractor" remuneration includes a guaranteed basic payment (fee). The basic payment is usually between £210 and £275/ha (£85-£110/acre) for combinable crops and should cover the fixed costs of the operation.

Following deduction of agreement running costs (variable costs, drying etc) and the Farmers Basic Payment, the surplus is split between the 2 parties. The split may typically be 70%-80% to the contractor and 20%-30% to the landowner. This incentivises good performance and management from the contractor. A second band of payment rate is sometimes introduced e.g. 50%:50% split above a set level of surplus.

One sometimes sees farmers' total power and machinery costs compared with stubble to stubble contractors' charges. It has of course to be remembered that the former include many cost items not included in the latter, e.g. the cost of farm vehicles, fixed plant such as grain stores and general farm maintenance.

3.   TRACTOR HOURS

per annum

Crops	per hectare	
	Average	Premium
Cereals	9	7
Straw Harvesting	3.5	2.5
Potatoes	25	15
Sugar Beet	20	12
Vining Peas	20	12
Dried Peas	10	8
Field Beans	9	7
Oilseed Rape	9	7
Herbage Seeds:		
1 year undersown or 3 year direct drilled	7	5
1 year direct drilled	11	8
Hops (machine picked)	125	—
Kale (grazed)	8	6
Turnips/Swedes: folded/lifted	12/35	10/25
Fallow	12	7
Ley Establishment:		
Undersown	2	1
Direct Seed	7	4
Making Hay	12	8
Making Silage:		
1st Cut	12	8
2nd Cut	9	6
Grazing:		
Temporary Grass	3	2.5
Permanent Grass	2	1.5

Livestock	per head Average
Dairy Cows	6
Other Cattle over 2 years	5
Other Cattle 1-2 years	4
Other Cattle ½-1 year	2.25
Calves 0-½ year	2.25
Housed Bullocks	3
Sheep, per ewe	1.25
Store Sheep	0.8
Sows	1.75
Other Pigs over 2 months	1
Laying Birds	0.04

1.   *For livestock*, annual requirements are the per head requirements above multiplied by average numbers during the year (i.e. average numbers at end of each month).

2. *As with labour,* the number of tractors required by a farm depends more on the seasonal requirements and number required at any one time than on total annual tractor hours. These can be calculated from the seasonal labour data provided earlier in this book. The soil type and size/power of tractors purchased are obviously other relevant factors.

Tractor Power Requirements

		hp/acre		hp/ha		kW/ha	
		av.	prem.	av.	prem.	av.	prem.
Combinable crops:	heavy land	0.75	0.65	1.85	1.5	1.4	1.1
	light land	0.5	0.45	1.25	1.0	0.95	0.75
Mixed cropping:	heavy land	1.0	0.75	2.5	1.85	1.85	1.4
	light land	0.7	0.5	1.75	1.25	1.3	1.95

UK Agricultural Tractor Sales per Year (over 50 HP)

Year	Average Tractor Size kW (HP)	Number of Units Sold	Per Cent change y/y
2003	94.0 (126.0)	14,445	+4.1%
2004	96.1 (128.8)	14,750	+ 2.1%
2005	95.2 (127.6)	13,068	-11.4%
2006	95.7 (128.3)	13,566	+ 3.8%
2007	100.0 (134.0)	15,540	+14.6%
2008	103.0 (138.1)	17,104	+10.1%
2009	107.0 (143.4)	15,013	-12.2%
2010	105.9 (142.0)	13,347	-11.1%
2011 (to May)		6,400	

(data from the Agricultural Engineers Association).

GRAIN HAULAGE COSTS

The average costs per tonne of grain (and oilseed) haulage in Great Britain over the past six seasons are summarised by the HGCA's haulage survey carried out each December. The summarised results for the years 2005 to 2010 are tabulated below:

Summary table of the HGCA Haulage Survey Results

	2005	2006	2007	2008	2009	2010
10 miles	£4.29	£4.09	£4.18	£4.83	£4.24	£4.54
20 miles	£4.77	£4.57	£4.69	£5.35	£4.81	£5.03
40 miles	£5.74	£5.53	£5.72	£6.40	£5.95	£6.01
60 miles	£6.71	£6.50	£6.74	£7.45	£7.09	£6.98
100 miles	£8.65	£8.43	£8.78	£9.54	£9.38	£8.94
150 miles	£11.08	£10.84	£11.34	£12.16	£12.23	£11.39

4.   TRACTOR COSTS

	Four-Wheel Drive Tractors			
	110 h.p.		130 h.p.	
Initial Cost............................	£49,400		£54,600	
	per year £	per hour £	per year £	per hour £
Depreciation............................	3,952	7.90	4,368	8.74
Insurance................................	371	0.74	410	0.82
Repairs and Maintenance..................	1,976	3.95	2,184	4.37
Fuel and Oil............................	4,250	8.50	5,023	10.05
Total	10,548	21.10	11,984	23.97

	Crawler			
	165 h.p.		265 h.p.	
Initial Cost............................	£70,200		£158,600	
	per year £	per hour £	per year £	per hour £
Depreciation............................	5,616	11.23	12,688	25.38
Insurance................................	527	1.05	1,190	2.38
Repairs and Maintenance..................	2,808	5.62	6,344	12.69
Fuel and Oil............................	6,374	12.75	11,024	22.05
Total	15,324	30.65	31,245	62.49

Figures are estimates calculated for 2012. Depreciation assumes all tractors are sold for 20% of their original value after 10 years of life. This is based on the depreciation schedule shown on page 189 which demonstrates the average annual fall in value of machinery over its life (column 2 is applicable to tractors).

Annual repair costs have been calculated at 4% of initial cost for all tractors. No interest on capital has been included. Fuel is charged at 66p/litre plus a 5% allowance for oil.

The hourly figures are based on a use of 500 hours per year. A greater annual use than this will mean higher annual costs but possibly lower hourly costs. On some large arable farms and within many contracting businesses, many tractors do up to, and even over, 1,000 hours per year. Earlier replacement at a given annual use will increase depreciation costs per hour but should reduce repair costs. The hourly figures are averages for all types of work: heavy operations such as ploughing obviously have a higher cost than light work.

5.   ESTIMATING ANNUAL MACHINERY COSTS

Annual machinery costs consist of depreciation, repairs, fuel and oil, contract charges, and vehicle tax and insurance. These can be budgeted in three ways;

1)   using information on past machinery costs on the farm (e.g. management accounts),

2)   per hectare, by looking up an average figure for the district, according to the size and type of farm. Approximate levels are shown in the tables of whole farm fixed costs (page 197). This is obviously a rough and ready measure.

3)   Fully detailed calculation, costing and depreciating each machine in turn, including tractors, estimating repairs and fuel costs for each, and adding the charges for any contract work. The following tables give, for different types of machine, estimated life, annual depreciation, and estimated repairs according to annual use.

ESTIMATED USEFUL LIFE OF POWERED MACHINERY IN NORMAL USE

Estimated Useful Life (years)	Annual Use (hours)				
Equipment	25	50	100	200	300
Group 1:					
Ploughs, cultivators, toothed harrows, hoes, rolls, ridgers, potato planting attachments, grain	12+	12+	12+	12	10
Group 2:					
Disc harrows, corn drills, grain drying machines, food grinders and mixers	12+	12+	12	10	8
Group 3:					
Combine harvesters, pick-up balers, rotary cultivators, hydraulic loaders	12+	12+	12	9	7
Group 4:					
Mowers, forage harvesters, swath turners, rakes, tedders, hedge cutting machines, semi-automatic potato planters and transplanters, unit root drills, mechanical root thinners	12+	12	11	8	6
Group 5:					
Fertilisers, combine drills, FYM spreaders, elevator potato diggers, spraying machines, pea cutter windrowers	10	10	9	8	7
Miscellaneous:					
Beet harvesters	11	10	9	6	5
Potato harvesters	—	8	7	5	—
Milking machinery	—	—	—	—	20+

	Annual Use (hours)				
	500	750	1,000	1,500	2,000	2,500
Tractors	12+	12	10	7	6	5
Electric motors	12+	12+	12+	12+	12	12

DEPRECIATION: AVERAGE ANNUAL FALL IN VALUE

(per cent of new price)

Age of Machine	Complex. High Depreciation Rate e.g. potato harvesters, mobile pea viners, etc.	Established machines with many moving parts, e.g. tractors, combines, balers, forage harvesters	Simple equipment with few moving parts, e.g. ploughs, trailers
	%	%	%
1	40	30	20
2	27½	20	15
3	20*	16*	12½
4	17½†	14½	11½
5	15‡	13†	10½*
6	13½	12	9½
7	12	11	9
8	11	10‡	8½†
9	(10)	9½	8
10	(9½)	8½	7½‡

* Typical frequency of renewal with heavy use.

† Typical frequency of renewal with average use.

‡Typical frequency of renewal with light use.

DEPRECIATION: PERCENTAGE RATES

Straight-Line

Trade-in, Second-hand or Scrap Value as % of New Price

Years Retained	5%	10%	20%	25%	33%	40%	50%	60%
3	—	—	—	—	—	20	16	13
4	—	—	—	—	17	15	12	—
5	—	—	—	15	13	12	—	—
6	—	—	13	12	11	10	—	—
8	—	11	10	9	—	—	—	—
10	9	9	8	—	—	—	—	—
12	8	7	—	—	—	—	—	—
15	6	—	—	—	—	—	—	—

Example: If a machine costing £10,000 is retained for 8 years, at the end of which the trade-in value is 20% of the new price (i.e. £2,000), the average depreciation per annum has been £8,000 over 8 years = £1,000 (i.e. 10% per year of the new price).

Formula to calculate percentage = ((NP – TiV) / AoM) / NP x 100

NP	New Price
TiV	Trade in Value
AoM	Age of Machine

Diminishing Balances

Trade-in, Second-hand or Scrap Value as % of New Price

Years Retained	5%	10%	20%	25%	33%	40%	50%	60%
3	—	—	—	—	—	26	21	16
4	—	—	—	—	24	20	16	—
5	—	—	—	24	20	17	—	—
6	—	—	23	20	17	14	—	—
8	—	25	18	16	—	—	—	—
10	25	20	15	—	—	—	—	—
12	22	17	—	—	—	—	—	—
15	18	—	—	—	—	—	—	—

Example: If a machine costing £10,000 is retained for 4 years, at the end of which the trade-in value is 40% of the new replacement price, the annual depreciation on the diminishing balances method is:

Year 1, £2,000 (i.e. 20% of £10,000);

Year 2, £1,600 (i.e. 20% of £8,000 [the written-down value]);

Year 3, £1,280 (i.e. 20% of £6,400); Year 4, £1,024 (20% of £5,120).

The total written-down value at the end of Year 4 is therefore £4,096 (i.e. £10,000 less the total depreciation of £5,904). This is approximately 41% of the new price. (Taking the percentages in the above table to decimal places would give the trade-in prices stated more precisely).

ESTIMATED ANNUAL COST OF SPARES AND REPAIRS

These figures are based on a percentage of purchase price* at various levels of use

Tractors	Annual Use *(hours)*				Additional 100 hours use add
	500	750	1,000	1,500	
	%	%	%	%	%
	5	6.7	8	10.5	0.5

	Annual Use *(hours)*				Additional 100 hours use add
	50	100	150	200	
Harvesting Machinery:	%	%	%	%	%
Combine Harvesters, self-propelled and engine-driven	1.5	2.5	3.5	4.5	2
Combine Harvesters, p.t.o. driven, metered-chop forage harvesters, pick-up balers, potato & sugar beet harvesters	3	5	6	7	2
Other Implements and Machines:					
Ploughs, Cultivators, Toothed harrows, Hoes, Elevator potato diggers	4.5	8	11	14	6
Rotary cultivators, Mowers, Pea cutter-windrowers	4	7	9.5	12	5
Disc harrows, Fertiliser distributors, Farmyard manure spreaders, Combine drills, Potato planters with fertiliser attachment, sprayers, Hedge-cutting	3	5.5	7.5	9.5	4
Swath turners, Tedders, Side-delivery rakes, Unit drills, Flail forage harvesters, Semi-automatic potato planters and transplanters, Down-the-row thinners	2.5	4.5	6.5	8.5	4
Corn drills, Milking machines, Hydraulic loaders, Potato planting Attachments	2	4	5.5	7	3
Grain driers, Grain cleaners, Rolls, Hammer mills, Feed mixers Threshers	1.5	2	2.5	3	0.5

* When it is known that a high purchase price is due to high quality and durability or a low price corresponds to a high rate of wear and tear, adjustments to the figures should be made.

6. FIELD DRAINAGE

Estimated for 2012

1. Installation (costs per metre of excavating a trench, supplying and laying the pipe and backfilling with soil).

Plastic pipes:		
	60mm diameter	1.80—2.00
	80mm diameter	2.10—2.70
	100mm diameter	3.00—3.25
	125mm diameter	4.00—4.35
	150mm diameter	4.50—5.10
	300mm diameter	12.10—13.60

The above rates apply to schemes of 5 hectares or more; smaller areas and patching up work can cost up to 50% more.

Supplying and laying permeable backfill to within 375mm of ground level will add between £2.65 and £3.40 per metre to costs.

Digging new open ditches (1.8m top width, 0.9m depth) costs £2.00-£2.50 per metre compared with improving existing ditches at £1.40 to £2.00 per metre.

Mole draining will cost in the region of £80-£90 per hectare.

2. *Total Costs* per hectare for complete schemes will vary depending on the distance between laterals, soil type, size of area to be drained, region of the country and the time of year when the work is to be undertaken. The cost of a scheme with 20m spacing between laterals and using permeable backfill will typically be in the range £2,500 to £3,000 per hectare (£1000-£1,200 per acre).

Backfilling with soil, rather than with permeable material such as washed gravel, may reduce the cost by almost half but is only possible on certain types of soil. Equally, certain soil types which are particularly suitable for mole drainage may permit spacing between laterals to be increased to 40m or even 80m in some instances. Where this is possible costs will be reduced proportionately.

7. IRRIGATION COSTS

Estimated for 2012

Capital Costs

1. Pumps (delivering from 20 to 200 cubic metres per hour from a surface water source, all with portable suction and delivery fittings)

Tractor pto shaft driven c/w monitoring equipment	£3,000-5,700
Diesel engine driven c/w monitoring equipment	£5,300-23,000
Electric motor driven (c/w switch gear)	£2,800-40,000
Optional remote/wireless monitoring controls	£2,300-5,700

2. Pipelines (averages per m)
Portable: (excl. valve take offs) 50mm, £2.80; 75 mm, £3.35; 100 mm, £5.00; 125 mm, £6.00; 150 mm, £8.60; (incl. valve take offs) 75 mm, £5.20;
100 mm, £6.60; 125 mm, £7.60; 150mm, £11.00.
Permanent Underground P.V.C. pipe 12.5 bar rating (supply and laying) per metre: 75 mm, £5.00; 100 mm, £6.20; 150/160 mm, £8.50; 200 mm, £12.00; 250mm, £16.20.
Hydrants: 100 mm x 100 mm, £225; 150 mm x 125 mm, £275.

3. Application Systems
    (a) Traditional portable hand move sprinkler systems
    75mm (3 inch) diameter. Sprinkler line assemblies:

1 move/day/six day cycle	£880/ha
2 moves/day/six day cycle	£460/ha
3 moves/day/six day cycle	£320/ha

    (b) Solid set sprinkler lines – semi-permanent systems
    63mm dia. pipework assemblies at

18m x 18m triangulated spacing	£1,535/ha
As above but infra-red automated hand-held controls	£1,750/ha

    (c) Drip irrigation systems

16.5mm non-recoverable tape (excluding header mains, control valves and filtration equipment)	£420/ha

    (d) Hose reel systems using rain guns (average cost per machine)

		Manual controls	Electric Controls
Small	6-15m³/hr	£4,400	–
Medium	20-40m³/hr	£11,000	£12,900
Large	40-80m³/hr	£16,000	£18,000

    (e) Hose reel systems using irrigation booms (average cost per unit)

Small including	20m boom	£ 8,000
Medium including	40/50m boom	£18,000
Large including	70/80m boom	£32,000

    (f) Pivot and linear systems

Small pivot	200m radius (12.5ha)	£1,450/ha full circle
Large pivot	600m radius (113ha)	£870/ha full circle
Linear machine (dependent on length)		£1,660-2,350/ha

4. *Total*

If no source works are needed, as with water from a river, or pond, total capital costs are likely to vary between £1,150 and £2,250 per hectare requiring irrigation at regular intervals, depending on the levels of sophistication and automation of the system installed.

Water Sources

An abstraction licence is required if more than 20m^3 (4,000 gallons) of water per day are taken from surface or underground sources. If abstracting more than 10m^3 per day in Scotland, you must obtain authorisation from SEPA. If abstracting less than 10m^3 per day in Scotland, and comply with certain General Binding Rules (GBR), you do not require authorisation.

Abstraction charges vary widely (and have generally risen for 2011/12) calculated by a formula combining the following factors together:

- Volume – annual licensed
- the Source Factor; whether the source is Environment Agency unsupported, supported or tidal
- The Season Factor; summer, winter or all year round
- A minimum charge of £25

There were 32 regions 'supported' by the Environment Agency in 2011/12. Abstraction from these rivers is 3 times dearer than 'unsupported' sources. Abstraction from tidal sources costs 20% of 'unsupported' sources.

Winter abstraction charges (authorised for abstraction between 1 November to 31 March) cost 16% of all-year abstraction charges. Summer charges (1st April to 31 October) are 160% of the all-year charge.

An application charge of £135 and advertising administration charge of £100 is due, alongside a standard unit charge (SUC), a charge for the region in which the abstraction is authorised to be made and an Environmental Improvement Unit Charge (EIUC). For 2011/12 they are:

Region (£/1000m^3)	Standard Unit Charges	Environmental Improvement Unit Charge (EIUC)
Anglian	27.51	6.56
Midlands	14.95	4.26
Northumbria	25.98	0.00
Yorkshire	11.63	0.62
North West	12.57	0.72
Southern	19.23	5.76
South West including Wessex	19.71	7.25
Thames	13.84	0.83
EA Wales	13.89	4.04

Water Costs

A typical extraction cost for a non-tidal, non supported farm in East Anglia for 25mm per hectare (250m^3 per hectare) would be £1.36/ha for winter abstraction only (0.55p/m^3), £8.52 for all year abstraction (3.41p/m^3) and £13.63/ha (summer only abstraction)

(5.45p/m^3). The same for an acre-inch would equate to £0.56, £3.50 and £5.60 respectively. This is clearly just the cost for the water. The capital invested and the labour and any power requirement should also be accounted for which will vary according to individual circumstances. Mains water at 145p per m^3 would cost £363 per application of 25mm per hectare (£147/acre).

New time limited abstraction licences are difficult to obtain, especially for summer abstraction. Hence there is an increasing trend towards constructing reservoirs that can be used to store water abstracted during the winter months. The cost of clay-lined reservoirs varies widely but would typically be in excess of £1.20 per m^3 of water stored. This price could double if the reservoir is lined and fenced.

Overall Operating Costs

Because of variations in individual farm circumstances in terms of source works and the irrigation system used, the overall cost of applying 25mm per hectare can range widely, from £70 to £130. Very sophisticated systems distributing mains water over intensive specialist crops could be much more expensive.

Conversions and Calculations

The (approximate) imperial equivalents for metric values commonly used in irrigation are as follows:

- 1 cubic metre = 1,000 litres = 220 gallons (1 million gallons = 4,546 cubic metres).

- A pump capacity of 100 cubic metres per hour is equivalent to 22,000 gallons per hour (366 gallons per minute).

- 1,000 cubic metres is sufficient to apply 25 millimetres of water over 4 hectares, which is approximately equivalent to applying 1 inch over 10 acres. An acre inch is therefore 100 cubic meters (22,000 gallons), or a hectare centimetre is 100 cubic meters.

- The cost/volume conversion from a hectare of 25mm depth to an acre-inch is 0.411 or 2.433 from an acre-inch to a hectare 25mm.

8.   GRAIN DRYING AND STORAGE COSTS

Estimated for 2012

Drying

Capital Costs: vary widely according to type and capacity of drier. A standard 20 tonne per hour heated air drier, suitable for a 350 hectare arable unit would cost in the region of £120,000 including the wet bin and associated handling requirements (to feed drier and empty it). Over 10 years, this capital cost represents £5.35 for every tonne of grain regardless of drying requirements. Over 15 years it will fall to £3.57. Amortised (i.e. cost to repay capital and interest) at 6% and assuming only 75% of the grain requires drying, over the 15 year period, this figure rises to £7.35/tonne dried. This figure changes dramatically by changes to throughput and longevity.

Annual fixed costs: being fitted and immobile, grain dryers have a low resale value (mobile dryers do have some second hand value but generally used machines are difficult to find). *Depreciation* is calculated as the capital value divided by the longevity and tonnes per year. This ranges from £5.57 to £1.56 per tonne depending on capacity and annual throughput. *Maintenance* tends to be low at around 2% of purchase value, rising as the dryer ages. *Insurance*; 1.25% of the current value.

Running costs: *Fuel*: A useful 'rule of thumb' is 1 litre of fuel per 1% moisture per tonne. Thus drying each tonne by an average of 5% points at 66ppl makes £3.30 per tonne. *Electricity* use is 17.5Kw/hr for the burner and dischargers, as much again for the handling apparatus, totalling 35Kw/hr. Over a season, (approximately 85 hours use) at 10p/kWh is £294. This represents 18p per tonne of grain dried. Little labour is required for modern automatic driers unless grain has to be passed over the drier several times.

Overall operating costs for a fixed machine of 20t/hr output (on a 350 ha arable farm) therefore equate to £10.11 per tonne of grain dried (assuming 75% dried). Per tonne of total grain produced by the farm the cost is £7.58. *Mobile dryers for smaller farm businesses would be cheaper to buy and therefore the capital cost per tonne is likely to be less than those quoted, but these machines will require a tractor to drive them plus labour, a forklift and even trailers to unload them, adding to their running costs.*

Central grain stores have grain drying services of about £6.00 to £12.00 per tonne for 5% moisture drying for members and non-members respectively. Contractors' charges are typically around £12.00 – 14.00 per tonne for drying grain by 5% moisture.

Storage

Capital Costs: from approximately £110 per tonne (on-floor storage in a purpose-built building) to over £300 per tonne for an elaborate plant, including pit, elevator, conveyors, ventilated storage bins, catwalk etc. in a new building. *Typical costs* are given on page 217.

Depreciation and Interest: £250/t depreciated over 25 years is £10.00/t per year. Interest/opportunity cost of £250 at 6% is £7.50/year (i.e. on the average capital employed). *Fuel and Repairs:* £2.50 per tonne (1%).

Interest on Grain Stored: 75p/month at £150/t grain at 6% interest to £1.13/month at £150/t grain, at 9% interest.

Contract Storage: typically £1.50 - 2.00/t per month with a handling charge of around £2.00 - £2.50 per tonne for loading into store and out of store.

VI.   OTHER FIXED COSTS DATA

1.   WHOLE FARM FIXED COSTS

The following are a broad indication of the levels of fixed costs per hectare (acre) for various types and sizes of farm, estimated for 2012, including the value of unpaid family manual labour, including that of the farmer and his wife. The figures are based on the actual results from the Farm Business Survey (FBS) for the 2009-10 year, adjusted for subsequent changes in costs. The FBS is based on a sample of farms which does change over time, so there is not a consistent sample. This just emphasises that the costs given below should be used only as an indication and must be adjusted according to individual situations; see also further notes on the use of this data below.

The FBS is conducted by a consortium of Universities and Colleges across England on behalf of DEFRA. Although the survey is limited to England, the figures within this section are likely to be broadly applicable to most parts of the UK. The FBS has undergone an overhaul in recent years. Specific regional reports are no longer published - although they can be accessed via the FBS website (see www.farmbusinesssurvey.co.uk). In addition, the farm types have been standardised across the country. They are now based on DEFRA's standard farm classifications. This has meant that some categories of farm have disappeared (mainly the 'mixed' ones such as dairy & arable, and arable & lowland livestock). All of these costs can of course vary widely according to many factors, especially the intensity of farming, e.g. the number of cows per 100 hectares on dairy farms, or the hectares of intensive crops on general cropping farms.

The figures provided are averages. 'Premium' farms of the same level of intensity can have labour, machinery and general overhead costs at least 20% lower. However, the most profitable farms are often more intensive. They therefore have higher fixed costs associated with the great intensity - but with substantially higher total farm gross margins. Thus it is the net amount (Gross Margin – Fixed Costs) that matters.

The 'small' farm categories relate only to full-time holdings and do not include very intensive holdings occupying very small areas.

The term 'fixed costs' is used here as it is in gross margin analysis and planning; a full explanation of the differences between fixed and variable costs in this context is given on pages 1 and 2. Note that all casual labour and contract work has been included under fixed costs. In calculating enterprise gross margins on the individual farm these costs are normally allocated as variable costs if they are specific to a particular enterprise and vary approximately in proportion to its size, i.e. are approximately constant per hectare of a particular crop or per head of livestock. Otherwise they are included as fixed costs. In both cases, however, they could be regarded as substitutes for regular labour and/or the farmer's own machinery - which are both items of fixed cost. It is therefore simpler if both are included, fully, as fixed costs. If one is comparing results from accounts set out on a gross margin basis, and some or all of the casual labour and contract work have been included as variable costs (especially on cropping farms, e.g. for potato harvesting using casual labour or a contractor's machine), the necessary adjustments need to be made in making the comparisons.

Notes on the Schedules

1. *Unpaid Labour:* Refers to the value of unpaid family manual labour, including that of the farmer and his wife.

2. *Machinery Depreciation:* This is based on current (i.e. replacement) cost. This gives a truer reflection of the real loss of value of machinery (as is apparent when replacement becomes necessary). It also allows easier comparison between different businesses. However, many farm accounts calculate depreciation on the 'historic' (i.e. original)

cost of the machinery. This will tend to produce a lower figure. Depending on the age of the machine, and bearing in mind recent strong increases in machinery prices, the historic method may underestimate depreciation by 10-20%. Note that both the Depreciation item and Repairs include vehicles.

3. *Leasing Charges:* The capital element, but not the interest, is included in depreciation; the proportion paid as interest varies according to the rate of interest paid and the length of the leasing period, but is typically 7%-10%.

4. *Machinery Running Costs:* This includes fuel, oil, repairs, servicing and vehicle tax and insurance. Separate figures for these elements are no longer available. As a general rule, fuel might make up a little over half of all such costs.

5. *General Overheads:* include general farm maintenance and repairs, office expenses, water, insurance, fees, subscriptions, etc.

6. *Rent & Interest:* Rent now only relates to the actual rent paid by the average farm in that particular category. It is no longer an imputed rent for all land farmed by the business; thus, a fully owned-occupied farm will have no rental costs. Interest used to be excluded but now actual interest paid by the average farm in that particular category is shown.

In making comparisons with fixed costs taken from farm accounts it is important to note that in the figures below unpaid manual labour is included; farm accounts will rarely include unpaid labour. Also the figures below include average rent and interest; in farm accounts these will vary widely depending on the farm tenure and borrowing. Very low 'target' figures given in press articles often omit these items and can therefore be misleading; usually, too, they relate only to large, very well appointed farms. If an 'opportunity cost' for owner-occupied land (often fully paid for many years ago) is included, then the cost level rises further. Note too that the figures given below do not include management, whether paid or unpaid. The margin after deducting the fixed costs below from the total gross margin plus any other farm receipts represents the total return to management and own capital in the business.

Labour, machinery and buildings are the main items of 'fixed' costs subject to change with major alterations in farm policy. Each has a separate section in this book.

Mainly Dairying

	Under 75 ha (Under 185 acres)		75 - 125 ha (185 - 310 acres)		Over 125 ha (Over 310 acres)	
Regular Labour (paid)	60	(24)	100	(40)	200	(81)
Regular Labour (unpaid)	700	(283)	460	(186)	270	(109)
Casual Labour	25	(10)	30	(12)	25	(10)
Total Labour	**785**	**(318)**	**590**	**(239)**	**495**	**(200)**
Machinery Depreciation	140	(57)	150	(61)	140	(57)
Machinery Running Costs	130	(53)	140	(57)	140	(57)
Contract	100	(40)	125	(51)	125	(51)
Total Power & Machinery...	**370**	**(150)**	**415**	**(168)**	**405**	**(164)**
Farm Maintenance	30	(12)	40	(16)	45	(18)
Water & Electricity	145	(59)	140	(57)	125	(51)
General Overhead Expenses ..	85	(34)	85	(34)	70	(28)
Total Overheads	**260**	**(105)**	**265**	**(107)**	**240**	**(97)**
Rent & Interest	145	(59)	150	(61)	165	(67)
Total Fixed Costs	**1560**	**(631)**	**1420**	**(575)**	**1305**	**(528)**

Mainly Cereals

	Under 175 ha (Under 430 acres)		175 - 300 ha (430 - 740 acres)		Over 300 ha (Over 740 acres)	
Regular Labour (paid)	40	(16)	55	(22)	90	(36)
Regular Labour (unpaid)	250	(101)	160	(65)	110	(45)
Casual Labour	15	(6)	10	(4)	15	(6)
Total Labour	**305**	**(123)**	**225**	**(91)**	**215**	**(87)**
Machinery Depreciation	105	(42)	110	(45)	110	(45)
Machinery Running Costs	90	(36)	100	(40)	95	(38)
Contract	80	(32)	70	(28)	60	(24)
Total Power & Machinery...	**275**	**(111)**	**280**	**(113)**	**265**	**(107)**
Farm Maintenance	20	(8)	20	(8)	20	(8)
Water & Electricity	65	(26)	60	(24)	55	(22)
General Overhead Expenses ..	65	(26)	70	(28)	60	(24)
Total Overheads	**150**	**(61)**	**150**	**(61)**	**135**	**(55)**
Rent & Interest	90	(36)	100	(40)	105	(42)
Total Fixed Costs	**820**	**(332)**	**755**	**(306)**	**720**	**(291)**

Large-Scale Cereal Farms (over 500 ha (1,250 acres))

Data from the Farm Business Survey indicates there are further economies of scale for cereals farms at even larger farm sizes. There are likely to be wide variations depending on the precise scale of these businesses (some of which are very large). The following figures may be used as a guide; Labour - £155 per ha (of which paid labour £95); Power & Machinery - £220 per ha; Other Overheads - £120 per ha; Rent & Interest - £100 per ha. This totals £595 per ha (£240 per acre).

Data for larger-scale General Cropping farms (see below) is not so conclusive. Costs on a 'per ha' basis do not necessarily seem to fall as farm size increases. This may be due to the larger proportion of (higher cost) root crops and vegetables seen on larger farm sizes.

General Cropping

	Under 150 ha (Under 370 acres)		150 - 225 ha (370 - 560 acres)		Over 225 ha (Over 560 acres)	
Regular Labour (paid)	45	(18)	85	(34)	110	(45)
Regular Labour (unpaid)	350	(142)	230	(93)	165	(67)
Casual Labour	25	(10)	35	(14)	60	(24)
Total Labour	**420**	**(170)**	**350**	**(142)**	**335**	**(136)**
Machinery Depreciation	150	(61)	125	(51)	140	(57)
Machinery Running Costs	135	(55)	135	(55)	130	(53)
Contract	90	(36)	100	(40)	100	(40)
Total Power & Machinery...	**375**	**(152)**	**360**	**(146)**	**370**	**(150)**
Farm Maintenance	20	(8)	25	(10)	25	(10)
Water & Electricity	80	(32)	80	(32)	70	(28)
General Overhead Expenses ..	70	(28)	90	(36)	85	(34)
Total Overheads	**170**	**(69)**	**195**	**(79)**	**180**	**(73)**
Rent & Interest	115	(47)	135	(55)	140	(57)
Total Fixed Costs	**1080**	**(437)**	**1040**	**(421)**	**1025**	**(415)**

* With potatoes and/or sugar beet and/or field vegetables; grade 1 or 2 land.

Mainly Sheep/Cattle (lowland)

	Under 90 ha (Under 220 acres)		90 - 125 ha (220 - 310 acres)		Over 125 ha (Over 310 acres)	
Regular Labour (paid)	25	(10)	45	(18)	45	(18)
Regular Labour (unpaid)	450	(182)	300	(121)	250	(101)
Casual Labour	10	(4)	15	(6)	10	(4)
Total Labour	**485**	**(196)**	**360**	**(146)**	**305**	**(123)**
Machinery Depreciation	80	(32)	85	(34)	90	(36)
Machinery Running Costs	70	(28)	85	(34)	100	(40)
Contract	45	(18)	45	(18)	55	(22)
Total Power & Machinery...	**195**	**(79)**	**215**	**(87)**	**245**	**(99)**
Farm Maintenance	20	(8)	15	(6)	20	(8)
Water & Electricity	65	(26)	60	(24)	60	(24)
General Overhead Expenses ..	60	(24)	45	(18)	35	(14)
Total Overheads	**145**	**(59)**	**120**	**(49)**	**115**	**(47)**
Rent & Interest	65	(26)	70	(28)	95	(38)
Total Fixed Costs	**890**	**(360)**	**765**	**(310)**	**760**	**(308)**

Mainly Sheep/Cattle (upland)					
	Under 130 ha (Under 320 acres)		130 - 230 ha (320 - 570 acres)		Over 230 ha (Over 570 acres)
Regular Labour (paid)	25	(10)	25	(10)	45	(18)
Regular Labour (unpaid)	350	(142)	210	(85)	150	(61)
Casual Labour	5	(2)	5	(2)	10	(4)
Total Labour	**380**	**(154)**	**240**	**(97)**	**205**	**(83)**
Machinery Depreciation	60	(24)	50	(20)	55	(22)
Machinery Running Costs	55	(22)	45	(18)	60	(24)
Contract	25	(10)	20	(8)	20	(8)
Total Power & Machinery...	**140**	**(57)**	**115**	**(47)**	**135**	**(55)**
Farm Maintenance	10	(4)	10	(4)	10	(4)
Water & Electricity	40	(16)	30	(12)	30	(12)
General Overhead Expenses ..	25	(10)	20	(8)	15	(6)
Total Overheads	**75**	**(30)**	**60**	**(24)**	**55**	**(22)**
Rent & Interest	45	(18)	45	(18)	55	(22)
Total Fixed Costs	**640**	**(259)**	**460**	**(186)**	**450**	**(182)**

Other Farm Types

The other main DEFRA farm types are '*Mixed*', *Pigs*, *Poultry and Horticulture*. As the name suggests, the Mixed category includes all farms where one enterprise is not sufficiently dominant for it to be allocated to one of the categories above. As it includes many different mixes of enterprises, the figures are unlikely to be useful for budgeting purposes.

Due to the intensity and variability of the Pig, Poultry and Horticultural farm types, the presentation of average 'per ha' figures would not be useful. Detailed historic FBS data for the different pig, poultry and horticulture systems found in England are published on line at the addresses given on page 4. For pigs, Askham Bryan: for poultry and horticulture, Reading, or go to www.farmbusinesssurvey.co.uk.

2. RENTS

One of the main factors affecting the rental level of agricultural land is the type of tenancy it is let on. There are three main types of agricultural tenancy in England and Wales: Full or Agricultural Holdings Act (AHA) 1986, Farm Business Tenancies (FBTs, under the 1995 Act) and Seasonal Lets of less than 1 year. Since the introduction of the 1995 Act no new AHA tenancies can be created.

The influence of the Single Payment Scheme provisions which started in 2005 also needs to be taken into account when comparing rent levels. The situation will vary from farm to farm and differ between the different regions of the countries of the UK. The tenant is the only person who can claim the Single Payment (SP), except in some seasonal agreements where the landlord may be able to claim. In an AHA tenancy agreement the rental is struck independently of the Single Payment in that the tenant will have been awarded the Single Payment entitlements in 2005 and at the end of the tenancy the ownership remains with the tenant or his/her successors. With FBTs the assumption is that the tenant is claiming a 'full' SP, and if land becomes available without SP entitlements then rental levels will be lower than those shown below.

Unless otherwise stated the figures in this section relate to farms let with a combination of crops, grass and rough grazing in England; they include housing and buildings, as available.

Agricultural Holdings Act Tenancies:

It should be borne in mind that rough grazing may be included in the figures given in the table below and the figures relate to the 2009/10 (Feb-Feb) year mainly covering 2009. Some farms are likely to be let at below competitive rates, for various reasons. Rents for land had been tending to fall up to 2007 but this was offset by higher rents for housing and buildings so that overall per hectare rents were stable. Since then improving commodity prices have seen them increase, albeit with a pause from mid-2008 to mid-2009 as rapid input cost increases (especially fuel, fertiliser and feed) led to reduced farm profitability and thus lower rental settlements.

The average rent for lowland, excluding woodland and rough grazing for farms under full Agricultural Tenancies is likely to be approximately £185 per ha, *£75 per acre*, in 2011. The levels on large mixed arable farms (i.e. including potatoes, sugar beet and/or vegetables) on very good soil, or well-equipped dairy farms, will tend to average £200 to £275 per hectare, *£80 to £110 per acre*. Rents on moderate, below average, quality farms, particularly with full repairing and insuring leases are likely to average £125 to £150 per hectare, *£50 to £60 per acre*.

Farm Business Tenancies:

On average FBT rents will remain higher than those above for AHA tenancies. Although, not always the case especially for lowland cattle and sheep land and dairy land. Farmers who already own land, with little or no mortgage, can afford to offer a higher figure than bidders with no other farms. For cereals land of reasonable quality recent offers have tended to follow the price of a tonne of wheat per acre, but offers of over £450 per hectare (*£182 per acre*) have been reported for 3-5 year agreements. However typically FBT rentals for arable land are lower and a 2011 opinion-based survey from RICS (reported below) gives the average for England and Wales for arable FBT rents at £249 per hectare, *£101 per acre*.

Farm Business Survey 2009-10:

The figures are rounded to the nearest £10/ha in line with current DEFRA practice.

Average Rent by Type of Agreement: £/ha *(acre)*

Full Agricultural Tenancies ....   140 *(57)*
Farm Business Tenancies for 1 year and over ....   160 *(65)*
Seasonal Lets of less than one year ....   100 *(40)*

Average Rent by Farm Type: (£ per ha [acre])	Full Agricultural Tenancies	Farm Business Tenancies*
Cereal	150 *(61)*	170 *(69)*
General Cropping	170 *(69)*	220 *(89)*
Dairy	160 *(65)*	170 *(69)*
Cattle and Sheep (Lowland)	130 *(53)*	120 *(49)*
Cattle and Sheep (LFA)	50 *(20)*	70 *(28)*
All	140 *(57)*	160 *(65)*

* for a year and over

Source of Data

DEFRA (Farming Statistics): Farm rents 2009 – England. In the past DEFRA rental statistics were collected via the Tenanted Land Survey (TLS) and these were reported on in previous editions of the Farm Management Pocketbook. Following a review in early 2009 DEFRA decided that the Farm Business Survey (FBS) data should be the main source and the Tenanted Land Survey (TLS) should be discontinued. The FBS is an annual survey conducted by trained Interviewers. The FBS collects data at business level and collects data for up to 15 agreements per business, with a sample of around 1,900 farm businesses. The next publication is due in January 2012 for the 2010-11 survey.

RICS Rural Land Market Survey :

The following were average rents for England and Wales for the first half of 2011 but should be treated with caution as they are opinion based, and reflect recently struck rental levels.

Average Rent	Full Agricultural Tenancy £ per Ha (acre)	Farm Business Tenancy £ per Ha (acre)
Arable	157 (64)	249 (101)
Pasture	128 (52)	180 (73)

3.   LAND PRICES

SALE VALUE OF FARMLAND, ENGLAND AND WALES

Auction Sales (with Vacant Possession only) :
  Oxford Institute/Savills(1) series, 1937-2000

Year	Current Prices		Real Values(2)		Index (3)	Year	Current Prices		Real Values(2)		Index (3)
1937-9	0	(24)	2030	(822)	33	1982	4557	(1844)	8373	(3389)	136
1945	111	(45)	2246	(909)	37	1983	5145	(2082)	9041	(3659)	147
1955	198	(80)	3274	(1325)	53	1984	4888	(1978)	8180	(3310)	133
1960	198	(80)	2643	(1070)	43	1985	4781	(1935)	7542	(3052)	123
1965	304	(123)	3608	(1460)	59	1986	4193	(1697)	6398	(2589)	104
1970	581	(235)	5857	(2370)	95	1987	4944	(2001)	7242	(2931)	118
1971	605	(245)	4872	(1972)	79	1988	6716	(2718)	9376	(3794)	153
1971	647	(262)	4761	(1927)	77	1989	6558	(2654)	8493	(3437)	138
1972	1473	(596)	9603	(3886)	156	1990	6346	(2568)	7505	(3037)	122
1973	1871	(757)	11793	(4773)	192	1991	6007	(2431)	6708	(2715)	109
1974	1572	(636)	8529	(3452)	139	1992	5441	(2202)	5859	(2371)	95
1975	1332	(539)	5817	(2354)	95	1993	5456	(2208)	5783	(2340)	94
1976	1814	(734)	6798	(2751)	111	1994	5028	(2035)	5204	(2106)	85
1977	2449	(991)	7922	(3206)	129	1995	6140	(2484)	6140	(2485)	100
1988	3279	(1327)	9794	(3964)	160	1996	8797	(3560)	8591	(3477)	140
1979	4371	(1769)	11513	(4659)	188	1997	8065	(3263)	7636	(3090)	124
1980	4265	(1726)	9521	(3853)	155	1998	7250	(2934)	6637	(2686)	108
1981	4272	(1729)	8525	(3450)	139	1999	13920	(5634)	12565	(5085)	205
						2000	7895	(3196)	7125	(2885)	116

(1) Savills after 1988. (2) At 1995 general price levels. (3) Real Values, 1995 = 100.

From 1970, figures were based on sales reports in the Estates Gazette and the Farmers Weekly, plus some unpublished sales, with a minimum size of 10 hectares. This series was discontinued after 2000.

Current Agricultural Land Prices

A CALP/RICS Farmland Price Index (England and Wales) began in 1995. It covers sales of vacant possession land in England and Wales, excluding residential value where more than 50% of total sale price; value of milk quota excluded. It is calculated by dividing total value of sales by total area sold. Figures for the most recent half-yearly periods are subject to revision as further information becomes available.

As can be seen from the table below, the volume of land traded in any year, and included in the Index, is low – probably only between 0.1%-0.2% of the total agricultural area of England and Wales. The relative scarcity of land for sale has helped contribute to the increases in prices seen since the early 2000's. Such a 'thin' market can also make the prices sensitive to a small number of large transactions. For this reason, in recent years, the RICS has moved away from the transaction-based figures presented below, to using opinion-based data as its headline land price figures.

Farmland prices have weathered the economic downturn of recent times far better than other classes of property. Strong commodity prices during 2007 and up to mid 2008 meant that farmland prices were the last to react to the downturn in the economic climate. 'Lifestyle' purchasers were replaced by farmers keeping the demand for and the price of land high. Prices faltered in the first half of 2009 with the increase in farm inputs and the fall in commodity prices. Since then, continued tight supplies, improving farm commodity prices and a partial return of non-farming buyers has seen farmland prices move forward again. An increase in price is expected to continue through 2011 and 2012, although the rate of increase may level-off.

CALP/RICS Farmland Price Index 1995-2011 – Transaction based.

		Number of Sales	Area sold '000		Weighted Average Price £		Index 1995
			Ha	(acres)	Ha	(acres)	=100
1995	Q1	73	3.9	(9.6)	5,187	(2,099)	100
1998	Q1	113	5.2	(12.8)	7,364	(3,033)	145
	Q2	133	5.5	(13.6)	7,545	(3,053)	146
	Q3	164	7.1	(17.5)	6,411	(2,594)	124
	Q4	149	7.9	(19.5)	6,812	(2,757)	131
1999	Q1	84	3.6	(8.9)	6,376	(2,580)	123
	Q2	138	4.5	(11.1)	7,337	(2,969)	141
	Q3	152	9.0	(22.2)	7,186	(2,908)	139
	Q4	15	6.9	(17.0)	7,204	(2,915)	139
2000	Q1	90	3.9	(9.6)	7,660	(3,100)	148
	Q2	120	4.9	(12.1)	7,211	(2,918)	139
	Q3	134	7.2	(17.8)	7,082	(2,866)	137
	Q4	128	5.9	(14.6)	6,461	(2,615)	125
2001	Q1	73	4.5	(11.1)	7,273	(2,943)	140
	Q2	70	4.3	(10.6)	7,967	(3,224)	154
	Q3	137	7.5	(18.5)	7,169	(2,901)	138
	Q4	130	5.8	(14.3)	7,327	(2,965)	141
2002	Q1	71	3.0	(7.4)	7,906	(3,200)	152
	Q2	87	3.4	(8.4)	7,579	(3,067)	146
	Q3	135	6.6	(16.3)	7,694	(3,114)	148
	Q4	154	6.0	(14.8)	6,390	(2,586)	123
2003	Q1	69	2.5	(6.2)	7,817	(3,163)	151
	Q2	80	3.4	(8.4)	7,910	(3,201)	152
	Q3	67	3.3	(8.2)	7,629	(3,087)	147
	Q4	85	4.1	(10.1)	8,367	(3,386)	161
2004	Q1	46	1.8	(4.4)	9,526	(3,855)	184
	Q2	75	2.8	(6.9)	9,255	(3,745)	178
	Q3	53	2.1	(5.2)	10,670	(4,318)	206
	Q4	89	2.6	(6.4)	9,828	(3,977)	189
2005	H1	141	6.0	(14.8)	8,967	(3,629)	173
	H2	164	8.7	(21.5)	9,647	(3,904)	186
2006	H1	173	9.4	(23.2)	9,408	(3,807)	181
	H2	234	15.0	(37.1)	10,376	(4,199)	200
2007	H1	141	7.0	(17.3)	11,153	(4,513)	215
	H2	230	10.8	(26.7)	14,138	(5,721)	273
2008	H1	233	8.9	(21.9)	15,824	(6,404)	305
	H2	278	11.7	(28.9)	16,342	(6,713)	315
2009	H1	181	6.3	(13.8)	15,199	(6,151)	293
	H2	256	11.4	(28.2)	16,126	(6,526)	311
2010	H1	293	5.5	(14.0)	15,177	(6,142)	293
	H2	256	11.4	(28.2)	16,126	(6,526)	311
2011	H1	293	5.5	(14.0)	15,177	(6,142)	293

Other Land Price Series

In past editions of the Pocketbook, Inland Revenue and Valuation Office (VO) land price returns have been published, covering 30 years up to 1996/97 and 1993-2004 respectively. These series contained detailed splits between vacant possession and tenanted land, farms (including houses and buildings) and bare land, and also by size, land class and region. This information is still available from past editions of the Pocketbook. Data in the VO series does not continue beyond 2004, although limited information is available on the website, www.voa.gov.uk

Much of the data included in this section is available in **Farmland Market**, a Farmers Weekly publication in association with RICS, and includes other land and rental statistics, articles and opinion.

SALE VALUE OF FORESTS AND WOODLANDS

Forests

The figures in this section relate to planted land sold (over 25 hectares) so that values include the value of the property (land) and the timber. The decline in timber prices was reversed in 2010 due to the high price of imported timber; a consequence of a weak Pound. An increase in the demand for timber is expected into 2012. Forest property values have held their own. There has been more movement in the market for larger, more commercial forests helped by more favourable grants being offered for these kinds of properties. Investors still see land and trees as a safe haven during the difficult economic climate, although lifestyle buyers are finding it more difficult to obtain funding.

Forestry continues to be attractive to investors especially due to the tax benefits available to owning woodland. Income tax is not payable on timber sales. There is potentially 100% relief on Inheritance Tax (IH) and any gains attributable to standing or felled timber are exempt from Capital Gains Tax (CGT).

The number of transactions reduced significantly in the year to September 2010 with the area sold down 32% to 9,950ha from 14,600ha in 2009. The total market value for 2010 was 28% down.

Average forest prices were up 5% in the year to September 2010 compared to 2009 to £3,470 per Ha. The figures below are for the UK and are predominantly upland with at least 50% coniferous content. Values vary with many factors and only size of block and age are recorded here, but yield class is also important.

Value of Forestland:

By Size Range (approx.)	2009	2010
	£/ha (£/acre)	£/ha (£/acre)
Below 51 hectares	6,000 (2,430)	5,100 (2,060)
51 to 100 hectares	3,600 (1,460)	4,700 (1,900)
101 to 200 hectares	3,500 (1,420)	3,400 (1,380)
Above 200 hectares	2,900 (1,170)	3,000 (1,210)

By Age Band	2009	2010
	£/ha (£/acre)	£/ha (£/acre)
Young (1 to 10 years)	1,850 (750)	3,300 (1,340)
Mid-rotation (11 to 20 years)	3,450 (1,400)	2,800 (1,130)
Semi-mature (21 to 30 years)	2,750 (1,110)	3,000 (1,210)
Mature (over 30 years)	3,150 (1,280)	2,950 (1,190)
Mature (over 40 years)	4,950 (2,000)	5,600 (2,270)

Woodlands

The value for small woodland decreased last year as demand from lifestyle buyers for less commercial, more amenity and sporting woodland was hit by the economic climate. Values remain at their highest adjacent to centres of population and for properties of high amenity value. Sales in the South of England are often recorded in the £8-12,000/ha range, whereas £2-5,000/ha is more typical for more remote properties or where amenity values are lower.

Source: UPM Tilhill and Savills, Forest Market Report (2010)

4. BUILDINGS

BUILDING COSTS

Building costs are notoriously variable. Many factors influence a contractor's price, including distance from his yard, size of contract, site access, site conditions, complexity of work, familiarity with the type of work and his current work load. There will also be differences in efficiency and standard of work between contractors and, as is often the case with farm buildings, the absence of detailed specification by the client may mean different contractors will not have quoted for identical buildings. The number of extras that are found to be required after a contract has been agreed will also vary.

The costs given below are an approximate guide. They refer to new buildings, erected by contractor on a clear level site and exclude VAT and grants that may be available. More detailed information is available in the following publications. The books and journals giving general building cost information generally assume knowledge of how to take off quantities for building work.

Specialised Information on Farm Buildings

- Farm Building Cost Guide. Published by SAC Building Design Services, Aberdeen.

- Standard Costs. Published by the Scottish Government. Used when claiming government grants on a standard-cost basis. It can be found at www.scotland.gov.uk/Resource/Doc/158202/0042819.pdf

- The Farm Buildings Handbook. Published by the Rural and Industrial Design and Building Association, Stowmarket.

General Building Cost Information

Books are produced by a number of publishers with annual or more frequent new editions and updates. Examples are Laxton's Building Price Book, Spon's Architects' and Builders' Price Book, and Wessex Comprehensive Building Price Book. Regularly updated cost information is also given in several professional and trade journals.

Constituent Parts

Frame, Roof and Foundations   *per m² floor area*

1. Open-sided timber framed pole barn with round pole uprights on concrete bases, sawn timber rafters and purlins, high-tensile galvanised steel cladding to roof and gable ends above eaves, hardcore floor, eaves height 4.8 m, 9 m span, no side cladding, rainwater drainage to soakaways.   £70

2. Open-sided steel portal-framed building with fibre-cement or plastic coated steel cladding to roof and gables above eaves, hardcore floor, eaves height 4.8 m, no side cladding, rainwater drainage to soakaways.

9 m span	£120
13.2 m span	£105
18 m span	£100

3. Cost breakdown of 2 above;

Materials:	portal frame and purlins	26%
	foundations	3%
	roofing	16%
	rainwater and drainage	3%

	hardcore and blinding	2%
	Total Materials	50%
Erection:	portal frame and purlins	19%
	foundations	2%
	roofing	19%
	rainwater and drainage	5%
	hardcore and blinding	5%
	Total Erection	50%

Roof cladding   *per m²*

1. Natural grey fibre-cement, 146 mm corrugations fixed with drive screws

Materials	£14.00	
Fixing	£12.50	
Total		£26.50

2. Extra for coloured sheet   £2.50
3. Deduct for translucent sheets   £0.55
4. Deduct for PVC-coated steel   £3.00
5. Deduct for high-tensile corrugated galvanised steel sheeting   £4.00

per m run

6. PVC 150 mm half-round gutter on fascia brackets, including stop-ends and outlets   £25.00
7. PVC 100 mm rainwater pipe with fixings, swan-neck and shoe   £44.00
8. Fibre-cement close-fitting ridge   £37.00
9. Fibre-cement ventilating ridge   £42.50

Walls and Cladding   *per m²*

1. Concrete blockwork, fair faced and pointed both sides

150 mm thick	£45.00
215 mm thick	£65.00
215 mm thick hollow blocks	£66.00
215 mm thick hollow blocks, filled and reinforced	£83.50

2. Extra for rendering or roughcast to blockwork on one side   £23.00
3. Vertical spaced boarding 21x 145 mm with 19 mm gaps including horizontal rails, all pressure treated   £26.50
4. Fibre-cement vertical cladding, including rails   £41.50
5. Corrugated high-tensile steel side cladding, including rails   £34.00
6. Wall element: 215 mm thick blockwork, including strip foundation (base 750 mm below ground level), 2.5 m height above ground level   £166 per m run

Floors   *per m²*

1. Concrete floor 100 mm thick, Gen 3 mix, on 150 mm hardcore, including excavation: £33.50

Breakdown:
(a)	excavate, level and compact	£3.00
(b)	hardcore	£4.90
(c)	blinding	£2.40
(d)	damp-proofmembrane	£2.10
(e)	premixed concrete spread and compacted	£18.00
(f)	float finish	£4.00

2. Extra to above for
(a)	150 mm instead of 100 mm	£5.50
(b)	laying concrete to falls	£1.70
(c)	broom or textured finish	£2.00
(d)	Carborundum dust non-slip finish	£3.50
(e)	insulating concrete	£10.50

3. Reinforced concrete slatted floors for cattle
(a)	cattle loading	£73.00
(b)	tractor loading	£80.00

4. Reinforced concrete slats for pigs   £54.00

5. Insulating floor, including excavation and base
(a)	27 mm expanded polystyrene, 38 mm screed	£48.50
(b)	insulating concrete with lightweight aggregate	£40.00
(c)	as (b) with 20 mm screed	£49.00

6. Form channel in concrete   £5.00 per m run

7. Excavate for cast 1 m3 in-situ concrete bases for stanchions   £128.00 each

Services and Fittings   *per m²*

1. Drainage: 100 mm PVC pipe laid in trench, including 750 mm deep excavation and backfil   £26.50 per m run
Breakdown:
(a)	excavate and backfill	£17.00
(b)	100 mm PVC pipe laid	£10.00

Extras:
(c)	add to (a) for 1 m deep	£3.60
(d)	add to (b) for 150 mm pipe	£6.70

2. Excavate soakaway and fill with stones   £109 each

3. Trap and grid top, 100 mm PVC   £26 each

4. Yard gully with heavy duty road grating 400 x 300 mm   £198 each

5. Inspection chamber 900 mm deep, 450 x 600 mm opening and medium duty cast iron cover   £390 each

6. Above-ground vitreous enamel slurry tank on concrete base, 1000 m³   £52,000 each

7. Reception pit, 20 m³   £4,940 each

8. Slurry channel beneath (not including) slats, 1.8 m deep, 3m wide   £450 per m run

9. Lighting: 1.5 m 60W single fluorescent unit, including wiring and switch   £135 each
Extras:
(a)	PVC conduit	£6.30
(b)	screwed steel conduit	£11.50

10. Power: 13A switched outlet — £23.00 each
11. Diagonal feed fence, fixed, including posts (painted) — £125 per m run
12. Tombstone feed fence, fixed, including posts (painted) — £130 per m run
13. Feed bunker — £73 per m run
14. Hay rack, wall fixing — £83 per m run
15. Cubicle division, galvanised, fixed in place — £104 each
16. Fencing: three-rail timber with posts, all pressure treated — £28.50 per m run
17. Gate, 3 m wide, galvanised steel, including posts set in concrete
     (a) medium duty — £240 each
     (b) heavy duty — £312 each
     Deduct for painted instead of galvanised finish — £31

Complete Buildings

Fully Covered and Enclosed Barn

Portal frame, 18 m span, 6 m bays, 6 m to eaves, 3 m high blockwork walls with sheet cladding above, 6 m sliding doors at either end, 150mm thick concrete floor — £180 per m² floor area

Cows and Cattle Housing

1. Covered strawed yard, enclosed with ventilated cladding, concrete floor, pens only, with 4.0 m² per head floor area — £728 per head
2. Extra to 1 for 4.0 m wide double-sided feeding passage, barrier and troughs — £300 per head
3. Kennel building — £440 per head
4. Portal framed building with cubicles — £1,450 per head
5. Extra to 4 for feed stance, feeding passage, barriers and troughs — £610 per head
6. Extra to 4 for slatting of cubicle passages — £625 per head
7. Covered collecting yard, 1.1 m² per cow — £220 per head
8. Milking parlour building, example: 5.5 x 11.5 m for 8/16 parlour — £18,500
9. Parlour equipment, herringbone parlours:
    (a) low level, 1 stall per point — £3,750 per point
    (b) pipeline — £3,350 per point
    (c) extra for meter and auto cluster removal — £2,080 per point
    (d) auto feed dispenser — £860 per point
10. Dairy building — £320 per m² floor area
11. Bulk tank and washer — £8.30 per litre
12. Loose box, 16 m² floor area laid to falls, rendered walls — £330 per m² floor area
13. Bull pen and open run — £12,500
14. Cattle crush and 20 m race — £6,000
15. Slatted floor cattle building for 120 growing cattle (1.7 m² pen space per head) with drive-through feed passage/troughs — £1,450 per head

Silage   *per tonne stored*

1.   Timber panel clamp on concrete base with effluent tank   £73
2.   Precast concrete panel clamp with effluent tank   £100
3.   Glass-lined forage tower and unloader   £235

Waste Storage   *per m³ stored*

1.   Lined lagoon with safety fence   £40.00
2.   Glass-lined steel slurry silo
      small (400 m³)   £56.00
      medium (1,200 m³)   £50.00
      large (3,600 m³)   £46.00
3.   GRP below-ground effluent tank, encased in concrete
      small (12 m³)   £480
      large (36 m³)   £420

Sheep Housing

1.   Penning, troughs, feed barriers and drinkers installed in
      suitable existing building   £35.00 per ewe
2.   Purpose-built sheep shed with 1.35 m² pen space per ewe
      concentrate troughs, feed passage and barrier for   forage
      feeding   £220 per ewe
      Extras:
      (a)   softwood slatted floor panels, materials only   £9.00 per m²
      (b)   slatted panels as (a), made up, plus supports   £29.50 per m²

Pig Housing   *per sow and litter*

1.   Farrowing and rearing
      (a) Prefabricated farrowing pens with crates, side creep
           areas, part-slatted floors, including foundations,
           electrical and plumbing work   £3,350
      (b) Steel-framed farrowing house with insulated
           blockwork walls, part-slatted pens with side creeps
           in rooms of eight with off main passage   £3,700
      (c) Flat-deck rearing house 3-6 weeks with fully
           perforated floors to pens, 0.25 m² per pig pen area   £145 per weaner
      (d) Prefabricated verandah house including foundations,
           electrical and plumbing work, 0.3m² per pig internal
           lying area   £115 per weaner

2. Finishing   *per baconer*

    (a) Prefabricated fattening house with part-slatted floors,
         trough feeding   £250

    (b) Prefabricated fattening house with part-slatted floors,
         floor fed   £235

    (c) Steel framed building with insulated blockwork walls,
         part-slatted floors, trough fed   £104

    (d) Automatic feeding systems for items (a), (b) and (c)
         above:
         dry-feed system with ad-lib hoppers   £650
         dry on-floor feeding   £15.00
         wet feeding   £21

3. Dry sows and boars   *per sow*
    (a) Yards with floor feeding   £350
    (b) Sow cubicle system   £585
    (c) Yards with electronic feeders   £990
    (d) Yards with individual feeders   £1,150
    (e) Two-yard system with flat-rate feeding   £1,300
    (f) Boar pens as part of sow house   £2,600 each

4. Complete pig unit

    Building costs calculated on basis of three-week weaning,
    23 pigs per sow per year to bacon, excl. external slurry or
    dung storage, feed storage and handling/weighing facilities:
    (a) Breeding and rearing only   £1,990 per sow
    (b) Breeding with progeny to bacon   £3,500 per sow

Poultry Housing and Equipment   *per bird*

1. Intensive enriched cages with automatic feeding and egg
    collection; (new traditional cages were banned from 1st
    January 2003;only enriched cages complete with nest box,
    perches and scratching area are now allowed)   £22.00-£26.00

2. Perchery/barn   £20.70-£25.00

3. Free Range: new sites stocked at 9 birds per m²,   £25.50-£33.00
    existing sites stocked at 11.7 birds per m²   £21.00-£27.00
     smaller mobile units will cost   £30.00 plus

4. Broiler Breeders, deep litter, 0.167 m² per bird   £27.00

5. Pullets (cage and floor reared)   £15.00

6. Broilers, deep litter, 0.05 m² per bird   £8.50-£9.50

7. Turkeys, 20,000 pole barn fattening unit
    (cost varies with size of unit and degree of automation)   £20.00-£26.50

Grain Storage and Drying   *per tonne stored*

1. Intake pit, conveyor, elevator, overhead conveyor and catwalk,
    storage bins within existing building   £210
    extra for low volume ventilation of bins   £84

2.	As 1 in new building	£310
3.	Portable grain walling for on-floor storage in existing building	£52
4.	On floor grain storage in purpose-built building	£115
	Extras:	
	(a) low volume ventilation	£8.30-£9.40
	(b) on-floor drying with above-ground main duct and laterals	£125
	(c) add to (b) for below-ground laterals	£15.50
5.	Sealed towers for moist grain, including loading and unloading equipment	£150-£190

Potato Storage	*per tonne stored*
1. Pallet-box store with recirculation fans	£225
Pallet boxes, 1 tonne	£80
2. Bulk store, building only	£210
Ventilation system: fans, main duct, below-floor lateral ducts	£52

Roads and Fences	*per m length*
3.2 m wide hardcore road with drainage ditches using locally excavated material	£31.00
using imported hardcore (£6.15/m³)	£46.00
extra for bitumen macadam surfacing, two coats	£52.00
Traditional 7-wire stock fence	£7.20
High tensile 7-wire stock fence	£5.10

Construction Equipment Hire	*hourly rate, with driver*
Excavator	£26.00-£33.50
Tipping lorry	£36.00-£52.00
10-tonne crane	£41.00
	weekly rate
Concrete mixer, 100 litre (5/3)	£43
Compressor and heavy breaker	£130

STANDARD COSTS

Standard costs are published by the Scottish Government on the basis of the cost of farm or casual labour and new materials. They do not include an allowance for overheads and profit: in most cases building contractors would add 15-30% to cover them. Standard costs are therefore usually lower, sometimes by a larger percentage than this, particularly where the labour content of the item is high. The following examples are based on standard costs issued for 2002. Farm buildings costs generally will have risen by about 40% between that year and mid-2009. Crown copyright material is reproduced from 'Standard Costs' with permission of the Controller of HMSO and the Queen's Printer for Scotland.

	per m² floor area
Open-sided framed building with cladding to roof and gable peaks only, hardcore floor, rainwater drainage to soakaways:	
9 x 18 m	£36
13.2 x 24m	£33.50

	per m² wall or roof
Corrugated cladding to roof or walls, including supports (purlins or rails):	
fibre cement sheeting	£17.00
extra for coloured sheeting	£1.00
extra for PVC coated steel instead of fibre cement	£0.70
deduct for metallic coated (e.g. galvanised) steel	£5.00
Spaced boarding	£19.00
Wall element, concrete block-work 190-324 mm thick with strip foundation (base 750 mm below ground level) and 2.5 mm height above ground level	£95 per m run
Extra for rendering block-work on one side	£6.70 per m²
Concrete floor, 100 mm thick, including excavation, hardcore and waterproof membrane	£12.00 per m²
Concrete floor, 150 mm thick as above	£16.00 per m²
Reinforced concrete slats for cattle (supports not included)	£49.50 per m²
Yard gully with heavy grating	£260 each
Drainage pipes, 100 mm, jointed in UPVC, clay-ware or spun concrete including 900 mm trench and backfill	£11.70 per m run
Drainage pipes 150 mm as above	£19.90 per m run
Tank for water, effluent etc., 20 m³	£3,100 each
Gate, 3 m wide, steel, including posts concreted in: light duty	£110.00 each
cattle yard type	£147.00 each

	per m² floor area
Fully covered enclosed building with concrete floor, and rainwater drainage to soakaways	
10 x 18 m	£75.00
15 x 24 m	£56.70

STORAGE REQUIREMENTS

Bulk (cubic metres (feet) per tonne):

		M³/tonne	Ft³/tonne
Beans		1.2	(43)
Wheat, peas		1.3	(46)
Barley, rye, oilseed rape, linseed, fodder beet		1.4	(50)
Oats		1.9	(68)
Potatoes		1.6	(57)
Dry bulb onions		2.0	(71)
Concentrates:	meal	2.0	(71)
	cubes	1.6	(57)
Grass silage:	18% DM	1.3	(46)
	30% DM	1.6	(57)
Maize silage		1.3	(46)
Silage: large round bales		2.5	(88)
Wheat straw ⎫		13.0	(464)
Barley straw ⎬ small bales		11.5	(411)
Hay ⎭		6.0	(214)
Wheat straw ⎫		20.0	(714)
Barley straw ⎬ large round bales		18.0	(643)
Hay ⎭		8.0	(286)
Brewers' grains		0.9	(32)

(With straw and hay the storage requirement clearly depends on the packing density; the above are simply typical averages).

Boxes (floor area in square metres (feet) per tonne):

Potatoes:	0.5 tonne boxes, 5 boxes high	0.52	(5.6)
	1.0 tonne boxes, 4 boxes high	0.52	(5.6)
	1.0 tonne boxes, 5 boxes high	0.45	(4.8)

Bags (floor area in square metres (feet) per tonne):

Feedstuffs:	2 bags high	1.6	(17)
Fertiliser:	6 bags high	1.1	(12)
	10 bags high	0.7	(8)

VII.   TAXATION

Note: no responsibility can be taken for any errors or omissions in the information presented in this section or for any action taken on the basis of the information provided. Professional advice should always be sought before taking any decision that may affect your tax position.

1.   INCOME TAX

RATES OF INCOME TAX (2011-12)

	Income Band	Dividends	Interest	Other Income
Basic rate	£0 to £35,000	10	20	20
Higher rate	£35,001-150,000	32.5	40	40
Additional rate	over £150,000	42.5	50	50

For 2011-12 a lower rate of 10% still applies to other savings income (primarily bank and building society interest) up to a limit of £2,560. This 10% rate is not available if taxable non-savings income exceeds £2,560.

ALLOWANCES AND RELIEFS (2011-12)

Personal Allowance

This is £7,475 for 2011-12. If aged 65 to 74 it is £9,940, and £10,090 if aged over 75 on 5th April 2012, subject to total income not exceeding the statutory income limit (£24,000 for 2011-12). The basic personal allowance for income tax is gradually reduced to nil for individuals with adjusted net incomes in excess of £100,000. The reduction is £1 for every £2 over the limit.

Married Couples Allowance

This was abolished from the tax year ended 6th April 2001 except for couples where at least one spouse was born before 6th April 1935. From 2005-06 the allowance is available to couples in a civil partnership where at least one partner was born before 6th April 1935. The relief is given as a reduction in income tax restricted to the lower of 10% of the allowance (£2,800 for 2011-12) or the total tax liability.

Personal Pension Schemes

Tax relief is obtainable for contributions to a pension. The rules on maximum contributions have been simplified and the annual allowance has been reduced from 2011-12 onwards. The annual allowance is £50,000 for 2011-12 (£255,000 for 2010-11). The lifetime allowance is now £1,800,000. Maximum contributions under the simplified Stakeholder Pension rules are £3,600 per year.

2.   PRIVATE COMPANY TAXATION

RATES OF CORPORATION TAX (2011-12)

The rates set out in the table below apply to profits made in any financial year (FY) ending 1st April to 31st March. FY12 therefore covers 1st April 2011 to 31st March 2012. Profits are chargeable at the following rates;

Corporation Tax Bandings

	Profits band	per cent tax	
		FY11	*FY12*
Small companies' rate	Up to £300,000	20	*20*
Upper marginal rate	£300,000 to £1.5m	27.5	*26.25*
Main companies' rate	Over £1.5m	26	*25*

Note: The marginal rates shown above are divided by the number of associated companies.

COMPANY TAXATION – OTHER ISSUES

Capital Gains

Capital gains of companies are charged at the appropriate rate of Corporation Tax. The indexation allowance is still available to reduce capital gains made by Companies.

Quotas

Milk quota purchased by a company after 1st April 2002 will attract Corporation Tax relief at the rate of depreciation selected in the accounting policies of the company or 4% per year if not depreciated in the accounts of the company.

Distributions

Dividends are not deductible in arriving at the amount of Corporation Tax profit. However, the recipient of distributions will be credited with a tax payment of 10% of distributions received, which will be deemed to discharge the liability of basic rate (20%) taxpayers. Higher rate taxpayers are liable to pay tax at 32.5% on that part of their dividend income falling above the higher rate limit. Taxpayers with income in excess of £150,000 will be liable to tax on dividends at 42.5%.

Losses

Carry back restricted to one year. However the 2009 Budget introduced an extension to the loss relief provisions for two years. Where a company made a trading loss in its accounting periods ending in the period 24th November 2008 to 23rd November 2010 the trading loss can be carried back and offset against profits of the 3 preceding years. The amount of losses that can be carried back to the first preceding year remains unlimited. After carry back to the preceding year, a maximum of £50,000 of the balance of the unused losses is available for carry back to the earlier two years. The £50,000 limit applies separately to the unused losses of each 12 month period.

Losses can be carried forward and offset against profits of the same trade.

3. AGRICULTURAL BUSINESSES: OTHER ITEMS

ASSESSING SELF-EMPLOYED PROFITS

Self-employed people are assessed for tax in any tax year on the basis of the profits recorded in the annual accounts which end in that tax year, i.e. on a 'current year basis'.

LIVESTOCK

Dairy cows or breeding livestock may be treated on the herd basis or on a trading stock basis;

Herd Basis

Under the herd basis valuation changes are not included in the trading account, nor are additions to the herd, but sales from the herd and replacements are. On the sale of all or a substantial proportion (normally taken as 20% or more) of the herd, no tax is paid on any profit over the original cost price, nor is there any relief for loss.

Editorial Note: The high values of cattle at present make it less likely that a new farming business will want to elect for the herd basis although each case must be judged on its merits.

Trading Stock Basis

Purchases, sales and valuation changes are all included in the trading account. Under this method stock should be valued at the lower of cost (or cost of production) and net realisable value. Where animals are home-produced and it is not possible to ascertain actual costs from farm records the 'deemed' cost may be used. This is 60% of market value for cattle and 75% for sheep and pigs.

STOCK VALUATION: CROPS

Crops should generally be valued at the cost of production (or net realisable value, if lower). Costs which are directly attributable to buying, producing and growing the crops should be included. The deemed cost method allows 75% of market value to be used although this method should only be used where it is not possible to ascertain actual costs.

ALLOWANCES FOR CAPITAL EXPENDITURE

Machinery and Plant

1. The same rules apply whether the machinery and plant is new or second hand. An annual writing down allowance of 20% p.a. is available on a reducing balance basis on capital expenditure incurred on the provision of plant and machinery. Qualifying expenditure is added to the asset 'pool' and the writing down allowances are given on the residue of expenditure in that pool.

2. The Annual Investment Allowance ('AIA') was introduced from 6th April 2008 (1st April 2008 for companies). This gives 100% relief for the first £100,000 (£50,000 from 6th April 2008 to 5th April 2010) of qualifying expenditure incurred in an accounting period. This will be reduced to £25,000 from 6th April 2012. The limit is proportionally increased or decreased where the chargeable period is longer or shorter than a year. A group of companies can only receive a single allowance. Expenditure on cars does not qualify, although expenditure on long life assets, or on 'integral features' can be claimed.

3. A 10% rate applies to expenditure incurred on certain listed 'integral features' in a building and on long life assets on or after April 2008. Long life asset expenditure brought forward will obtain the 10% rate (6% up to April 2008).

5. 100% first year allowances can be claimed for expenditure incurred by any business on designated energy-saving plant and machinery and environmentally beneficial technologies and products. The lists of items which qualify can be found on the Government's Energy Technology Product lists, which is at www.eca.gov.uk.

6. For chargeable periods beginning on or after 6th April 2008 (1st April 2008 for Companies), a Writing Down Allowance of up to £1,000 can be claimed in respect of the main pool and/or the special rate pool where the unrelieved expenditure in that pool is £1,000 or less.

Cars

Motor cars purchased before 1st April 2009 for companies and 5th April 2009 for unincorporated businesses, costing more than £12,000 are included in a separate 'pool' in the year of purchase, on which a 20% writing down allowance is available. The allowance is restricted to a maximum of £3,000 for motor cars with a written-down value of more than £12,000. Special rules apply where a motor car is only partly used for business purposes. There is a 100% first year allowance for new cars with emissions of less than 110g/km CO_2 (120g/km for expenditure incurred before 1st April 2008). This applies to cars registered after 16th April 2002.

For expenditure on motor cars purchased after 1st April 2009 for companies and 5th April 2009 for unincorporated businesses, the regime for cars costing over £12,000 is abolished. Cars with CO_2 emissions exceeding 160gm/km will be allocated to the 10% special rate pool. All other cars will go into the general pool. For unincorporated businesses, cars will have their own separate pools where there is an element of private use.

Machinery Leasing

Tax allowances for rental payments on financial leases are spread to reflect the commercial depreciation of the asset. This may mean that full tax relief for rental payments may not be gained in the years in which the payments are made.

Buildings

Farm buildings, fencing, drainage and other improvements (including up to one-third of farmhouses) used to qualify for a writing-down allowance of 4% annually, given equally over 25 years. These allowances have now been completely phased out.

LOSSES

Losses can normally be set off against other income in the year they are incurred and in the prior year. If other income is insufficient in the year when the loss occurs and in the prior year, any unrelieved losses can be carried forward and set off against future profits from the same trade. Special rules apply to prevent abuse of loss relief provisions by 'hobby' farmers who are not running their farms on a commercial basis with a view to producing a profit: normally losses are disallowed against other income after 5 consecutive years of loss. Trading losses may be set against capital gains in the same year as the loss.

The 2009 Budget introduced an extension to the loss relief provisions for two years. Where an unincorporated business makes a trading loss in the 2008-09 and/or 2009-10 tax years, the trading loss can be carried back and offset against profits of the 3 preceding years. The amount of losses that can be carried back to the first preceding year remains unlimited. After carry back to the preceding year, a maximum of £50,000 of the balance of the unused losses is available for carry back to the earlier two years. The £50,000 limit applies separately to the unused losses of each tax year.

PROFIT AVERAGING

This relief is to enable farmers, other than companies, to average their taxable profits over two consecutive years. Where the difference between the profits of two consecutive years is 30% or more of the higher profits, the total profits for the two years are equally divided between the two years. Marginal relief is available where the difference is less than 30% but more than 25% of the higher profits. Profit for the purposes of tax averaging calculations is after the deduction of capital allowances. There is a two year limit in which to make the claim.

4. CAPITAL GAINS TAX

APPLICATION AND RATES

Applies to capital gains made by an individual. Capital gains accruing to companies are chargeable to Corporation Tax. A capital gain is the difference between the acquisition value and the sale price. The first £10,600 of capital gains realised by an individual in a tax year are covered by their annual exemption.

The rate of capital gains tax for disposals between 6th April 2008 and 22nd June 2010 is 18%. Disposals of non-business assets on or after 23rd June 2010 will attract capital gains tax of 18% for basic rate taxpayers or 28% for higher and additional rate taxpayers. The rate of CGT is 18% where total taxable gains and income, after taking into account all allowable deductions including losses, personal allowances and the CGT annual exemption, are less than the upper limit of the income tax basic rate band. The 28% rate will apply to gains or any parts of gains above this limit.

Exempt assets include a principal private residence (e.g. farm house, if non-exclusive business occupation applies) if occupied as such, normal life assurance policies, animals and tangible movable properly (i.e. chattels) disposed of for £6,000 or less.

Capital Gains Tax is chargeable only on the disposal (including gifts) of assets. Capital Gains Tax is not payable on death.

Payment of Capital Gains Tax is due on 31st January following the tax year of disposal.

RELIEFS

Losses

Should a transaction produce a loss, this may be set against any long term chargeable gains arising in the same year or, if these are insufficient, those accruing in subsequent years. Losses brought forward will be used only to the extent necessary to reduce untaxed gains for the year to £10,600.

Where a trading loss can be set against other income in the same or prior year for income tax purposes, any unused loss can be set against capital gains for those years.

Improvements

Spending that has increased the value of the asset can be offset against any gain. In the case of agricultural property, allowance would be made for any capital expenditure undertaken to improve the property.

Indexation and Taper Relief

Indexation and Taper relief for individuals has now been abolished for any disposals taking place on or after 6th April 2008. Indexation allowance is still available for capital gains arising in companies.

Entrepreneurs Relief

Entrepreneur's relief applies to certain disposals of business assets by an individual. The relief, which must be claimed, gives a reduced effective rate of Capital Gains Tax of 10% for eligible gains of up to £2m for disposals between 6th April 2010 and 22nd June 2010. Gains arising in the period from 6th April 2008 to 5th April 2010 are subject to a limit of £1m. For qualifying disposals between 23rd June 2010 and 5 April 2011, a 10% rate of tax applies on the first £5m of lifetime gains. The limit of lifetime gains increased to £10m from 6 April 2011. The limit is a lifetime limit per individual. The assets which qualify for entrepreneurs' relief are in line with those which qualified for business asset taper relief. This covers:

- a trading business carried on by an individual alone or in partnership;
- assets of such a trade following cessation;
- shares or securities in a trading company where the individual owns 5% or more and is an officer or employee

The conditions for the relief must have been satisfied throughout a qualifying period of a year before the disposal. The relief operates by reducing the amount of qualifying gains by four-ninths to arrive at the effective rate of 10% for gains arising before 22nd June 2010. For gains arising on or after 23rd June 2010, a new rate of 10% now applies.

Editorial Note: The new rules for Entrepreneur relief are complex, particularly in cases of disposals of part of the business. The rules are similar to the previous Retirement Relief and are particularly tricky in cases of disposals of farmland and related assets and trade. It is recommended that professional advice is sought where it is anticipated claiming this relief, particularly as given the increase in the lifetime allowance combined with the increase in tax rate for non-business assets, the tax savings can be greatly increased.

Rollover

Payment of tax may be deferred on gains accruing from the sale of business assets (including land and buildings occupied and used for trade purposes, fixed plant and machinery, milk quotas, and from the sale of shares in a family business) if part or all of the proceeds are spent on acquiring new qualifying assets. The tax is deferred by deducting the gain from the acquisition price of the new asset. It can only be claimed if the new asset is acquired within 12 months before and 3 years after the disposal of the old assets. Disposal and acquisition dates for Capital Gains purposes are generally contract, not completion, dates.

Holdover

Payments of tax may be deferred where disposal is by gift. This relief only applies to gifts of business assets, land which qualifies for agricultural property relief at either the 100% or 50% rate under Inheritance Tax (see next section) and gifts which lead to an immediate charge to Inheritance Tax (e.g. gifts into a discretionary trust). The amount of the chargeable gain which would normally have accrued to the donor will be held over; the value at which the donee is deemed to acquire the asset will be its market value reduced by the amount of the donor's chargeable gain held over. Where deferral is not available, payment of tax by interest bearing annual instalments over 10 years will be allowed for gifts of land, controlling share holdings and minority share holdings in unquoted companies.

5.   INHERITANCE TAX

APPLICATION AND RATES

This tax is charged on lifetime gifts and transfers on death. The rate for 2011-12 is 40%, but there is a nil-rate band below £325,000.

The nil rate band is potentially increased for surviving spouses or civil partners who died on or after 9th October 2007. From this date the nil rate band may be increased by the unused proportion of the deceased spouse or civil partners nil rate band.

Outright gifts to individuals are exempt from tax at the time of the gift. If the donor lives for a further seven years then the transfer is fully exempt. Gifts into accumulation and maintenance trusts and interest in possession trusts no longer receive special treatment - all other gifts will be taxed at half the above rates at the time of the transfer.

Tax is charged on the value of an individual's estate at death plus the value of all gifts made within seven years of death. Allowance is made for any tax paid on lifetime gifts included in the value of the estate on death. Relief is given for outright gifts made more than three years before death according to the following scale:

Years between gift and death	0-3	3-4	4-5	5-6	6-7
Percentage of the full tax charge	100%	80%	60%	40%	20%

Exemptions include: transfers between husband and wife; the first £3,000 of gift made by a donor in the income tax year and separately up to £250 per year to any number of persons; gifts made out of income which form part of normal expenditure; marriage gifts within limits of £5,000 for a parent, £2,500 for a lineal ancestor and £1,000 for other donors.

RELIEFS

Agricultural Property Relief

Relief may be available for agricultural land. Subject to a general rule that the agricultural land must have been occupied by the transferor (or by his controlled company) for two years, or owned by the transferor for 7 years and occupied for agricultural purposes by someone else before any relief is granted. The relief is at two different rates. If the basis of valuation is vacant possession (or there is the right to obtain it within 12 months), the taxable value of the land is reduced by 100%. If the basis of valuation is tenanted value, the taxable value of the land is reduced by 50% of that tenanted value. Ownership and occupation periods normally include prior periods of ownership or occupation by husbands and wives. From 1st September 1995, 100% relief applies to new lettings of agricultural land as Farm Business Tenancies.

The 2009 Budget extended Agricultural relief to include agricultural land situated in the European Economic Area (EEA).

Editorial Note: *There has been much publicised activity and tax cases concerning APR claims, particularly attempts by the Inland Revenue to reduce or deny the relief on claims for farmhouses. Care must be taken to protect the relief particularly where the attached land is either let out on a Farm Business Tenancy or under a contract farming arrangement.*

Business Property Relief

Relief is also available in respect to 'business property' transferred during lifetime or on death. The relief extends to the business assets of a proprietor and the interest of a partner or controlling shareholder in the business capital of a company. The value of such property, providing certain tests are satisfied (e.g. it has been owned by the transferor for two years preceding transfer), is reduced by 100%. Where a partner or controlling shareholder owns assets (e.g. land) that the business uses, the value will be reduced by 50%. Shareholdings in unquoted companies receive a 100% reduction in market value.

Lifetime gifts of property eligible for Agricultural and Business Property Relief have to be retained (or replaced by similar property) until the death of the donor (or earlier death of the donee) if those reliefs are to be available when the tax (or additional tax) becomes payable subsequent to the donor's death

In the case of the transfer of property eligible for APR and BPR, the tax can be paid by annual instalments over ten years free of interest.

6.   STAMP TAXES

Stamp Duty is charged at 0.5 per cent of consideration paid on the transfer of shares and securities.

Stamp Duty Land Tax is charged on the transfer of an interest in land; both sales and leases. With sales of property the tax is levied on a percentage of the sale value of the property (special rules apply to land in disadvantaged areas). The rates applicable to transactions from 6th April 2010 are:

Residential property	Rate	Non-residential and mixed use	Rate
Value up to £125,000...........	nil	Value up to £150,000..............	nil
£125,001 to £250,000..........	1%	£150,001 to £250,000..............	1%
£250,001 to £500,000..........	3%	£250,001 to £500,000..............	3%
£500,001 to £1,000,000.......	4%	£500,001 or more....................	4%
£1,000,001 or more..............	5%		

Stamp Duty Land Tax is payable on leases calculated according to the net present value of the rent payable over the term of the lease.

7.   VALUE ADDED TAX

Agricultural businesses with a turnover of taxable goods and services in excess of £73,000 per annum from 1st April 2011 (£70,000 from 1st April 2010 to 31st March 2011), must register for VAT. Businesses with a turnover below this limit may apply for voluntary registration. The standard VAT rate is 20% since 4th January 2011. Most agricultural products are zero rated for VAT purposes. VAT has to be paid on certain inputs. Registered businesses are eligible to reclaim the tax paid where the goods or services purchased have been used in the production of zero-rated supplies.

A flat rate scheme is available to farmers as an alternative to registering for VAT. Farmers under the flat rate scheme do not have to submit tax returns or account for VAT and consequently cannot reclaim tax. They can, however, charge (and keep) a flat rate addition of 4% when they sell to VAT registered customers goods and services which qualify. This addition is not VAT but acts as compensation for losing input tax on purchases. The registered person paying the flat rate amount to the farmer can recover it as if it were VAT, subject to the normal rules for reclaiming. The local VAT office may refuse to issue a certificate to participate in the flat rate scheme if this would mean the farmer would recover substantially (£3,000) more than through the normal system.

A new flat rate scheme operates for small businesses generally and is an alternative that farmers can use if they have taxable supplies of no more than £150,000 and a total business income of no more than £187,500. This scheme operates in a different way to the flat rate scheme for farmers in that a business charges the normal rate of VAT on sales. However, the VAT which the business has to remit to Customs and Excise is calculated by multiplying the value of gross sales by a rate specified for each particular trade sector. The rate for agriculture is 6.5% from 4th January 2011 except for businesses supplying agricultural services, when the rate is 11%.

Editorial Note: Farmers and landowners must always consider the VAT implications when considering any new or more farming activities on the land or within the buildings, particularly where supplies are made the public who cannot recover any VAT which may be charged on the service or goods provided from the farm.

8.   NATIONAL INSURANCE

The tables below set out the National Insurance contributions for the 2011-12 year;

Class 1 (not contracted out)

Employee's weekly earnings	Employee	Employer
£139.00 or less..................................	Nil	Nil
£139.01 to £817.00	12%	13.8%
Over £817.00	2%	13.8%

Class 2

Self-employed flat rate .... £2.50 a week

Class 3

Non-employed (voluntary) flat rate.................... . £12.60 a week

Class 4

Self-employed. On profits or gains
between £7,225 and £42,475 .... 9%
over £42,475 .... 2%

Acknowledgement: The Author is grateful to *Howard Worth Chartered Accountants Agricultural Department* for their assistance in updating this section of the Pocketbook. Drake House, Gadbrook Park, Northwich, Cheshire, CW9 7RA.   Tel: 01606 369 000. www.howardworth.co.uk

VIII.   FARM BUSINESS MANAGEMENT

1.   DEFINITIONS OF FARM MANAGEMENT TERMS

VALUATIONS AND CAPITAL

Valuations

Valuation is essentially a process of estimation. Alternative bases are possible, according to the purpose intended. The basis should be consistent throughout the period of any series of figures.

1. *Saleable crops in store.* At estimated market value less costs still to be incurred, e.g. for storage and marketing. Both may be estimated either at the expected date of sale or at the date of valuation.

2. *Growing crops.* Preferably at variable costs to the date of valuation, although estimated total cost can alternatively be used.

3. *Saleable crops ready for harvesting* but still in the ground. Preferably as valued in point 1 above, less estimated harvesting costs, although they can alternatively be treated as described in point 2 above.

4. *Fodder stocks (home-grown).* Preferably at variable costs when calculating gross margins. Alternatively at estimated market value (based on hay-equivalent value according to quality). Fodder crops still in the ground, e.g. kale, treated as point 2 above.

5. *Stocks of purchased materials (including fodder).* At cost (net of discounts).

6. *Machinery and equipment.* Original cost (net of investment grants), less accumulated depreciation to date of valuation – this gives a valuation on the 'historic' cost basis. Alternatively at estimated market value.

7. *Livestock.* At current market value, less cost of marketing. Fluctuations in market value expected to be temporary should be ignored.

Capital

Tenant's Capital. The estimated total value of capital on the farm, other than land and fixed equipment. There is no easy way of determining this sum precisely and estimates are made in several ways depending on the information available and the purpose for which the estimate is required. One method is to take the average of the opening and closing valuations (at either market value or cost) of livestock, crops, machinery and stores (feed, seed, fertilisers). See also pages 229 (following section).

Landlord's Capital. Value of the land and fixed equipment (including buildings).

OUTPUT TERMS

Revenue (or Income). Receipts adjusted for debtors at the beginning and end of the accounting period. Items such as CAP support, revenue grants, contract receipts and wayleaves are included.

Returns. Revenue adjusted for valuation changes (add closing, deduct opening, valuation).

Gross Output. Returns plus the value of produce consumed in the farmhouse or supplied to workers for which no payment is made, less purchases of livestock, livestock products and other produce bought for resale.

Enterprise Output. The total value of an enterprise, whether sold or retained on the farm. It therefore equals Gross Output of the enterprise plus the market value of any of the products kept on the farm (transfers out). Following 'decoupling' the Single Payment should not be apportioned to individual enterprises, but coupled support such as protein and energy crop payments should be. Products transferred from another enterprise to be used in the production of the enterprise whose output is being calculated are deducted at market value (transfers in). Instead of the accounting year the "harvest year" can be used for crops which means valuations may not be relevant.

(Enterprise) Output from Forage. Primarily the sum of the enterprise outputs of grazing livestock, but includes keep let and occasional sales, e.g. of surplus hay, together with an adjustment for changes in the valuation of stocks of home-grown fodder. However, fortuitous changes in stocks caused by yield variations due to the weather, the severity or length of the winter, or minor changes in livestock numbers or forage area can be either ignored (if small in relation to total annual usage) or included in miscellaneous output.

Adjusted Forage (Enterprise) Output is Output from Forage less rented keep and purchases of bulk fodder.

Standard Output. The average enterprise output per hectare of a crop or per head of livestock calculated from either national or local average price and average yield data.

INPUT TERMS

Expenditure. Payments adjusted for creditors at the beginning and end of the accounting period. Capital expenditure is not included.

Costs. Expenditure adjusted for valuation changes (add opening, deduct closing, valuation), with the following adjustments. Add: depreciation on capital expenditure including machinery, any loss made on machinery sales (add to depreciation) and the value of payments in kind to workers if not already included in their earnings. Deduct: purchases of livestock, livestock products and other produce bought for resale, any profit made on machinery (deduct from depreciation), allowance for private use of farm vehicles (deduct from machinery costs), the value of purchased stores used in the farmhouse (e.g. electricity) or sold off the farm (deduct from the relevant item).

Inputs. Costs with the following adjustments, made in order to put all farms on a similar basis for comparative purposes. Add: the value of unpaid family labour, including the manual labour of the farmer and his wife, and, in the case of owner-occupiers, an estimated rental value (based on average rents of similar farms in the area), less any cottage rents received. Deduct: any mortgage payments and other expenses of owner-occupation, interest payments and the cost of paid management. A proportion of the rental value of the farmhouse may also be deducted.

Fixed Costs. See pages from 197 whole Farm Fixed Costs.

Variable Costs. See page 1.

MARGIN TERMS

Management and Investment Income. Gross Output less Inputs. It represents the reward to management and the return on tenant's capital invested in the farm, whether borrowed or not. It is mainly used for comparative purposes, all farms having been put on a similar financial basis by the adjustments made to costs in calculating Inputs.

Net Farm Income. Management and Investment Income, less paid management, plus the value of the manual labour of the farmer and his wife. It represents the return to all tenant's type capital and the reward to the farmer for his manual labour and management.

Profit (or Loss). Gross Output less Costs. This represents the surplus or deficit before imputing any notional charges such as rental value or unpaid labour. In the accounts of owner-occupiers it includes any profit accruing from the ownership of land.

Farm Business Income. This term is increasingly being used in FBS costings, and is similar to 'Profit' above. It represents the return to all unpaid labour and to all their own capital in the farm business including land and farm buildings.

Gross Margin. See page 1.

Net Margin. A term sometimes used to denote Gross Margin less direct labour and machinery costs charged to an individual enterprise. This is not, however, nationally accepted terminology. Increasingly Net Margin in the enterprise context is being used to denote the profit of an enterprise by taking its gross output less its 'complete enterprise costs', but see page 2.

AREA TERMS

Total Hectares. All hectares comprising the farm.

Hectares. Total hectares less areas of woods, waste land, roads, yards, buildings, etc.

Adjusted Hectares. Hectares reduced by the conversion of rough grazings into the equivalent hectares of average quality grassland. This is the figure often used for lowland farms when calculating "per hectare" results.

Forage Hectares. Total hectares of forage crops grown, less any hectares exclusively used by pigs or poultry and the area equivalent of any home-grown fodder fed to livestock reared in cereal systems. Also, the area of rough grazings is converted to its grassland equivalent (see Adjusted Hectares). Forage crops are all crops including grass, rough grazing, maize and whole crops grown specifically for grazing livestock, but excluding catch crops and crops harvested as grain and pulses.

Adjusted Forage Hectares. Forage hectares adjusted as follows. Add area equivalent of keep rented, deduct area equivalent of keep let; deduct the area equivalent of occasional sales of fodder, e.g. surplus hay, and seed cuts (note: hay and seed grown regularly for sale should be regarded as cash crops, not forage crops); add or deduct the area equivalent of planned changes in the valuation of stocks of home-grown fodder (fortuitous changes in stocks resulting from weather conditions may be ignored); convert rough grazings into their grassland equivalent if not already done. The following adjustments also may be made: add the area equivalent of catch crops and of grazing from cash crops of hay or seed: add the area equivalent of purchased fodder.

In calculations such as Gross Margins per Forage Hectare, Adjusted Forage Hectares are usually used. If the area equivalent of purchased fodder has been added the cost of purchased fodder must not be charged as a variable cost: this is probably the best calculation for comparative purposes. Alternatively, when considering all the grazing enterprises taken together, purchased fodder can be deducted as a variable cost and no addition made for its area equivalent.

2. CAPITAL REQUIREMENT AND RETURN

TENANT'S CAPITAL

1. *Machinery.* Costs of new machinery are given on pages 174. Written-down values in 2012 are likely to be averaging £500-£600 per hectare (£200-£250/acre) taking all farm types together. Average values for different farm types are given on the next page.

2. *Breeding Livestock.* The 2012 average of breeding livestock value per hectare can be anything up to £1,600 (£650/acre) for an intensive dairy farm. Approximate average market values of various categories of breeding livestock (of mixed ages in the case of adult stock) are as follows (actual value will vary according to average age and weight, quality and breed):

Average market values of various breeding livestock

Holstein/Friesian Dairy Cows:	£1,150
Channel Island Dairy Cows:	£800
Other Dairy Cows:	£900
Beef Cows:	£900

	Holstein Friesians	Replacements Ayrshires and C.I. Breeds	Beef Cattle
In Calf Heifers	£1,400	£1,000	£1,100
1-2 years	£950	£750	£800
6-12 months	£600	£475	£575
Under 6 months	£300	£225	£325

	Other Livestock
Ewes (2 ½ years old / one lamb crop)	£105
Rams (2 ½ years old / one mating season)	£350
Sows and In-Pig Gilts	£225
Boars	£550

3. Working Capital. This is defined as the current assets of a business less its current liabilities. It is the liquid capital needed to finance the cash flow through the production cycle, the length of which varies considerably between different crop and livestock enterprises and different combinations of these enterprises. It can include the cost of purchased fattening stock, feed, seed, fertilisers, regular labour, machinery running costs, general overhead costs, rent and living expenses. This capital will vary between farm business types. Specialist root crop and vegetable farm businesses will have significantly higher working capital requirements than livestock and combinable cropping businesses. The only accurate way to estimate working capital requirement is to complete a full cash flow estimate for the production cycle of the business.

Average Tenants Capital per Hectare

Average Tenant's Capital for different English farm types, for 2012:

Farm Type Group	Average No. Hectares	Livestock	Crops, Cultivns., Stores	Machinery and Equipment*	Total Tenant's Capital	
		£/ha	£/ha	£/ha	£/ha	£/acre
Mainly Dairying:						
under 75 ha	60	1,200	170	760	2,130	863
75 to 125 ha	85	1,350	250	830	2,430	984
Over 125 ha	170	1,400	255	910	2,565	1039
Mainly Cereals:						
under 175 ha	160	33	500	600	1,133	459
175 to 300 ha	250	40	500	610	1,150	466
over 300 ha	600	46	505	560	1,111	450
General Cropping:						
under 150 ha	110	-	425	780	1,205	488
150 to 225 ha	180	-	580	700	1,280	518
over 225 ha	475	-	435	750	1,185	480
Mainly Sheep/Cattle (Lowland):						
Under 90 ha	90	430	75	475	980	397
90 to 125 ha	135	430	90	490	1,010	409
Over 125 ha	250	385	25	400	810	328
Mainly Sheep/Cattle (Upland LFA):						
under 130 ha	115	375	45	325	745	302
130 to 230 ha	180	360	35	230	625	253
over 230 ha	320	380	30	205	615	249

* Based on current (i.e. replacement) costs.

The above (deliberately rounded) data is based on Farm Business Survey results for England compiled annually by University/Colleges centres (as listed on page 4). The values of milk quota and Single Payment entitlements are excluded as are other assets not named above, such as debtors.

RETURN ON CAPITAL

Tenant's Capital.

Return on tenant's capital is calculated by taking the management and investment income (MII) of a business as a percentage of the tenant's capital (see definitions in section VIII.1). Because MII is before deduction of any interest, this return is 'gross', i.e. before allowing for cost of finance. However, it should be borne in mind that MII includes no charge for management but that a rental value for owner-occupied land and the value of the unpaid labour of the farmer and wife have been deducted.

Landlord's Capital

The return on landlord's capital is calculated by taking the rental income, less any ownership expenses (mortgage, insurance, repairs etc.), expressed as a percentage of the land value. With farmland in 2012 averaging, possibly £15,000 per hectare (£6,070 per acre) (see page 204) with vacant possession (assuming no special amenity or house value), an average lowland rent of, say, £200 per hectare (£80 per acre) (see page 202), and assuming ownership expenses at £75 per hectare (£30 per acre), the (net) return (£125 per hectare (£50 per acre) averages 0.83%.

If land is taken at its tenanted value, with an assumed vacant possession premium of say one-third foregone, the return increases to 1.26%. If farm business tenancy rents were paid, at say 40% above the average level for established tenants (i.e. £280/ha [£112/acre]), the return would average 1.37% with land at the vacant possession price assumed and 2.07% with land at the tenanted value assumed. Full repairing and insurance leases clearly raise the returns above these levels. Above average quality farms acquire higher rents but also obviously command higher prices than the average levels quoted above.

Return on Capital to Individual Enterprises

On a mixed farm it is almost impossible to ascertain the return on enterprise capital, except perhaps for a full-time pig or poultry enterprise, nor would it be of very much use even if it could be determined. It would require the arbitrary allocation both of costs and capital inputs that are common to several, in some cases all, of the enterprises on the farm.

What is relevant and important is the extra (net) return from an enterprise either to be introduced or expanded, as calculated by a partial budget, related to the extra (net) capital needed. The 'net' in brackets relates, as regards return, to the addition to gross margins less any addition to (or plus any reduction in) 'fixed' costs, bearing in mind that another enterprise may have to be deleted or reduced in size; and, as regards capital, to the fact that deletion or reduction of another enterprise may release capital.

In most cases of 'marginal' substitution, it is differences in the value of breeding livestock and differences in variable costs that are particularly relevant, but the timing of both inputs and sales are also obviously very important.

'Marginal' Capital Requirements

These are for small changes in crop areas or livestock numbers and can be estimated as follows:

- Crops: variable costs till sale.
- Dairy Cows and Egg Production: value of the cow* or hens, plus food until payment of product.
- Other Breeding Livestock: average value of stock*, plus variable costs to sale (payment) of the progeny (e.g. lambs) – or their transfer to another enterprise (e.g. weaners to the pig fattening enterprise).
- Rearing Breeding Livestock (e.g. heifers, shearlings, gilts, pullets): cost of the calf, lamb, weaner or chick, plus variable costs until they produce their first progeny/milk/eggs.
- Fattening Livestock and Production of Stores: cost of stock, plus variable costs till sale.

* Value of breeding stock, including dairy cows: either the average value over their entire breeding or milk producing life (see table on page 229) or their value when they first produce progeny can be taken. The latter will give the lower return on (marginal) capital and is thus the severer test.

Home-reared stock: where stock to be used for milk or egg production, breeding or fattening are home-reared, there are two possibilities:

(a) either they can be valued at variable costs of production when they are transferred from the rearing to the 'productive' enterprise; in this case the return on (marginal) capital will be estimated over the combined rearing and 'productive' enterprise.

(b) or they can be valued at market value at point of transfer. This is the procedure if one wishes to work out a return on (marginal) capital for the rearing and the 'productive' enterprises separately.

Return on 'Marginal' Capital.

This is sometimes expressed as the gross margin less fuel and repair costs of the enterprise expanded as a percentage of the 'marginal', or extra, capital. However, two points have to be remembered:

(a) If another enterprise has had to be reduced in size to enable the enterprise under consideration to be expanded, the capital released and the gross margin forfeited by reducing the size of the first enterprise must be brought into the calculation in estimating the net result of the change.

(b) All the above statements on 'marginal' capital refer to small changes. If the change is large enough to cause changes in labour, machinery or building requirements the capital changes brought about may be considerably greater.

Return on Investments in Medium-Term and Long-Term Capital.

This calculates the Rate of Return and the Discounted Yield.

Example: If a £5,000 investment results in an annual net return of £500 (after deducting depreciation, but ignoring interest payments):

$$\text{Rate of Return on Initial Capital} = \frac{500}{5,000} \times 100 = 10\%$$

$$\text{Rate of Return on Average Capital} = \frac{500}{2,500} \times 100 = 20\%$$

It is more accurate to calculate the '*Discounted Yield*', which is the discount rate that brings the present value of the net cash flows (which means ignoring depreciation) to the value of the investment. The tables on pages 238 may be used.

'Short-Cut' Estimates of the Discounted Yield on Depreciating Assets

The Discounted Yield falls between the simple Rates of Return on Initial and Average Capital. In fact, for investments lasting 5 to 15 years, when the Rate of Return on Initial Capital is 10 per cent and on Average Capital 20 per cent, the Discounted Yield will be almost exactly halfway between, i.e. about 15 per cent. However, this is only so providing the anticipated annual net cash earnings are fairly constant — or fluctuate unpredictably around a fairly constant level.

There are three circumstances when the Discounted Yield will get closer to the Rate of Return on Initial Capital (i.e. the lower per cent return) and further from the Rate of Return on Average Capital:

(a) The longer the life of the investment.

(b) The higher the Rate of Return.

(c) The higher the net cash flow is in the later years of the investment compared with the earlier years.

When the opposite circumstances obtain, the Discounted Yield will be closer to the Rate of Return on Average Capital (i.e. the higher per cent return).

Granted that there are inevitably varying degrees of estimation and uncertainty in calculating future net annual earnings of investments, the following short-cuts might reasonably be used where the annual net cash earnings are expected to be fairly constant —

or fluctuate unpredictably (e.g. through weather effects on yields) around a fairly constant level. (W.O. period = write-off period; R.R.I.C. = rate of return on initial capital).

1. Where

    (i)   the W.O. period is 5 years or less,

    (ii)   the W.O. period is 6 - 10 years and the R.R.I.C. is 15 per cent or less,

    (iii)   the W.O. period is 11 - 20 years and the R.R.I.C. is 10 per cent or less,

    calculate the Return on Capital as being approximately midway between the Rates of Return on Initial and Average Capital, i.e. by calculating the Rate of Return on 2/3 of the original investment.

    For example, following the earlier example above:

$$\frac{500}{3,333} \times 100 = 15\%.$$

2. Where

    (i)   the W.O. period is 6 to 10 years and the R.R.I.C. exceeds 15 per cent,

    (ii)   the W.O. period is 11 to 20 years and the R.R.I.C. is between 10 per cent and 25 per cent,

    (iii)   the W.O. period exceeds 20 years and the R.R.I.C. is 10 per cent or less,

    calculate the Return on Capital on 80 per cent of the original investment.

    For example, again following the earlier example:

$$\frac{500}{4,000} \times 100 = 12.5°\%.$$

3. Where

    (i)   the W.O. period is 11 to 20 years and the R.R.I.C. exceeds 25 per cent,

    (ii)   the W.O. period exceeds 20 years and the R.R.I.C. exceeds 10 per cent, take the Return on Capital to be the R.R.I.C.

In borderline cases, use method 1 rather than 2, or 2 rather than 3 if there is a tendency for the cash flow to be higher in the earlier years, e.g. because of tax allowances on machinery. Take 2 rather than 1, and 3 rather than 2, if the likelihood is that the cash flow will be lower in earlier years and increase in later years.

However, where the annual cash flow is expected to vary (apart from unpredictable fluctuations) it is safer to make the full D.C.F. calculation. This is particularly so where the variation is both up and down and where further periodic investments are to be made during the life of the project.

3.   INTEREST RATES

Rate of interest on Bank Loans.

Typically 3.0% to 3.5% above Base Rate. Main range is 1.5% above to 4.0% above. Extremes are likely to be 0.8% above (minimum) and 7% above (maximum). Since the banking crisis in 2008 and the reduction in Base Rate to 0.5%, interest rates have become more variable depending often on the relationship with the bank. Banks are demanding wider margins generally and low margins over base are becoming extremely rare, especially for new lending agreements.

Annual Percentage Rate (APR)

This is the effective rate of interest calculated on an annual basis and should be used when seeking to make a true comparison between interest charges on money borrowed from different sources. The APR allows for the fact that when interest is applied to accounts at half yearly, quarterly or monthly intervals an element of compounding will arise.

For example, £100 borrowed for one year at a quoted annual nominal interest rate of 6% (e.g. 5.5% over base rate of 0.5%) with interest charged quarterly, will lead to an accumulated interest charge of £6.136 (i.e., giving an APR of just under 6.14%). The higher the annual nominal interest rate and the more frequently the interest charges are applied to the account, the more pronounced the compounding element becomes. For example, an annual nominal interest rate of 10% produces an APR of 10.25% with half yearly charging, 10.38% with quarterly charging and 10.47% with monthly charging.

In the case of some loans and hire purchase agreements, interest charges may be quoted as a flat rate on the original amount borrowed. The APR will be considerably greater than the flat rate if the loan is repaid by equal periodic instalments, comprising part capital and part interest, so that the borrowing is completely repaid by the end of the agreed term. For example, the APR for a loan at a flat rate of interest of 8% repaid by monthly instalments over 5 years will be 15%. The shorter the repayment period, and the more frequent the payments, the higher is the APR compared with the flat rate.

The Real Rate of Interest.

When preparing simple profit and loss budgets to estimate how worthwhile an investment in a fixed asset (machinery, buildings, land) is, it is usual to price inputs and outputs at present-day values even when most costs and returns are expected to rise due to inflation over the life of the investment. Where this real terms approach is adopted a more realistic estimate of the effect on profitability can be gained by basing charges for capital on the real rate of interest rather than the APR.

The real rate of interest is the APR adjusted for the annual rate at which prices relevant to the investment are expected to increase. A crude estimate of the real rate of interest can be obtained by simply subtracting the expected rate of price increase from the APR; for example, if the APR were 8% and the expected rate of inflation 3%, the real rate of interest would be $8 - 3 = 5\%$.

4.   FINANCIAL RATIOS

Common Ratios

The following ratios are often quoted as rough guidelines:

		% of Gross Output
Variable Costs		30-40%
Labour	15-17½%	
Machinery	15-17½%	} 30-40%
Sundry Fixed Costs	5%	
Rent & Interest		15%
Margin*		15%

* to cover drawings, tax, capital repayments, reinvestments

It has to be borne in mind that these are indeed only rough guidelines and need to be considered with great care. Values vary, with type of farming and size of farm. It is often unclear how certain items are being measured, especially whether unpaid manual labour of the farmer and family has been included or whether a rental value has been allowed for owner-occupied land. In the table above variable costs at 30% or less would be found on cereals type farms, leaving 40% for labour, machinery and sundry fixed costs. On intensive livestock farms variable costs of 40% would be expected, leaving only 30% for fixed costs.

Farm Survey Ratios

The following are rounded averages based on farm surveys in recent years on a large sample of all types of farm, assuming a Management and Investment Income (see page 227) of 10% of Total Output is made. It is to be noted that Total Output includes the market value of any production retained for use/consumption on the farm (e.g. cereals for feed or seed), Unpaid Labour (value of manual labour supplied by the farmer and spouse) is included. Rent includes the rental value of owner-occupied land and Interest charges are not included in the costs. Casual labour and all Contract work are included in fixed costs. Obviously, costs are a lower proportion and the margin a higher proportion in profitable years, and vice-versa in low profit years. Obviously, too, within years the more profitable farms have lower percentage costs, leaving higher percentage margins and vice-versa.

Average Financial Ratios from Farm Business Survey (England)

	% Total Output	% Total Gross Margin	% Total Fixed Costs
Variable Costs:			
(excl. casual labour and contract work)	32.5		
Fixed Costs:			
Labour: Paid (inc. casuals) }	20	30	33
Labour: Unpaid			
Power & Machinery			
(inc. contract work)	20	30	33
Labour & Machinery	40	60	66
Rent/Rental Value	12.5	19	21
General Overheads	7.5	11	13
Total Fixed Costs	60	90	100
Margin	**7.5**	**10**	-

Total Gross Margin = 67.5% of Total Output

Lending Criteria

Another set of standards widely used by lending and leasing institutions looks at total Finance Charges (rent, interest, leasing charges, etc.), as a percentage of Gross Output and Gross Margin;

Finance as a % of Gross Output	Finance as a % of Gross Margin	Lending Criteria
0-10%	0-15%	Normally very safe
11-15%	16-22.5%	Common range, should be safe
16-20%	23-29%	Care required
20% plus	30% plus	Potentially dangerous

As lenders will be well aware, however, these ratios too must be regarded with caution and in conjunction with the farm's level of net worth (% equity) and its trend in recent years, recent trends in its profitability and the potential borrower's record of expenditure both on and off the farm, together with his or her character and potential. Also, of course, some enterprises / types of farming are more risky than others.

DISCOUNTING TABLE

Discount Factors for Calculating the Present Value of Future (irregular) Cash Flows

Year								Percentage									
	3%	4%	5%	6%	7%	8%	9%	10%	11%	12%	13%	14%	15%	16%	18%	20%	25%
1	0.971	0.962	0.952	0.943	0.935	0.926	0.917	0.909	0.901	0.893	0.885	0.877	0.870	0.862	0.847	0.833	0.800
2	0.943	0.925	0.907	0.890	0.873	0.857	0.842	0.826	0.812	0.797	0.783	0.769	0.756	0.743	0.718	0.694	0.640
3	0.915	0.889	0.864	0.840	0.816	0.794	0.772	0.751	0.731	0.712	0.693	0.675	0.658	0.641	0.609	0.579	0.512
4	0.888	0.855	0.823	0.792	0.763	0.735	0.708	0.683	0.659	0.636	0.613	0.592	0.572	0.552	0.516	0.482	0.410
5	0.863	0.822	0.784	0.747	0.713	0.681	0.650	0.621	0.593	0.567	0.543	0.519	0.497	0.476	0.437	0.402	0.328
6	0.837	0.790	0.746	0.705	0.666	0.630	0.596	0.564	0.535	0.507	0.480	0.456	0.432	0.410	0.370	0.335	0.262
7	0.813	0.760	0.711	0.665	0.623	0.583	0.547	0.513	0.482	0.452	0.425	0.400	0.376	0.354	0.314	0.279	0.210
8	0.789	0.731	0.677	0.627	0.582	0.540	0.502	0.467	0.434	0.404	0.376	0.351	0.327	0.305	0.266	0.233	0.168
9	0.766	0.703	0.645	0.592	0.544	0.500	0.460	0.424	0.391	0.361	0.333	0.308	0.284	0.263	0.225	0.194	0.134
10	0.744	0.676	0.614	0.558	0.508	0.463	0.422	0.386	0.352	0.322	0.295	0.270	0.247	0.227	0.191	0.162	0.107
11	0.722	0.650	0.585	0.527	0.475	0.429	0.388	0.350	0.317	0.287	0.261	0.237	0.215	0.195	0.162	0.135	0.086
12	0.701	0.625	0.557	0.497	0.444	0.397	0.356	0.319	0.286	0.257	0.231	0.208	0.187	0.168	0.137	0.112	0.069
13	0.681	0.601	0.530	0.469	0.415	0.368	0.326	0.290	0.258	0.229	0.204	0.182	0.163	0.145	0.116	0.093	0.055
14	0.661	0.577	0.505	0.442	0.388	0.340	0.299	0.263	0.232	0.205	0.181	0.160	0.141	0.125	0.098	0.078	0.044
15	0.642	0.555	0.481	0.417	0.362	0.315	0.275	0.239	0.209	0.183	0.160	0.140	0.123	0.108	0.084	0.065	0.035
20	0.554	0.456	0.377	0.312	0.258	0.215	0.178	0.149	0.124	0.104	0.087	0.073	0.061	0.051	0.037	0.026	0.012
25	0.478	0.375	0.295	0.233	0.184	0.146	0.116	0.092	0.074	0.059	0.047	0.038	0.030	0.024	0.016	0.010	0.004
30	0.412	0.308	0.231	0.174	0.131	0.099	0.075	0.057	0.044	0.033	0.026	0.020	0.015	0.012	0.007	0.004	0.001

Example: The Present Value of £500 received 10 years from now, at 12 per cent discount rate of interest = 500 x 0.322 = £161.

Conversely, £161 invested now, at 12 per cent compound interest, will be worth £500 in 10 years' time.

DISCOUNTING TABLE B

Discount Factors for Calculating the Present Value of Future Annuity (i.e. Constant Annual Cash Flow) Receivable in Year 1 to n inclusive.

Year	Percentage																
	3%	4%	5%	6%	7%	8%	9%	10%	11%	12%	13%	14%	15%	16%	18%	20%	25%
1	0.971	0.962	0.952	0.943	0.935	0.926	0.917	0.909	0.901	0.893	0.885	0.877	0.870	0.862	0.847	0.833	0.800
2	1.913	1.886	1.859	1.833	1.808	1.783	1.759	1.736	1.713	1.690	1.668	1.647	1.626	1.605	1.566	1.528	1.440
3	2.829	2.775	2.723	2.673	2.624	2.577	2.531	2.487	2.444	2.402	2.361	2.322	2.283	2.246	2.174	2.106	1.952
4	3.717	3.630	3.546	3.465	3.387	3.312	3.240	3.170	3.102	3.037	2.974	2.914	2.855	2.798	2.690	2.589	2.362
5	4.580	4.452	4.329	4.212	4.100	3.993	3.890	3.791	3.696	3.605	3.517	3.433	3.352	3.274	3.127	2.991	2.689
6	5.417	5.242	5.076	4.917	4.767	4.623	4.486	4.355	4.231	4.111	3.998	3.889	3.784	3.685	3.498	3.326	2.951
7	6.230	6.002	5.786	5.582	5.389	5.206	5.033	4.868	4.712	4.564	4.423	4.288	4.160	4.039	3.812	3.605	3.161
8	7.020	6.733	6.463	6.210	5.971	5.747	5.535	5.335	5.146	4.968	4.799	4.639	4.487	4.344	4.078	3.837	3.329
9	7.786	7.435	7.108	6.802	6.515	6.247	5.995	5.759	5.537	5.328	5.132	4.946	4.772	4.607	4.303	4.031	3.463
10	8.530	8.111	7.722	7.360	7.024	6.710	6.418	6.145	5.889	5.650	5.426	5.216	5.019	4.833	4.494	4.192	3.570
11	9.253	8.760	8.306	7.887	7.499	7.139	6.805	6.495	6.207	5.938	5.687	5.453	5.234	5.029	4.656	4.327	3.656
12	9.954	9.385	8.863	8.384	7.943	7.536	7.161	6.814	6.492	6.194	5.918	5.660	5.421	5.197	4.793	4.439	3.725
13	10.635	9.986	9.394	8.853	8.358	7.904	7.487	7.103	6.750	6.424	6.122	5.842	5.583	5.342	4.910	4.533	3.780
14	11.296	10.563	9.899	9.295	8.745	8.244	7.786	7.367	6.982	6.628	6.302	6.002	5.724	5.468	5.008	4.611	3.824
15	11.938	11.118	10.380	9.712	9.108	8.559	8.061	7.606	7.191	6.811	6.462	6.142	5.847	5.575	5.092	4.675	3.859
20	14.877	13.590	12.462	11.470	10.594	9.818	9.129	8.514	7.963	7.469	7.025	6.623	6.259	5.929	5.353	4.870	3.954
25	17.413	15.662	14.094	12.783	11.654	10.675	9.823	9.077	8.422	7.843	7.330	6.873	6.464	6.097	5.467	4.948	3.985
30	19.600	17.292	15.372	13.765	12.409	11.258	10.274	9.427	8.694	8.055	7.496	7.003	6.566	6.177	5.517	4.979	3.995

Example: The Present Value of £500 a year for the next 10 years, at 12 per cent discount rate of interest = 500 x 5.650 = £2,825. This is the same answer that would be obtained by multiplying 500 by each discount factor (at 12 per cent) in Table A for each year from 1 to 10, and adding together the ten resulting figures to obtain the Discounted Yield of a constant annual net cash flow, divide this into the original investment and look up the resulting figure in the table above, against the number of years. Example: an investment of £1,000 is estimated to produce £80 a year additional profit over 10 years (before charging interest). Add £100 depreciation a year = £180 annual net cash flow. 1000 / 180 = 5.56. This equals just over 12 per cent (the 10 years /12 per cent figure being 5.650).

COMPOUNDING TABLE

The Future Money Value of £1 after n Years with no additional payments made

Rate of Interest

Year	3%	4%	5%	6%	7%	8%	9%	10%	11%	12%	13%	14%	15%	16%	18%	20%	25%
1	1.03	1.04	1.05	1.06	1.07	1.08	1.09	1.10	1.11	1.12	1.13	1.14	1.15	1.16	1.18	1.20	1.25
2	1.06	1.08	1.10	1.12	1.14	1.17	1.19	1.21	1.23	1.25	1.28	1.30	1.32	1.35	1.39	1.44	1.56
3	1.09	1.12	1.16	1.19	1.23	1.26	1.30	1.33	1.37	1.40	1.44	1.48	1.52	1.56	1.64	1.73	1.95
4	1.13	1.17	1.22	1.26	1.31	1.36	1.41	1.46	1.52	1.57	1.63	1.69	1.75	1.81	1.94	2.07	2.44
5	1.16	1.22	1.28	1.34	1.40	1.47	1.54	1.61	1.69	1.76	1.84	1.93	2.01	2.10	2.29	2.49	3.05
6	1.19	1.27	1.34	1.42	1.50	1.59	1.68	1.77	1.87	1.97	2.08	2.19	2.31	2.44	2.70	2.99	3.81
7	1.23	1.32	1.41	1.50	1.61	1.71	1.83	1.95	2.08	2.21	2.35	2.50	2.66	2.83	3.19	3.58	4.77
8	1.27	1.37	1.48	1.59	1.72	1.85	1.99	2.14	2.30	2.48	2.66	2.85	3.06	3.28	3.76	4.30	5.96
9	1.30	1.42	1.55	1.69	1.84	2.00	2.17	2.36	2.56	2.77	3.00	3.25	3.52	3.80	4.44	5.16	7.45
10	1.34	1.48	1.63	1.79	1.97	2.16	2.37	2.59	2.84	3.11	3.39	3.71	4.05	4.41	5.23	6.19	9.31
11	1.38	1.54	1.71	1.90	2.10	2.33	2.58	2.85	3.15	3.48	3.84	4.23	4.65	5.12	6.18	7.43	11.64
12	1.43	1.60	1.80	2.01	2.25	2.52	2.81	3.14	3.50	3.90	4.33	4.82	5.35	5.94	7.29	8.92	14.55
13	1.47	1.67	1.89	2.13	2.41	2.72	3.07	3.45	3.88	4.36	4.90	5.49	6.15	6.89	8.60	10.70	18.19
14	1.51	1.73	1.98	2.26	2.58	2.94	3.34	3.80	4.31	4.89	5.53	6.26	7.08	7.99	10.15	12.84	22.74
15	1.56	1.80	2.08	2.40	2.76	3.17	3.64	4.18	4.78	5.47	6.25	7.14	8.14	9.27	11.97	15.41	28.42
20	1.81	2.19	2.65	3.21	3.87	4.66	5.60	6.73	8.06	9.65	11.52	13.74	16.37	19.46	27.39	38.34	86.74
25	2.09	2.67	3.39	4.29	5.43	6.85	8.62	10.83	13.59	17.00	21.23	26.46	32.92	40.87	62.67	95.40	264.7
30	2.43	3.24	4.32	5.74	7.61	10.06	13.27	17.45	22.89	29.96	39.12	50.95	66.21	85.85	143.4	237.4	807.8

COMPOUNDING TABLE B

The Future Money Value of £1 after n Years*

Year									Rate of Interest								
	3%	4%	5%	6%	7%	8%	9%	10%	11%	12%	13%	14%	15%	16%	18%	20%	25%
1	1.03	1.04	1.05	1.06	1.07	1.08	1.09	1.10	1.11	1.12	1.13	1.14	1.15	1.16	1.18	1.20	1.25
2	2.09	2.12	2.15	2.18	2.21	2.25	2.28	2.31	2.34	2.37	2.41	2.44	2.47	2.51	2.57	2.64	2.81
3	3.18	3.25	3.31	3.37	3.44	3.51	3.57	3.64	3.71	3.78	3.85	3.92	3.99	4.07	4.22	4.37	4.77
4	4.31	4.42	4.53	4.64	4.75	4.87	4.98	5.11	5.23	5.35	5.48	5.61	5.74	5.88	6.15	6.44	7.21
5	5.47	5.63	5.80	5.98	6.15	6.34	6.52	6.72	6.91	7.12	7.32	7.54	7.75	7.98	8.44	8.93	10.26
6	6.66	6.90	7.14	7.39	7.65	7.92	8.20	8.49	8.78	9.09	9.40	9.73	10.07	10.41	11.14	11.92	14.07
7	7.89	8.21	8.55	8.90	9.26	9.64	10.03	10.44	10.86	11.30	11.76	12.23	12.73	13.24	14.33	15.50	18.84
8	9.16	9.58	10.03	10.49	10.98	11.49	12.02	12.58	13.16	13.78	14.42	15.09	15.79	16.52	18.09	19.80	24.80
9	10.46	11.01	11.58	12.18	12.82	13.49	14.19	14.94	15.72	16.55	17.42	18.34	19.30	20.32	22.52	24.96	32.25
10	11.81	12.49	13.21	13.97	14.78	15.65	16.56	17.53	18.56	19.65	20.81	22.04	23.35	24.73	27.76	31.15	41.57
11	13.19	14.03	14.92	15.87	16.89	17.98	19.14	20.38	21.71	23.13	24.65	26.27	28.00	29.85	33.93	38.58	53.21
12	14.62	15.63	16.71	17.88	19.14	20.50	21.95	23.52	25.21	27.03	28.98	31.09	33.35	35.79	41.22	47.50	67.76
13	16.09	17.29	18.60	20.02	21.55	23.21	25.02	26.97	29.09	31.39	33.88	36.58	39.50	42.67	49.82	58.20	85.95
14	17.60	19.02	20.58	22.28	24.13	26.15	28.36	30.77	33.41	36.28	39.42	42.84	46.58	50.66	59.97	71.04	108.7
15	19.16	20.82	22.66	24.67	26.89	29.32	32.00	34.95	38.19	41.75	45.67	49.98	54.72	59.93	71.94	86.44	137.1
20	27.68	30.97	34.72	38.99	43.87	49.42	55.76	63.00	71.27	80.70	91.47	103.8	117.8	133.8	173.0	224.0	428.7
25	37.55	43.31	50.11	58.16	67.68	78.95	92.32	108.2	127.0	149.3	175.8	207.3	244.7	289.1	404.3	566.4	1318
30	49.00	58.33	69.76	83.80	101.1	122.3	148.6	180.9	220.9	270.3	331.3	406.7	500.0	615.2	933.3	1418	4034

* Equal payments made at the beginning of each year.

240

AMORTISATION TABLE

Annual Charge to write off £1,000

Write-off Period	Rate of Interest															
	3	4	5	6	7	8	9	10	11	12	13	14	15	16	18	20
5 years	218	225	231	237	244	250	257	264	271	277	284	291	298	305	320	334
6	185	191	197	203	210	216	223	230	236	243	250	257	264	271	286	301
7	161	167	173	179	186	192	199	205	212	219	226	233	240	248	262	277
8	142	149	155	161	167	174	181	187	194	201	208	216	223	230	245	261
9	128	134	141	147	153	160	167	174	181	188	195	202	210	217	232	248
10	117	123	130	136	142	149	156	163	170	177	184	192	199	207	223	239
11	108	114	120	127	133	140	147	154	161	168	176	183	191	199	215	231
12	100	107	113	119	125	133	140	147	154	161	169	177	184	192	209	225
13	94	100	106	113	120	127	134	141	148	156	163	171	179	187	204	221
14	89	95	101	108	114	121	128	136	143	151	159	167	175	183	200	217
15	84	90	96	103	110	117	124	131	139	147	155	163	171	179	196	214
16	80	86	92	99	106	113	120	128	136	143	151	160	168	176	194	211
17	76	82	89	95	102	110	117	125	132	140	149	157	165	174	191	209
18	73	79	86	92	99	107	114	122	130	138	146	155	163	172	190	208
19	70	76	83	90	97	104	112	120	128	136	144	153	161	170	188	206
20	67	74	80	87	94	102	110	117	126	134	142	151	160	169	187	205
25	57	64	71	78	86	94	102	110	119	127	136	145	155	164	183	202
30	51	58	65	73	81	89	97	106	115	124	133	143	152	162	181	201
40	43	51	58	66	75	84	93	102	112	122	131	141	151	160	180	200

Example: £3,000 is borrowed to erect a building. The annual charge to service interest and capital repayment on the £3,000, repayable over 10 years at 12%, is 3 x £177 = £531. Where the write-off period of the building (10 years) is equal to the repayment period of the loan, then the average annual depreciation and interest will also equal £531.

The proportion of the total annual charge representing the average amount of capital repaid per annum can be readily determined by dividing the sum borrowed by the number of years of the loan: (in the above example this is £3,000 ÷ 10 = £300/year). The remainder is clearly the average amount of interest paid per annum: (in the above example, £531 — £300 = £231/year). The year to year variations between the two items (i.e. capital repaid and interest) are shown in the tables on pages 228 to 230, which demonstrate the way in which the capital repayment part increases and the interest part decreases over time.

SINKING FUND TABLE

The sum required to be set aside at the end of each year to make £1,000

								Rate of Interest								
No. of Years	3	4	5	6	7	8	9	10	11	12	13	14	15	16	18	20
5	188	185	181	177	174	170	167	164	161	157	154	151	148	145	140	134
6	155	151	147	143	140	136	133	130	126	123	120	117	114	111	106	101
7	131	127	123	119	116	112	109	105	102	99	96	93	90	88	82	77
8	112	109	105	101	97	94	91	87	84	81	78	76	73	70	65	61
9	98	94	91	87	83	80	77	74	71	68	65	62	60	57	52	48
10	87	83	80	76	72	69	66	63	60	57	54	52	49	47	43	39
11	78	74	70	67	63	60	57	54	51	48	46	43	41	39	35	31
12	70	67	63	59	56	53	50	47	44	41	39	37	34	32	29	25
13	64	60	56	53	50	47	44	41	38	36	33	31	29	27	24	21
14	59	55	51	48	44	41	38	36	33	31	29	27	25	23	20	17
15	54	50	46	43	40	37	34	31	29	27	25	23	21	19	16	14
16	50	46	42	39	36	33	30	28	26	23	21	20	18	16	14	11
17	46	42	39	35	32	30	27	25	22	20	19	17	15	14	11	9
18	43	39	36	32	29	27	24	22	20	18	16	15	13	12	10	8
19	40	36	33	30	27	24	22	20	18	16	14	13	11	10	8	6
20	37	34	30	27	24	22	20	17	16	14	12	11	10	9	7	5
25	27	24	21	18	16	14	12	10	9	7	6	5	5	4	3	2
30	21	18	15	13	11	9	7	6	5	4	3	3	2	2	1	1
40	13	11	8	6	5	4	3	2	2	1	1	1	1	—	—	—

MORTGAGE REPAYMENT DATA

Items per £1000 invested; where I = Interest, P = Principal repaid, L = Loan outstanding

Loan of	4%			5%			6%			8%			10%			12%		
	I	P	L	I	P	L	I	P	L	I	P	L	I	P	L	I	P	L
5 years																		
1	40	185	815	50	181	819	60	177	823	80	170	830	100	164	836	120	157	834
2	33	192	623	41	190	629	49	188	635	66	184	645	84	180	656	101	175	670
3	25	200	424	31	200	424	38	199	435	52	199	447	66	198	458	80	197	469
4	17	208	216	21	210	220	26	211	224	36	215	232	46	218	240	56	221	248
5	9	216	0	11	220	0	13	224	0	19	232	0	24	240	0	30	248	0
10 years																		
1	40	83	917	50	80	920	60	76	924	80	69	931	100	63	939	120	57	934
2	37	87	830	46	83	837	55	80	844	75	75	856	94	69	868	113	64	879
3	33	90	740	42	88	749	51	85	758	69	81	776	87	76	808	106	71	808
4	30	94	646	37	92	657	46	90	668	62	87	689	79	84	709	97	80	728
5	26	97	549	33	97	561	40	96	572	55	94	595	71	92	617	87	90	638
6	22	101	448	28	101	459	34	102	471	48	101	494	62	101	516	77	100	538
7	18	105	342	23	107	353	28	108	363	39	110	384	52	111	405	65	112	425
8	14	110	233	18	112	241	22	114	249	31	118	266	40	122	282	51	126	299
9	9	114	119	12	117	123	15	121	128	21	128	138	28	134	148	36	141	158
10	5	119	0	6	123	0	8	128	0	11	138	0	15	148	0	19	158	0

MORTGAGE REPAYMENT DATA (CONTINUED)

Loan of	4%			5%			6%			8%			10%			12%		
	I	P	L	I	P	L	I	P	L	I	P	L	I	P	L	I	P	L
20 years																		
1	40	34	966	50	30	970	60	27	973	80	22	978	100	17	983	120	14	986
5	34	39	818	43	37	833	53	34	847	72	30	872	92	26	893	112	22	912
10	26	48	597	33	47	620	41	46	642	58	44	683	76	41	722	95	38	756
15	15	58	328	20	60	347	26	61	367	38	64	407	51	66	445	66	68	483
20	3	71	0	4	76	0	5	82	0	8	94	0	11	107	0	14	120	0
25 years																		
1	40	24	976	50	21	979	60	18	982	80	14	986	100	10	990	120	7	993
5	36	28	870	45	25	884	55	23	897	75	19	920	95	15	938	116	12	952
10	30	34	712	38	33	736	47	31	760	66	27	802	86	24	838	107	21	868
15	22	42	519	29	41	548	37	41	576	54	40	629	72	39	677	91	37	720
20	13	51	285	18	53	307	23	55	330	35	59	374	48	62	418	63	65	460
25	2	62	0	3	68	0	4	74	0	7	87	0	10	100	0	14	114	0

MORTGAGE REPAYMENT DATA (CONTINUED)

Loan through	6%			8%			10%			12%			14%			16%		
	I	P	L	I	P	L	I	P	L	I	P	L	I	P	L	I	P	L
30 years																		
1	60	13	987	80	9	991	100	6	994	120	4	996	140	3	997	160	2	998
5	57	16	929	77	12	948	97	9	963	118	7	974	138	5	986	158	3	987
10	51	21	833	71	18	872	92	14	903	113	11	927	134	9	951	155	7	960
15	44	29	706	63	26	760	83	23	807	104	20	846	126	17	890	147	15	903
20	34	38	535	51	38	596	69	37	652	88	36	701	108	35	751	130	32	782
25	21	51	306	33	56	355	46	60	402	61	63	488	83	60	494	95	66	530
30	4	69	0	7	82	0	10	96	0	13	111	0	16	127	0	22	140	0
40 years																		
1	60	6	994	80	4	996	100	2	998	120	1	999	140	1	999	160	0	1000
5	58	8	964	79	5	977	99	3	986	119	2	992	139	2	995	160	1	997
10	56	11	915	76	8	944	97	5	964	118	4	977	138	3	989	159	2	991
15	52	15	850	73	11	895	94	9	928	115	6	951	136	5	973	157	3	978
20	47	20	762	67	17	823	88	14	871	110	11	906	130	11	942	153	7	951
25	40	26	645	59	24	718	80	22	778	102	20	826	123	18	874	145	15	894
30	31	35	489	48	36	563	66	36	628	86	35	685	109	32	742	129	31	775
35	20	47	280	31	53	335	45	58	388	60	61	437	85	56	487	95	66	525
40	4	63	0	6	78	0	9	93	0	13	108	0	18	123	0	22	138	0

Note—All figures rounded to nearest £.

6.   FARM RECORDS

The following records should be kept for management purposes:

Basic Whole Farm Financial Position

1.   Cash Analysis Book, fully detailed.

2.   Petty Cash Book.

3.   Annual Valuation, including physical quantities of

    i.   Harvested crops in store

    ii.   Livestock (breeding and fattening) at (near) market value, less any variable costs yet to be borne.

    iii.   Fertilisers, seeds, sprays, casual labour or contract work applied to growing crops should be recorded, but "cultivations" and manurial residues can be ignored for management purposes.

    iv.   Fertiliser, seed, sprays and other sundry direct items in store,

4.   Debtors and creditors at the end of the financial year.

Other Financial and Physical Records

5.   Output (quantities and value) of each crop and livestock enterprise for the "harvest year" (or production cycle). It may be possible to get information of sales from a fully detailed cash analysis book (although, for crops, the financial year figures will then have to be allocated between crops from the current harvest and those from the harvest in the previous financial year, in order to check on the accuracy of the opening valuation of crops in store; this is particularly a problem with Michaelmas ending accounts). The following records of internal transfers and consumption will also be required:

    (a)   Numbers and market value of livestock transferred from one livestock category to another, e.g. dairy calves to dairy followers or beef enterprise, or dairy heifers to dairy enterprise.

    (b)   Quantity and market value of cereals fed on farm and used for seed.

    (c)   Quantity and market value of milk and other produce consumed by the farmer or his employees, used on the farm (e.g. milk fed to calves), or sold direct.

6.   A monthly record of livestock numbers; preferably reconciled with the previous month according to births, purchases, deaths, sales and transfers.

7.   Costs and quantities of concentrate feed to each category of livestock, including home-grown cereals fed on the farm.

8.   Allocation of costs of seed, fertiliser, sprays, casual labour and contract work specific to an enterprise. This is in order to calculate gross margins, where required.

9.   Breeding record for cows, including bulling dates, date(s) served, type of bull used, pregnancy testing, estimated calving date, actual calving date, and date when dried off.

10. For each crop, total output and yield per hectare, in both quantity and value. Include each field where the crop has been grown and its approximate yield, where this can be satisfactorily obtained.

11. For each field, keep one page to cover a period of say, ten years. Record on this, each year, crop grown, variety sown, fertiliser used, sprays used, date sown, date(s) harvested, approximate yield (if obtainable), and any other special notes that you feel may have significance for the future.

12. A rotation record. On a single page, if possible, list each field down the side and say, ten years along the top. Colour each field-year space according to the crop grown, e.g. barley yellow, potatoes red, etc.

13. It is important to note that other farm records are required for legislative and cross compliance purposes including:

    i.   Livestock movements, identification, flock and herd records etc

    ii.   Nitrate Vulnerable Zone (NVZ) records and calculations including livestock loadings, manure storage, fertiliser plans and usage etc

    iii.   Pesticide application and storage records, risk assessments

    iv.   Farm waste storage and disposal records and necessary exemptions / permits / transfer certificates

    v.   Integrated Pollution and Prevention Controls (IPPC) records (for pig and poultry units)

    vi.   Soil Protection reviews and risk assessments

    vii.   Financial (HMRC) records including VAT, PAYE, NI etc

IX.   MISCELLANEOUS DATA

1.   CONSERVATION COSTS

Note: Costs vary widely, depending on geographical location and the type and size of the job. Markets for such services can be highly localised, sparse in some areas, competitive in others.

Hedges

Hedge Cutting. From £320 per day at an average of 3 miles per day.

Hedge Laying (Making hedges stock proof and rejuvenated by selective cutting and positioning). Depends on hedge thickness (single or double). Mechanical Laying: up to 250m/day (2 people) £360 plus materials. Manual hedge laying approximately 20m/day at £12.50/metre (contract).

Hedge Planting. Transplants av. £44/100; netlon guards 53p; canes 11p; fencing (labour and materials): stock proof £3.90/metre, rabbit proof (dug in) up to £6.00/metre. Overall, £2.60/metre unguarded and unfenced, £10.00/metre guarded and fenced. Contract labour: planting up to £2.44/metre, fencing up to £2.80/metre. Contractor 100-150 metres/day. Pref Oct./March. Above includes repair.

Hedge Coppicing. By hand: 2 men and a chain saw, £5.25-6.30/metre plus burning debris. Contractor: tractor mounted saw, driver and 2 men, 13 metres/ hour, £39.00/hour.

Dry Stone Walls

Dry Stone Walling. This is one of the most variable costs depending on stone type, stone grading availability, structure, vehicular access to site and local competition (people pay more for private walls in gardens than fields). As a guide, the following figures apply: Cost of graded stone approximately £100/tonne, varying regionally and depending on local stone, type and availability. Cost of wall building is (normally quoted per square meter but grants awarded per linear meter) from as low as £30 (highlands) to £170 (Cotswolds) per square metre. Most are around £70-85/m². Partial grants are available in ELS, UELS, HLS and some local grants e.g. within National Parks.

Trees

Amenity Tree Planting; (half acre block or less). Transplants av. 95p; shelter plus stake and tie £1.25; stake 53p; whip 78p. rabbit spiral guard 34p; netlon guard av. 52p; cane av. 13p. Trees per man day: farmer 200, contractor 400; (large-scale, 33 man days/ha). Optimal time November to April.

Shelter Belts. Per 100 metre length: 100 large species (oak, lime, etc.) £53; 66 medium species (cherry, birch, etc.) £45; 100 shrubs, £36; 166 tree stakes, shelters and ties, £275; (site preparation, weed control, labour and fencing extra). DEFRA standard costs £700/ha; windbreaks £37.00/ha.

Woodland Establishment. Conifers £210/1,000. To supply and plant oak or beech transplants (2-3ft tall) in tubes £3.60-£4.20 each, dependent on shelter size. Rabbit fencing £6.00/metre (dug in). Contract labour: conifers at 2m (inc. trees) £1,560/ha; broadleaves at 3m (inc. trees) £1,050/ha; forest transplants (not inc. trees) £290/1,050. 12.5 days/ha (contractor). Optimal timing November to April. (Above not including maintenance).

Forestry, General. Contract labour: chain sawing £22/hr., brush cutting £13.00/hr, extracting timber/pulp £4.70-£11.00/tonne, chemical spot weeding 8p-11p/tree, rhododendron control £660-£885/acre.

Pollarding and Tree Surgery. Pollard: £47-£70/stool; surgery: £170/ tree. Pollarding: 2 or 3 trees/day. Surgery: 2 days/tree. Winter. Pollard every 20-40 years.

Ponds and Ditches

Pond Construction. Butyl lining (0.75mm) £5.40/m^2; other linings up to £3.40/m^2. Contract labour: 150 Komatsu £29/hr.; bulldozer D6 LGP £46/hr, 13t 360° excavator £41/hr (excluding haulage), Flailmowers from £18.25/hr. Autumn (dry ground conditions).

Pond Maintenance. Hymac £40/hr.; Backhoe £23.50-26/hr. 100 m^2/day (contractor). Timing: probably winter; time depends on ground condition and species whose life cycles may be disturbed. Every 5 to 50 years.

Ditch Maintenance. Backhoe excavator £22.00/hr; 13 tonne 360° excavator £32.50/hr.; labour £11.50/hr. preferably in winter. Every 3 to 7 years on rotation.

Grassland

Permanent Grass Margins at Field Edges. To provide wildlife benefits and help control pernicious weeds, reducing herbicides at the field edge. (A sterile strip provides virtually no wildlife benefit and the initial establishment costs may be offset by savings in maintenance costs in future years.) Costs per 100 metres of seeds as follows.

- Establishment: 2m grass margins, £6.00-£8.00;
- 6m grass margins, £20-£26;
- beetle banks, £5.50-£8.00 (6m wide).
- Maintenance: 2m margins, 70p to 90p;
- 6m margins, £2.30-£2.70.

Establishment of Wildlife Grassland Meadow. £180-275/ha for ground preparation, depending on weed burden, more for heavy land or exceptional weed burden. Seed costs very variable, but as a guide:

- Native Perennial wild flowers and grasses, £15.50/kg, 25kg/ha = £385/ha
- Nectar mix for bumble bees and butterflies £16.00/kg, 25kg/ha = £400/ha
- Bird Seed sward £6.20/kg, 12kg/ha = £74/ha for single year crop, £4.40/kg, 50kg/ha = £220 for longer sward.
- Single species native grass seeds vary from £3.40/kg (e.g. Meadow Fescue) to £80/kg (Sweet Vernal).
- Single species native perennial wild flower seeds vary from £60/kg (Lady's Bedstraw) to over £600/kg (Cowslip)
- Buffer strip grass margin mix for cross compliance, ELS and HLS compliance, £4.40/kg drilled at 25kg/ha = £110/ha. Costs of ground preparation and drilling are usually higher than the seed.

Acknowledgement: Thanks to Cotswold Seeds, 0800 252 211 and FWAG 02476 696 699

2.   FERTILISER PRICES

Compounds		Analysis		Price Per Tonne
N	**P$_2$O$_5$**	**K$_2$O**		**£**
0	24	24		374
0	18	36		388
0	20	30		372
0	30	15		379
0	30	20		408
5	24	24		424
8	24	24		453
10	26	26	(B)	504
11	15	20	(B)	374
13	13	20		375
15	15	20		414
16	16	16	(B)	410
22	4	14	(B)	344
20	10	10	(B)	358
25	5	5	(B)	330
26	0	15		351

Straights	Price per tonne £
Ammonium Nitrate: UK (34.5% N)	340
Ammonium Nitrate: Imported (34.5% N)	326
NS grade: UK (27% N, 30% SO$_3$)	298
Sulphate of Ammonia (21% N, 60% SO$_3$)	270
Urea (46% N.): granular/ prills	453
Liquid Nitrogen (26% N, 5% SO$_3$)	261
Triple Superphosphate (TSP) (46% P$_2$O$_5$)	435
DAP (18/46/0)	612
MAP (12/52/0)	610
Muriate of Potash (MOP) (60% K$_2$O)	350

Average price (p) per kg:	N :	98.6	(UK AN)
	P$_2$O$_5$:	94.6	(TSP)
	K$_2$O :	58.3	(MOP)

The prices above are for fertiliser delivered in 600kg bags; delivery in bulk averages £7.00/tonne less; collection of bags by farmers £8/tonne less. They are based on forward prices in August 2011; they vary according to area and bargaining power. (B) is blended; prices for granular (where available) average around £4/tonne more. They assume delivery in 25-27 tonne loads; add approximately £3.50/tonne for 10 tonne loads, £8.50 for 6-9 tonne loads, £20 for 4-5 tonne loads.

3.   MANURE VALUE OF SLURRY

Nutrient Values of Common Farm Yard Manure Types

	Dry Matter %	Total N	*Available N*	Total P	*Available P*	Total K	*Available K*
		(kg N/t)		(kg P$_2$O$_5$/t)		(kg K$_2$O/t)	
Cattle FYM *	25	6.0	*0.6*	3.2	*1.9*	8.0	*7.2*
Pig FYM	25	7.0	*1.0*	6.0	*3.6*	8.0	*7.2*
Sheep FYM	25	7.0	*0.7*	3.2	*1.9*	8.0	*7.2*
Duck FYM	25	6.5	*1.0*	5.5	*3.3*	7.5	*6.8*
Horse FYM	30	7.0	*N/a*	5.0	*3.0*	6.0	*5.4*

*For manure stored for 3 months or more.   FYM = Farmyard Manure

Note: these nutrient contents are for guidance only and will vary between different livestock systems and storage methods. Analysis should be performed to understand the specific values of manure.

Manure Output per Head during the Housing Period

	Undiluted Excreta t or m³	N	P$_2$O$_5$	K$_2$O
			Total Kg	
1 dairy cow ~ *6,000 to 9,000 litres milk yield*	11.6	60	26	46
1 beef cow ~ *>500 kg*	8.2	41	15.5	33
1 finishing pig ~ *per place* ~ *86% occupancy*	1.6	10.6	5.6	5.6
1,000 broiler hens ~ *per hen place* ~ *85% occupancy*	19	330	220	340

Note: These figures should not be used for calculating NVZ compliance as they only allow for the time spent in the buildings and therefore exclude manure deposited in fields during grazing. Refer to the DEFRA NVZ guidance booklets for NVZ calculation methodology and annual manure output tables.

Lime

The cost of lime is divided between cost of the material, cost of hauling it to the field and the cost of application. The grade and quality varies greatly, with differing contaminants, and is milled more at differing grades, some through a maximum sieve of 4mm, others farm larger. As a guide, a reasonable grade of lime, delivered 12 miles and applied at 5 tonnes per hectare (2t/acre) would currently cost in the region of £17/tonne.

Biosolids (Sewage Sludge)

Biosolids act as good soil conditioner and fertiliser to farmers, whilst providing the most environmentally favourable method for water companies to dispose of the sludge. Biosolids vary in nutritional composition depending on processing and location, but RB209 describes its content as follows:

Biosolid Key Composition

	Digested Cake	Thermally Dried Pellets	Lime Stabilised
Dry Matter	25%	95%	40%
Total Nitrogen *kg/t*	*11*	*40*	*8.5*
Available N *kg/t*	1.6	2	0.9
Available P_2O_5 *kg/t*	9	35	13
Available K_2O *kg/t*	0.5	1.8	0.7
Available SO_3 *kg/t*	6	23	8.5
Guideline Price £/t applied	£3.50	£30	£3.50

Nutrient data taken from RB209(2010)

4. AGROCHEMICAL COSTS

Only the names of the active ingredients are given below, with their principal use. These materials should only be applied in accordance with the manufacturers' recommendations.

Application rates vary and there are differences between the prices of various proprietary brands. The list is not intended to be exhaustive and there is no implied criticism of materials omitted.

The variation in costs per hectare is because of varying application rates rather than price variation between suppliers. It is priced on the purchase of chemical alone, i.e., not the agronomy service. The separate service can be priced in various ways, but for cereal farms roughly £8.50-£9.00/ha is normal when the two are separated or a percentage of agrochemical sales when combined.

Crop	Function		Material	Cost £/ha per application
Cereals	Herbicides	General	Mecoprop-P	5.40-12.40
			Ioxynil+Bromoxynil	5.00-10.00
			Dicamba +Mecoprop-P + MCPA	18.20-22.75
			Metsulfuron-methyl	16.30
			Mesosulphuron + Idosulphuron	31.40
			Difflufenican	4.65 – 7.65
		Cleavers	Fluroxypyr	8.70 - 11.60
			Amidosulfuron	13.00-19.40
			Florasalum + Fluroxypyr	13.90-20.90
		Wild Oats	Pinoxaden	17.20-44.50
		Wild Oats & Blackgrass	Clodinafop-propargyl	42.00
			Fenoxaprop-P-ethy	14.00-21.00
	Growth Regulator		Chlormequat	2.20
			Chlormequat + Choline Chloride	3.20
			As above + Imazaquin	10.00
			2-chlorethylphosphonic acid	5.30-10.60
			2-chloroethyl phosphonic acid + Mepiquat Chloride	7.80-15.60
			Trinexapac-ethyl	14.90-19.00
	Fungicides		Azoxystrobin	35.20
			Fenpropimorph	15.00-20.00
			Epoxiconazole	25.00
			Tebuconazole	16.80
			Prothioconazole	18.50-37.30
			Chlorothalonil	6.30
		Seed Dressing	Fuberidazole + Triadimenol	7.30-11.60
			Fuberidazole + Triadimenol + Imidacloprid	16.00-25.60
			Prythoconazole + Clothianidin	12.00-20.00

Crop	Function	Material	Cost £/ha per application
		Silthiofam	23.45-37.40
		Imidacloprid + tebuconazole + triazoxide	13.00-20.80
		Fluquincolazole	15.40 – 24.60
		Fludioxonil + Tefluthrin	13.00 - 21.00
		Triticonazole + Prochloraz	6.40 – 10.30
		Manganese	6.20 – 10.00
	Aphicide	Deltamethrin	3.40-4.25
		Pirimicarb	8.80
		Chlorpyriphos	6.80-13.60
	Slug Killer	Metaldehyde	5.50
		Methiocarb	24.75
Oilseed Rape	Herbicides	Propyzamide	35.70
		Metazachlor	22.80-38.00
		Clomazone	21.70
	Insecticide	Deltamethrin	4.25
		Pirimicarb	8.80-13.20
		Alphacypermethrin	2.90-5.75
	Fungicide	Iprodione + thiophate-methyl	22.00-33.00
		Tebuconazole	8.40-16.80
		Flusilazole + Carbendazim	15.00-19.20
		Metconazole	20.00
	Dessicant	Glyphosate	5.50
Potatoes	Herbicides:	Metribuzin	13.70-27.40
		Linuron	18.00-34.50
		Diquat	9.20-18.40
		Clomazone	22.00
	Blight Control	Cymoxanil + Mancozeb	10.40
		Cymoxanil + Famoxadone	12.30-17.20
		Fluazinam	10.60
		Mancozeb+Metalaxyl	25.90
	Haulm Dessicant	Diquat	36.90
Sugar Beet			
	Herbicides: Pre-emergence	Chloridazon:	
		Overall	25.50-60.00
		band spray	8.50 - 20.00
	Post-emergence	Phenmedipham:	5.60-9.40
		Triflusulfron-methyl	21.00
	Insecticide	Oxamyl	38.60-57.90
		Pirimicarb	8.80

Crop	Function	Material	Cost £/ha per application
Beans	Herbicide	Bentazone	63.50
		Pendimethalin	16.40-19.70
		Clomazone	22.00
	Fungicide	Chlorothalonil	18.80
		Tebuconazole	16.80
		Azoxystobin	35.20
Peas and Beans			
	Herbicide	Pendimethalin + Imazamox	38.20
	Insecticide	Pirimicarb	8.80
		Deltamethrin	4.25 - 5.10
Maize	Herbicide	Prosulfuron + Bromoxynil	36.15
		Nicosulfuron	20.80 - 31.20
		Bromoxynil	21.50
		Mesotrione	32.40
Brassicas	Herbicides	Metazachlor	32.30
		Pyridate	70.70
Broadleaved Grass weeds and volunteer Crops			
	Cereals	Fluazifop-P-butyl	21.20 - 31.80
		Propaquizafop	10.40 - 22.30
		Cycloxydim	23.00 - 38.25
Grassland	Herbicides	MCPA	7.80 - 13.00
General	Weed and Grass Killer		
	Couch Grass Control	Glyphosate	5.50 - 15.00
		Clopyralid + Fluroxypyr + Fluroxypyr	27.00 - 54.00
		Isoxaben	110.00
		Aminotriazole	118 – 178

The above prices are based on retail prices paid by farmers (2011) and reflect the discounts available where there are competing products from several manufacturers. The range in prices per hectare reflects the varying application rates. This is the price for the product, not including the agronomic advice that often comes with it.

Acknowledgement: thanks to Bartholemews 01243 784 171

5. SEED ROYALTY RATES

Farm-saved seed payment rates for autumn 2011 and spring 2012

	£/ha	£/tonne
Wheat	6.31	37.33
Winter Barley	6.16	37.12
Spring Barley	7.77	42.47
Oats	5.09	34.60
Peas	8.68	36.18
Beans	10.29	49.21
Oilseed Rape	8.80	1,956
Linseed	7.58	145.80
Triticale	7.69	42.48
Potatoes	£18 to £272	(variety dependant)

Seed purchased from a merchant includes a component of royalty for the seed breeder. Those farmers who save seed from the previous season (farm saved seed) are legally obliged to pay the royalty. If the seed is cleaned and dressed, the royalty payment is taken at this point (per tonne), if not, the farmer is responsible for paying (per hectare). Many older varieties no longer have royalty payments payable. It is illegal to sell or buy seed unless under license. View eligible varieties at www.bspb.co.uk .

6. HOME SAVED SEED COSTS

	Value of Old Crop £/t	Cleaning & Dressing £/t	Testing £/t	Royalty £/t	Total Cost £/t
Feed Wheat	150	68	1.00	37	**256**
Milling Wheat	180	68	1.00	37	**286**
Spring Wheat	180	72	0.90	37	**290**
Winter Feed Barley	145	72	2.00	37	**256**
Winter Malting Barley	155	72	2.00	37	**266**
Spring Malting Barley	165	72	2.00	42	**281**
Winter Oats	155	75	3.90	35	**269**
Spring Oats	155	75	3.70	35	**268**
Winter Rape	400	4,250	62	1956	**6,668**
Spring Rape	400	4,250	114	1956	**6,720**
Winter Beans	230	50	2.60	49	**332**
Spring Beans	230	50	2.60	49	**332**
Blue Peas	180	45	2.20	36	**263**
Marofats	200	45	2.20	36	**283**

The old crop seed is the value of sales not made from 2011 harvest. Cleaning and dressing figures are based on costs for a mobile cleaner on a 350 hectare farm, and likely amounts of seeds required for each crop (the lower the tonnage, the higher the cost). Single purpose or basic seed treatments included. Testing costs assume a single test (one variety) per species (Germination only £30/test). Royalty rates as above.

7. SEED DRILLING RATES

		Thousand Grain Weight (g/1000 grains)											
		35	38	41	44	47	50	53	56	59	62	65	68	71
Seeds Planted per m²	150	53	57	62	66	71	75	80	84	89	93	98	102	107
	175	61	67	72	77	82	88	93	98	103	109	114	119	124
	200	70	76	82	88	94	100	106	112	118	124	130	136	142
	225	79	86	92	99	106	113	119	126	133	140	146	153	160
	250	88	95	103	110	118	125	133	140	148	155	163	170	178
	275	96	105	113	121	129	138	146	154	162	171	179	187	195
	300	105	114	123	132	141	150	159	168	177	186	195	204	213
	325	114	124	133	143	153	163	172	182	192	202	211	221	231
	350	123	133	144	154	165	175	186	196	207	217	228	238	249
	375	131	143	154	165	176	188	199	210	221	233	244	255	266
	400	140	152	164	176	188	200	212	224	236	248	260	272	284
	425	149	162	174	187	200	213	225	238	251	264	276	289	302
	450	158	171	185	198	212	225	239	252	266	279	293	306	320

Measured in Kg/Ha

8.   FEED PRICES

£ per tonne

			£ per tonne
Cattle	Dairy:	High Energy Parlour	220 - 240
		Medium Energy Blend	210 - 225
	Beef	Pellets (16% CP)	200 - 210
		Concentrate	185 - 205
	Calf	Milk Substitute (bags)	1,600 – 1,700
		High Fat (bags)	1,150 – 1,160
		Calf Weaner Pellets.	230 - 240
		Calf Rearer Nuts	230 - 235
Sheep	High Energy Lamb Pellets.		230 - 245
	Medium energy sheep		220 - 230
	Sheep/lamb cake		210 - 218
	Ewe cake		221 - 228
Horses	Horse and Pony Pencils		300 - 450
Goats	Goat Nuts		215 - 225
Pigs	Piglet Weaner		285 - 300
	Sow Nuts		225 - 250
	Early Grower Pellets (20-24% protein)		285 - 293
	Grower/Finisher Pellets		235 - 260
	Sow Concentrate		336 - 346
	Grower Concentrate		343 - 354
Poultry	Chick and Rearer Feeds		215 - 255
	Layers Feeds		230 - 270
	Broiler Feeds		315 - 325
	Turkey Feeds		280 - 290
Straight Feeds	Fishmeal (66/70% CP)		900-1,100
	Soya Bean Meal (Hipro; 50% CP)		285 - 300
	Rapeseed Meal (34-36% CP)		190 - 200
	Palm Kernel Meal/Cake (17% CP)		140 - 155
	Sunflower Seed Pellets (30/33% CP)		174 - 180
	Citrus Pulp Nuts/Pellets		190 - 200
	Wheatfeed Meal (14-18% CP)		130 - 136
	Wheatfeed Pellets (14-18% CP)		140 - 155
	Maize Gluten (19-20% CP)		190 - 195
	Molasses (Cane) (5% CP)		150 - 160
	Sugar Beet Pulp (Molassed Nuts/Pellets)		200 - 240
	Brewers' Grains		25 - 45
	Distillers wheat grain		205 - 230
	Distillers Barley Grains		190 - 210

Compound feed prices are approximate ranges in July 2011; the range incorporates differences in the ingredients. They are delivered prices for hauls more than 10 miles in 25 tonne loads. The additional farm delivered cost for bags ranges from £18.00 to £27.50 a tonne.

9. FEEDSTUFF NUTRITIVE VALUES

Typical Energy and Protein Contents of Some Common Feeds

Type of Feed	Dry Matter Content g/kg	Metabolizable Energy MJ/kg DM	Crude Protein g/kg DM
Forages:			
Barley Straw	860	7.0	10
Grass Silage (typical clamp)	250	10.8	150
Hay (typical meadow)	850	8.8	100
Maize Silage	300	11.0	90
Pasture (rotational grazed)	180	11.5	160
Whole-crop Wheat (fermented)	400	10.5	95
Cereals:			
Barley	860	13.2	120
Oats	860	12.5	120
Wheat	860	13.6	130
Maize	880	13.8	90
Roots:			
Fodder Beet	180	12.0	60
Potatoes	200	13.3	100
Wet By-Products:			
Brewers Grains	260	11.5	250
Pressed Sugar Beet Pulp	260	12.5	100
Straights:			
Cane Molasses	750	12.7	40
Distillers Barley Grains	900	12.2	260
Distillers Maize Grains	900	14.0	310
Distillers Wheat Grains	900	13.5	340
Dried Citrus Pulp	900	12.6	70
Dried Molassed Sugar Beet Pulp	900	12.5	100
Extracted Rapeseed Meal	900	12.0	400
Extracted Soyabean Meal	900	13.4	530
Extracted Sunflower Meal	900	10.0	390
Field Beans	880	13.3	290
Lupin Seed Meal	900	14.2	350
Maize Gluten Feed	880	12.8	210
Palm Kernel Meal	900	11.4	200
Wheat-feed	880	11.3	190

For relative values of different feeds, see previous page.

10. AGRISTATS

These basic agricultural statistics relate to the UK farming and food sectors. The main source of data is the Defra Publication 'Agriculture in the UK 2010'. This can be found online at - www.defra.gov.uk/statistics/foodfarm/cross-cutting/auk/. All figures are for the UK and relate to the 2010 year unless otherwise stated.

INDUSTRY STRUCTURE

Agriculture's Economic Contribution	UK	England	Wales	Scotland	N.I.
Gross Output (£m)	20.65	15.54	1.20	2.42	1.49
Total Income from Farming* (£m)....	4.38	3.31	0.18	0.62	0.28
Agriculture's Share of the Economy**	0.55%	0.53%	0.52%	0.61%	1.01%
Agriculture's Share of Employment..	1.52%	1.13%	4.29%	2.65%	5.58%

*   *Total Income from Farming (TIFF) is essentially the profit of the farming sector.*

** *Based on agriculture's share of gross value-added – 2009 data.*

The wider agri-food sector (including farming, food manufacturing, wholesaling, retailing and catering) comprised around 7% of the entire economy (gross value-added) in 2009, and employed 14% of the total UK workforce.

Agricultural Workforce (2010)	Male	Female	Total
Regular Full-time	52,000 ♦	11,000 ♦	64,000
Regular Part-time*	27,000 ♦	16,000 ♦	39,000
Seasonal, Casual and Gang	40,000	17,000	56,000
Salaried Managers			11,000
Total Employees			171,000
Farmers, Partners Directors and their Spouses			
Full-time			133,000
Part-time*			161,000
Total Farmers, Partners Directors and their Spouses			295,000
Total Labour Force			466,000

*   *Part-time is less than 39 hours in England and Wales, less than 38 hours in Scotland and less than 30 hours in Northern Ireland.*

♦   *2009 data*

NB: A change in survey methodology has taken 70,000 from the total workforce from the 2009 survey, by removing the very small farms from the data.

Crop Areas (June) – '000 Hectares	2005	2008	2009	2010
Wheat	1,867	2,080	1,775	1,939
Barley	938	1,032	1,143	921
Oats	90	135	129	124
Mixed Corn, Triticale and Rye	24	27	28	29
Total Cereals (excluding maize)....	*2,919*	*3,274*	*3,076*	*3,013*
Potatoes	137	144	144	138
Sugar Beet	148	120	114	118
Oilseed Rape	519	598	570	642
Peas (harvested dry)	41	21	27	23
Field Beans	184	118	186	168
Linseed	45	16	28	44
Vegetables & Salad grown in the open	121	122	125	121
Orchards, Small Fruit and Grapes ..	32	34	32	34
Other Horticulture	16	15	13	14
Maize	131	153	163	164
Other Crops	631	527	616	604
Set-aside (inc. non-food crops)	-	-	-	-
Bare Fallow	699	194	244	174
Total Tillage	*5,623*	*5,336*	*5,338*	*5,257*
Temporary Grass (under 5 years old)	1,193	1,141	1,241	1,232
Total Arable	*6,816*	*6,477*	*6,579*	*6,489*
Permanent Grass (5 years, and over)	5,711	6,036	5,865	5,925
Total Grass*	*6,904*	*7,177*	*7,106*	*7,157*
Total Tillage & Grass*	*12,527*	*12,513*	*12,444*	*12,414*
Sole Right Rough Grazing	4,354	4,359	4,131	4,055
Common Rough Grazing	1,236	1,238	1,237	1,228
Total Rough Grazing	*5,590*	*5,597*	*5,368*	*5,283*
Land for Outdoor Pigs	-	-	-	10
Utilisable Agricultural Area (UAA)	-	*17,703*	*17,325*	*17,234*
Woodland	583	705	726	774
Other Land on agricultural holdings	289	289	246	274
Total Agricultural Area**	**18,486**	**18,697**	**18,296**	**18,282**

*   *Excluding Rough Grazing*

The Utilisable Agricultural Area (UAA) comprised around 71% of the total UK land area in 2012. Of the remaining 29%, 4% is woodland and other land on agricultural holdings. The 25% of 'non-agricultural' land broadly splits equally between forest land, urban areas and 'other' land uses. The latter category includes villages, small towns, transport infrastructure, non-urban wasteland, and inland water. The total UK land area is approximately 24.3 million hectares.

Livestock Numbers (June) – '000 Head		2005	2008	2009	2010
Total Cattle and Calves......................		10,770	10,107	10,025	10,112
of which:	Dairy Cows	1,998	1,909	1,857	1,847
	Beef Cows.........................	1,751	1,670	1,626	1,657
Total Sheep and Lambs		35,416	33,131	31,445	31,084
of which	Female Breeding Flock....	16,935	15,616	14,636	14,740
Total Pigs		4,862	4,714	4,540	4,460
of which	Female Breeding Herd.....	470	420	427	427
Poultry	Broilers	111,475	109,859	98,754	105,309
	Laying Flock....................	29,544	44,321	42,663	47,107
	Other Poultry	10,928	12,019	11,335	11,451
Farmed Deer		33	31	31	31
Goats	....	96	96	82	93

Size Distribution of Holdings

By Area on Holding	Holdings - '000	Area - '000 Ha	% of Holdings	% of Area
Under 20 hectares	104.3	704	46.9	4.1
20 to 50 hectares	43.1	1,425	19.4	8.4
50 to 100 hectares	33.6	2,405	15.1	14.1
100 hectares and over	41.4	12,520	18.6	73.4
Total	222.4	17,054	100	100

By Labour Requirement	Holdings - '000	SLR - '000	% of Holdings	% of SLRs
Under 1 SLR	156.7	36.1	70.5	13.0
1 to under 2 SLRs	26.4	38.0	11.9	13.7
2 to under 3 SLRs	14.1	34.6	6.3	12.5
3 to under 5 SLRs	13.8	52.9	6.2	19.0
5 SLRs and over...............................	11.4	116.3	5.1	41.9
Total	222.4	277.8	100	100

The Standard Labour Requirement (SLR) for a farm business represents the labour requirement (in full-time equivalents) for all the agricultural activities on the farm, based on standard coefficients for each commodity on the farm.

Average Size of Enterprises

Hectares	2005	2010	*Number*	2005	2010
Cereals (excl. maize)	49.4	57.7	Dairy Cows	68	78
Oilseed Rape..............	34.4	43.0	Beef Cows................	27	27
Potatoes......................	11.6	14.3	Breeding Sheep	217	215
Sugar Beet..................	20.3	24.0	Breeding Pigs	80	71
			Broilers...................	37,953	41,024

FINANCE

Total Income From Farming (TIFF)

Calendar Year	Real Terms (2010 Prices)			Current Prices	
	Total - £m	per Farmer*	Index**	Total - £m	per Farmer
1975	6,787	22,300	100	1,037	3,400
1976	7,974	26,700	117	1,421	4,800
1977	7,029	23,900	104	1,451	4,900
1978	6,209	21,300	91	1,387	4,700
1979	5,070	17,600	75	1,285	4,500
1980	4,038	14,400	59	1,207	4,300
1981	4,577	16,500	67	1,531	5,500
1982	5,619	20,500	83	2,041	7,400
1983	4,705	17,200	69	1,788	6,500
1984	5,885	21,500	87	2,347	8,600
1985	3,095	11,300	46	1,309	4,800
1986	3,559	13,100	52	1,557	5,700
1987	4,062	15,100	60	1,851	6,900
1988	3,740	14,100	55	1,788	6,700
1989	3,794	14,600	56	1,955	7,500
1990	3,147	12,300	46	1,775	6,900
1991	3,232	12,700	48	1,930	7,600
1992	4,288	16,900	63	2,656	10,500
1993	6,051	24,100	89	3,807	15,100
1994	6,559	26,400	97	4,229	17,000
1995	7,561	31,000	111	5,041	20,600
1996	6,729	27,900	99	4,597	19,000
1997	3,960	16,600	58	2,790	11,700
1998	2,768	11,800	41	2,017	8,600
1999	2,706	11,900	40	2,002	8,800
2000	2,057	9,400	30	1,567	7,100
2001	2,282	10,600	34	1,770	8,200
2002	2,871	13,700	42	2,263	10,800
2003	3,518	17,100	52	2,854	13,900
2004	3,136	15,500	46	2,619	12,900
2005	2,832	14,200	42	2,432	12,200
2006	2,861	14,700	42	2,536	13,000
2007	3,124	16,400	46	2,886	15,100
2008	4,988	26,700	73	4,793	25,600
2009	4,575	24,800	67	4,373	23,700
2010	4,377	24,000	64	4,377	24,000

TIFF is the business profits plus remuneration to farmers, partners and directors and others with an entrepreneurial interest in the business. It is calculated on a calendar year basis and is the main aggregate measure of UK farming's income (profitability). There are no imputed charges (such as a rental value for owned land or value of the farmer's own labour).

* TIFF per full-time entrepreneur equivalent

** average 1975 = 100

TIFF Accounts - Inputs and Outputs *(2010 Provisional)*

Inputs	£m	Outputs	£m	%
Animal Feed	4,020	Wheat	1,683	8.6
Seeds	637	Barley	510	2.6
Fertilisers	1,342	Oats and other cereals	67	0.3
Pesticides	711	Oilseed rape	702	3.6
Hired Labour	2,129	Potatoes	780	4.0
Depreciation: equipment	1,449	Sugar beet	198	1.0
Depreciation: buildings	707	Fresh vegetables	1,257	6.4
Maintenance: materials	826	Fruit	575	2.9
Maintenance: buildings	510	Plants and flowers	975	5.0
Fuels	884	Other crops	819	4.2
Electricity	366	Cattle	2,255	11.6
Agricultural services	910	Sheep	945	4.8
Veterinary expenses	388	Pigs	985	5.0
Net rent	353	Poultry	1,812	9.3
Interest and Finance Fees	244	Milk	3,325	17.0
Other goods and services	2,752	Eggs	561	2.9
		Other livestock	247	1.3
		Other agricultural	910	4.7
		Non-ag income	920	4.7
Total Inputs	**18,229**	**Total Gross Output**	**19,523**	100.0
Total Income From Farming	4,377	Single Payment & subsidies	3,083	
	22,606	**Total Output**	**22,606**	
		Total crops	4,757	24.3
		Total horticulture	2,807	14.4
		Total livestock	6,243	32.0
		Total livestock products	3,886	19.9
		Other	1,830	9.4

Average UK Farm Business Income (FBI) (Real Terms 2009/10 Prices)

Farm Type	2006/07	2007/08	2008/09	2009/10 (provisional)
Dairy	34,600	58,400	62,300	47,700
Grazing Livestock (LFA)	15,800	17,400	21,800	29,600
Grazing L'stock (Lowland)	14,400	14,000	19,100	22,600
Cereals	48,000	74,200	65,500	42,100
General Cropping	65,000	82,200	87,800	55,100
Specialist Pigs	26,700	7,500	51,500	67,400
Specialist Poultry	108,200	143,600	47,600	66,300
Mixed	29,500	47,700	33,200	39,500

FBI is the main farm-level measure of farming income (profitability). It is similar to TIFF but is based on a March to February year.

Balance Sheet of UK Agriculture (2009 Provisional) £m £m

Assets:	Fixed:	Land and buildings......................	176,379	
		Plant, machinery and vehicles......	9,178	
		Breeding livestock.......................	9,842	
	Total Fixed Assets:			*195,399*
	Current	Trading livestock.........................	3,064	
		Crops and stores	2,999	
		Debtors and cash deposits	5,328	
	Total Current Assets:.......................................			*11,391*
	Total Assets:	....		***206,790***
Liabilities:	Long &	Bank loans	3,531	
	Med-term:	AMC and SASC	1,213	
		Other...	21	
	Total Long and Medium Term Liabilities			*6,156*
	Short-term	Bank overdrafts	3,053	
		Trade credit..................................	1,698	
		Hire purchase and leasing	1,031	
		Other...	103	
	Total Short-term Liabilities:..............................			*5,885*
	Total Liabilities:.......................................			***12,040***
Net Worth:				**194,749**

% Equity (Net worth as a % of Total Assets): 94.18%

Total Income from Farming (TIFF) 2009 as % of   a) Net Worth: 2.25%
           b) Total Assets:...... 2.12%
           c) Tenants Cap'...... 18.9%
Note: no charge has been made for farmers' own labour or management

PRODUCTIVITY

UK Crop Yields			average (harvest year)				*Average*
(tonnes per hectare)	2005	2006	2007	2008	2009	2010	*05-10*
Wheat............................	8.0	8.0	7.2	8.3	7.9	7.7	*7.9*
Barley (all)	5.9	5.9	5.7	6.0	5.8	5.7	*5.8*
Winter Barley..............	6.5	6.7	6.1	6.7	6.4	6.4	*6.5*
Spring Barley	5.4	5.3	5.3	5.4	5.5	5.2	*5.4*
Oats	5.8	6.0	5.5	5.8	5.8	5.5	*5.7*
Oilseed Rape*	3.2	3.3	3.1	3.3	3.4	3.5	*3.3*
Linseed*	1.8	1.4	1.6	1.8	2.0	1.6	*1.7*
Field Beans	3.8	3.4	3.0	4.5	3.7	3.0	*3.6*
Dried Peas	3.8	3.3	3.1	4.0	3.6	3.5	*3.6*
Potatoes (all)	43.7	40.8	39.7	42.8	44.3	44.0	*42.6*
Early Potatoes	14.3	15.7	12.5	13.3	15.0	23.0	*15.6*
Maincrop Potatoes	46.6	43.0	43.1	46.7	48.0	45.0	*45.4*
Sugar Beet**.................	58.5	56.6	53.8	63.8	74.0	54.0	*60.1*

* *Excluding non-food crops on set-aside to 2007*   ** *Adjusted to 16% sugar*

UK Livestock Output			average (harvest year)				*Average*
(kg unless stated)	2005	2006	2007	2008	2009	2010	*05-10*
Milk Yield (litres/cow)*	6,986	6,977	6,913	6,943	7,068	7,315	*7,034*
Beef Carcase Wgt**.....	331	330	342	349	342	346	*340*
Lamb Carcase Wgt Δ...	19	19	19	19	19	19	*19*
Pig Carcase Wgt ♦.........	75	75	76	76	78	78	*76*

    *   *litres per annum*   ** *steers, heifers & young bulls*
    Δ   *clean sheep and lambs*   ♦ *clean pigs*

FOOD

Self Sufficiency * (%)	2005	2010		2005	2010
All Food........................	*60.1*	*60.2*	*Indigenous-type Food*..	*73.1*	*74.4*
Crops:			*Livestock:*		
Wheat............................	110	117	Beef and Veal................	74	85
Barley............................	115	121	Mutton and Lamb..........	85	92
Oats	99	109	Pig-meat	48	53
Total Cereals.................	103	112	Poultry-meat.................	88	88
Oilseed Rape	107	104	Butter............................	59	60
Potatoes........................	85	85	Cheese	60	54
Sugar	71	55	Cream	125	103
Fresh Vegetables...........	59	60	Hen Eggs......................	86	82
Fresh Fruit.....................	10	12			

    *   *ratio of UK production to UK human consumption*

Food Spending *	2005	2006	2007	2008	2009	2010
Household Expenditure	20.91	21.55	22.14	23.00	23.86	-
Eating-Out Expenditure	7.79	8.00	7.96	8.16	8.26	-
All Expenditure...........................	28.70	29.55	30.10	31.17	32.12	-

    *   *expenditure on Food and Non-alcoholic Drinks (£ per person per week)*

Producers Share *	1990	1995	2000	2005	2008	2009	2010
Basket of Goods.....	*43*	*48*	*35*	*35*	*37*	*36*	*36*
Wheat (bread)	16	16	10	7	9	7	8
Potatoes.................	31	62	27	22	22	17	20
Carrots...................	31	44	38	43	47	42	41
Apples	51	48	40	43	43	42	42
Milk.......................	35	39	28	30	35	31	32
Beef.......................	57	57	44	44	50	50	48
Lamb	57	58	43	45	47	53	56
Pork	55	57	47	37	37	40	39
Chicken	44	46	37	42	38	38	38
Eggs.......................	36	31	29	32	24	29	27

    *   *farmer's share of retail price*

11. RATE OF INFLATION; PRICE AND COST INDICES

INFLATION DATA

Calendar Year	RPI*: % yearly change	RPI: Index 1987=100	CPI** % yearly change	CPI Index 2005=100	Agricultural Prices Index, 2005 = 100	
					Outputs	Inputs
1975...............	24.2	34	-	-	-	-
1976...............	16.6	40	-	-	-	-
1977...............	15.8	46	-	-	-	-
1978...............	8.3	50	-	-	-	-
1979...............	13.4	57	-	-	-	-
1980...............	18.0	67	-	-	-	-
1981...............	11.9	75	-	-	-	-
1982...............	8.6	81	-	-	-	-
1983...............	4.6	85	-	-	-	-
1984...............	5.0	89	-	-	-	-
1985...............	6.1	95	-	-	-	-
1986...............	3.4	98	-	-	-	-
1987...............	4.2	102	-	-	-	-
1988...............	4.9	107	-	-	95.3	73.8
1989...............	7.8	115	5.2	67	101.9	77.3
1990...............	9.5	126	7.0	72	103.9	81.0
1991...............	5.9	134	7.5	77	102.8	83.2
1992...............	3.7	139	4.3	80	104.3	85.7
1993...............	1.6	141	2.5	82	111.6	88.9
1994...............	2.4	144	2.0	84	112.2	89.1
1995...............	3.5	149	2.6	86	121.3	91.8
1996...............	2.4	153	2.5	88	118.9	96.1
1997...............	3.1	158	1.8	90	103.9	92.4
1998...............	3.4	163	1.6	91	95.3	87.9
1999...............	1.5	165	1.3	92	92.5	87.0
2000...............	3.0	170	0.8	93	90.5	88.4
2001...............	1.8	173	1.2	94	97.6	91.6
2002...............	1.7	176	1.3	95	94.5	91.2
2003...............	2.9	181	1.4	97	100.3	93.6
2004...............	3.0	187	1.3	98	103.6	99.6
2005...............	2.8	192	2.1	100	100.0	100.0
2006...............	3.2	198	2.3	102	104.5	103.6
2007...............	4.3	207	2.3	105	118.8	114.0
2008...............	4.0	215	3.6	109	143.3	139.9
2009...............	-0.5	214	2.2	111	135.8	129.9
2010...............	4.6	224	3.3	115	142.9	135.6
2011 (est.)	5.0		4.2		153.9	138.2

* Retail Price Index

** Consumer Price Index

DETAILED AGRICULTURAL PRICE AND COST INDICES

Producer Prices (2005 = 100)	2006	2007	2008	2009	2010
Feed Wheat	114.3	158.2	216.2	159.8	174.8
Feed Barley	111.3	162.7	189.9	133.1	158.6
All Cereals	111.8	166.7	207.1	150.1	171.8
Oilseed Rape	119.8	143.9	232.9	183.4	198.9
Potatoes (main crop)	131.1	146.7	154.3	123.4	141.2
Sugar Beet	96.2	74.8	77.3	83.2	81.3
Desert Apples	105.7	121.5	130.9	131.4	140.8
All Fresh Vegetables	109.1	122.1	117.5	113.9	131.9
All Fresh Fruit	104.1	107.4	126.4	124.6	129.6
All Crop Products	109.6	133.6	153.7	131.1	145.8
Milk	97.2	112.2	140.4	128.4	133.5
Cattle	108.2	109.9	141.9	151.4	144.2
Sheep	102.4	91.8	116.4	147.4	162.2
Wool	36.4	77.7	78.9	71.4	107.5
Pigs	101.0	103.4	121.6	140.2	135.9
Poultry	98.6	107.1	134.6	137.2	140.9
Eggs	104.0	118.3	140.4	144.7	137.8
All Animal Products	*101.0*	*108.5*	*136.0*	*139.1*	*140.9*
All Products	104.5	118.8	143.3	135.8	142.9
Input Prices					
Seeds	89.5	100.1	111.2	109.1	107.3
Fertilisers	105.7	119.8	272.5	189.8	182.4
Plant Protection Products	102.5	104.2	106.4	107.7	105.1
Energy and Lubricants	112.2	117.9	158.2	132.9	151.4
Animal Feeding Stuffs	104.6	129.7	167.3	152.5	160.1
Maintenance and Repair of Plant	105.8	109.9	116.3	121.5	126.9
Machinery and Other Equipment	104.5	110.3	117.5	122.1	125.3
Buildings	105.9	113.0	120.3	120.6	126.9
General Expenses	102.6	108.2	113.5	115.4	123.4

12. METRIC CONVERSION FACTORS

Metric to Imperial	*Imperial to Metric*

Area

1 hectare (10,000m²).... 2.471 acres	1 acre ....0.405 ha
	1 square mile ....259 ha
1 square km.............0.386 sq. mile	1 square mile ....2.590 sq. km
1 square m...............1.196 sq. yard	1 square yard ....0.836 sq. m
1 square m.............. 10.764 sq. feet	1 square foot ....0.093 sq. m

(m = metre, km = kilometre)

Length

1 mm. ....0.039 inch	1 inch. .... 25.4 mm
1 cm.............................0.394 inch	1 inch.. 2.54 cm
1 m................................3.281 feet	1 foot .... 0.305 m
1 m .... 1.094 yard	1 yard.................................... 0.914 m
1 km .... 0.6214 mile	1 mile..................................... 1.609 km

(mm = millimetre, cm = centimetre)

Volume

1 millilitre .... 0.0352 fluid oz	1 fluid oz .... 28.413 ml
1 litre......................... 35.2 fluid oz	1 fluid oz ....0.028 litre
1 litre.............................1.76 pints	1 pint.....................................0.568 litre
1 litre............................0.22 gallon	1 gallon............................... 4.546 litres
1 cubic m...................35.31 cu feet	1 cubic foot........................ 0.028 cu m
1 cubic m ....1.307 cu yard	1 cubic yard .... 0.765 cu m
1 cubic m......................220 gallons	1 gallon............................... 0.005 cu m
1 ha of 10mm water . 22,000gallons	1 acre-inch 102.75m³

Weight

1 gram ....0.0353 oz	1 oz.. 28.35 gm
1 kg 35.274oz	
1 kg ....2.205 lb	1 lb.. 0.454 kg
50 kg ....0.984 cwt	
1 tonne (1,000 kg)...........19.68 cwt	1 cwt. .... 50.80 kg
1 tonne............................ 0.984 ton	1 ton................................... 1.016 tonne

Milk

1 litre....................................1.03kg	
1kg .... 0.971 litre	
1 litre............................1.709 pints	1 pint.. 0.585kg
I tonne ....213.63 gallon	1 gallon.................................... 4.681kg

Yields and Rates of Use

1 tonne/ha	0.398 ton/acre	1 ton/acre	2.511 tonnes/ha
1 tonne/ha	7.95 cwt/acre	1 cwt/acre	0.125 tonne/ha
1 gram/ha	0.014 oz/acre	1 oz/acre	70.053 g/ha
1 kg/ha	0.892 lb/acre	1 lb/acre	1.121 g/ha
1 kg/ha	0.008 cwt/acre	1 cwt/acre	125.5 g/ha
1 kg/ha (fert.)	0.797 unit/acre	1 unit/acre	1.255 kg/ha
1 litre/ha	0.712 pint/acre	1 pint/acre	1.404 litre/ha
1 litre/ha	0.089 gal/acre	1 gal/acre	11.24 litres/ha

Power, Pressure, Temperature

1 kW	1.341 hp	1 hp	0.746 kW
1MW	1,000kW		
1 kilojoule	0.948 Btu	1 Btu	1.055 kilojoule
1 therm	10,000 Btu	1 Btu	0.0001 therm
1 lb f ft	1.356 Nm	1 Nm	0.738 lb f ft
1 bar	14.705 lb/sq.in.	1 lb/sq.in	0.068 bar
°C to °F	x1.8, + 32	°F to °C	-32, ÷ 1.8

13. CONTACT DETAILS
GENERAL

Agricultural Engineers' Association
Samuelson House, 62 Forder Way, Hampton, Peterborough, PE7 8JB
www.aea.uk.com   0845 644 8748

Agriculture and Horticulture Development Board ~ AHDB
Stoneleigh Park, Kenilworth, Warwickshire, CV8 2TL   0247 669 2051
www.ahdb.org.uk
Includes:
    Horticultural Development Company, HDC   www.hdc.org.uk
    English Beef and Lamb Executive EBLEX   www.eblex.org.uk
    English Pig Executive   www.bpex.org.uk
    DairyCo   www.dairyco.org.uk
    HGCA   www.hgca.com
    Potato Council   www.potato.org.uk

Agricultural Law Association
6 St. Peters Close, Chislehurst, Kent BR7 6PD   0208 467 0722
www.ala.org.uk

Agricultural Industries Confederation (AIC)
Confederation House, East of England Showground, Peterborough,
PE2 6XE
www.agindustries.org.uk   0173 3385 230

Agricultural Wages Board
Area 8A, 9 Millbank, c/o 17 Smith Square, London
SWlP 3JR   0207 238 6523
http://www.defra.gov.uk/food-farm/farm-manage/wages/

Association of Independent Crop Consultants
Agriculture Place, Drayton Farm, East Meon, Petersfield,
Hampshire, GU32 1PN
www.aicc.org.uk   0173 082 3881

BBC Radio 4 Farming To-day
The Mail Box, Birmingham B1 1RF   0121 432 8888
http://www.bbc.co.uk/radio4/news/farmingtoday/

British Agricultural and Garden Machinery Association (BAGMA)
Middleton House, 2 Main Road, Middleton Cheney, Banbury,
Oxon, OX17 2TN
www.bagma.com   0129 571 3344

British Association of Seed Producers
Manor House, Woodhall Spa, Lincolnshire, LN10 6PX.   0152 635 2368

British Crop Protection Council (BCPC)
7 Omni Business Park, Omega Park, Alton, Hampshire GU34 2QD   0142 059 3200
www.bcpc.org

British Deer Society
The Walled Garden, Burgate Manor, Fordingbridge, Hampshire
SP6 1EF   0142 565 5434
www.bds.org.uk

British Egg Industry Council (BEIC)
2nd Floor, 89 Charterhouse Street, London EC1M 6HR   0207 608 3760
http://www.britegg.co.uk/

British Grassland Society
Unit 32c, Stoneleigh Deer Park, Stareton, Kenilworth,
Warwickshire, CV8 2LY   0247 669 6600
www.britishgrassland.com

British Institute of Agricultural Consultants (BIAC)
Portbury House, Sheepway, Portbury, BS20 7TE   0127 537 5559
www.biac.co.uk

British Pig Association
Trumpington Mews, 40b High Street, Trumpington, Cambs. CB2 2LS   0122 384 5100
www.britishpigs.org.uk

British Poultry Council
Europoint House, 5 - 11 Lavington Street, London SE1 0NZ   0207 202 4760
www.britishpoultry.org.uk

British Sheep Dairying Association
c/o High Weald Dairy, Tremains Farm, Treemans Road,
Horsted Keynes, West Sussex, RH17 7EA   0182 579 1636
www.sheepdairying.com

British Society of Plant Breeders
Woolpack Chambers, 16 Market Street, Ely, Cambs. CB7 4ND   0135 365 3200
www.bspb.co.uk

British Sugar
Sugar Way, Peterborough, Cambs. PE2 9AY   0173 356 3171
www.britishsugar.co.uk

British Veterinary Association
7 Mansfield Street, London WlG 9NQ   0207 636 6541
www.bva.co.uk

British Wool Marketing Board
Wool House, Roydsdale Way, Euroway Trading Estate,
Bradford, West Yorkshire BD4 6SE   0127 468 8666
www.britishwool.org.uk

CAB International
Nosworthy Way, Wallingford, Oxon OX10 8DE   0149 183 2111
www.cabi.org

Campaign to Protect Rural England (CPRE)
128 Southwark Street, London SE1 0SW   0207 981 2800
www.cpre.org.uk

Central Association of Agricultural Valuers (CAAV)

Market Chambers, 35 Market Place, Coleford, Gloucestershire
GL16 8AA
www.caav.org.uk   0159 483 2979

Centre for Agricultural Strategy
University of Reading, P.O. Box 237, Whiteknights Road, Earley Gate,
Reading,Berks. RG6 6AR   0118 378 4549
www.apd.reading.ac.uk

Country Land and Business Association (CLA)
16 Belgrave Square, London SWlX 8PQ   0207 235 0511
www.cla.org.uk

Crop Protection Association UK
2 Swan Court, Cygnet Park, Hampton, Peterborough, PE7 8GX   0173 335 5370
www.cropprotection.org.uk

Dairy Industry Association Ltd.
93 Baker Street, London W1U 6QQ   0207 486 7244
www.dairyuk.org

Department of Agriculture and Rural Development (DARDNI)
Dundonald House, Upper Newtownards Road, Belfast BT4 3SB   0289 052 4999
www.dardni.gov.uk

Department of Environment, Food and Rural Affairs (DEFRA)
Nobel House, 17 Smith Square, London SW1P 3JR   0845 933 5577
www.defra.gov.uk

English Hops and Herbs Ltd
Hop Pocket Lane, Paddock Wood, Tonbridge, Kent TN12 6DQ   0189 283 3415
www.botanix.co.uk   intray@botanix.co.uk

Environment Agency
Horizon House, Deanery Road, Bristol, BS1 5AH   0370 850 6506
www.environment-agency.gov.uk

FACE (Farming and Countryside Education)
Arthur Rank Centre, Stoneleigh Park, Warks. CV8 2LG   0845 838 7192
www.face-online.org.uk

Family Farmers' Association
Osborne Newton, Aveton Gifford, Kingsbridge, Devon TQ7 4PE   0154 885 2794
www.familyfarmersassociation.org.uk

Farmers Club
3 Whitehall Court, London SW1A 2EL   0207 930 4730
www.thefarmersclub.com

Farmers Union of Wales
Llys Amaeth, Plas Gogerddon, Aberystwyth, Ceredigion SY23 3BT   0197 082 0820
www.fuw.org.uk

Farming and Wildlife Advisory Group (FWAG)
National Agricultural Centre, Stoneleigh Park, Warks. CV8 2RX   0247 669 6699
www.fwag.org.uk

Food and Drink Federation
Federation House, 6 Catherine Street, London WC2B 5JJ   0207 836 2460
www.fdf.org.uk

Food Standards Agency
Aviation House, 125 Kingsway, London WC2B 6NH   0207 276 8000
www.food.gov.uk

Forestry Commission
231 Corstorphine Road, Edinburgh EH12 7AT   0131 334 0303
www.forestry.gov.uk   enquiries@forestry.gsi.gov.uk

Grain and Feed Trade Association (GAFTA)
9 Lincoln's Inn Fields, London, WC2A 3BP   0207 814 9666
www.gafta.com

Guild of Agricultural Journalists
1 Rose Villa, Anchor Road, Spa Common, North Walsham,
North Walsham, Norfolk, NR28 9AJ   0169 240 2853
www.gaj.org.uk

Health and Safety Executive (Agriculture Sector)
National Agricultural Centre, Stoneleigh Park, Warks. CV8 2LG   0247 669 8350
www.hse.gov.uk

Institution of Agricultural Engineers
West End Road, Silsoe, Bedford MK45 4DU   0152 586 1096

Institute of Agricultural Management
Portway House Sheepway Portbury Bristol BS20 7TE   01275 843 825
http://www.iagrm.org.uk/   enquiries@iagrm.org.uk

Institute of Agricultural Secretaries and Administrators
Mill Lane, Little Shrewley, Warwickshire, CV35 7HN   0192 648 5543
www.iagsa.co.uk

Institute of Chartered Foresters
59 George Street, Edinburgh, EH2 2JG   0131 240 1425
www.charteredforesters.org

Land Drainage Contractors Association
National Agricultural Centre, Stoneleigh Park, Warks. CV8 2LG   0132 726 3264
www.idca.org   secretary@idca.org

Lantra
Lantra House, National Agricultural Centre, Stoneleigh Park,
Warks. CV8 2LG   0247 669 6996
www.lantra.co.uk   connect@lantra.co.uk

LEAF (Linking Environment and Farming)
National Agricultural Centre, Stoneleigh Park, Warks. CV8 2LZ   0247 641 3911
www.leafuk.org   enquiries@leafuk.org

National Agricultural Centre (NAC)
Stoneleigh Park, Warks. CV8 2LZ   0247 669 6969
www.stoneleighpark.com

National Association of Agricultural Contractors (NAAC)
The Old Cart Shed, Easton Lodge Farm, Old Oundle Road
Wansford, Peterborough, PE8 6NP   0845 644 8750
www.naac.org.uk

National Association of British & Irish Millers (NABIM)
21 Arlington Street, London SWlA lRN   0207 493 2521
www.nabim.org.uk   info@nabim.org.uk

National Beef Association
Mart Centre, Tyne Green, Hexham, NE46 3SG   0143 460 1005
www.nationalbeefassociation.com   info@nationalbeefassociation.com

National Cattle Association (Dairy)
Brick House, Risbury, Leominster, Herefordshire HR6 0NQ   0156 876 0632
www.nationalrural.org

National Dairy Council
164 Shaftesbury Avenue, London WC2H 8HL   0207 395 4030
www.nationaldairycouncil.org   ndc@dairyinformation.com

National Farmers' Retail and Markets Association (FARMA)
12 Southgate Street, Winchester, SO23 9EF   0845 458 8420
www.farma.org.uk

National Farmers' Union (NFU)
Agriculture House, Stoneleigh Park, Warks. CV8 2TZ   0247 685 8500
London Office, Kings Buildings, 16 Smith Square, London SW1P 3JJ   0207 808 6600
www.nfuonline.com

NNFCC
BioCentre, York Science Park, Innovation Way, Heslington,
York YO10 5DG   0190 443 5182

www.nnfcc.co.uk   enquiries@nnfcc.co.uk

NFU Scotland
Rural Centre, West Mains, Ingliston, Midlothian EH28 8LT   0131 472 4000
www.nfus.org.uk   webmaster@nfus.org.uk

National Federation of Young Farmers Clubs
YFC Centre, 10th street, National Agricultural Centre, Stoneleigh Park,
Warks. CV8 2LG   0247 685 7200
www.nfyfc.org.uk   post@nfyfc.org.uk

National Office of Animal Health (NOAH)
3 Crossfield Chambers, Gladbeck Way, Enfield, Middlesex EN2 7HF   0208 367 3131
www.noah.co.uk   noah@noah.co.uk

National Sheep Association
The Sheep Centre, Malvern, Worcs. WR13 6PH   0168 489 2661
www.nationalsheep.org.uk

Natural England
1 East Parade, Sheffield S1 2ET   0300 060 6000
www.naturalengland.org.uk   web@naturalengland.org.uk

Processed Vegetable Growers' Association Limited (PGVA)
133 Eastgate, Louth, Lincolnshire LN11 9QG   0150 760 2427
www.pvga.co.uk   postbox@pvga.co.uk

Renewable Energy Association
Capital Tower, 91 Waterloo Road, London, SE1 8RT   0207 925 3570
www.r-e-a.net

Royal Agricultural Benevolent Institution (RABI)
Shaw House, 27 West Way, Oxford OX2 0QH   0186 572 4931
www.rabi.org.uk   info@rabi.org.uk

Royal Agricultural Society of England (RASE)
National Agricultural Centre, Stoneleigh Park, Warks. CV8 2LZ   0247 669 6969
www.rase.org.uk   info@rase.org.uk

Royal Association of British Dairy Farmers
Unit 31, Abbey Park, Stareton, Kenilworth, Warks CV8 2LY   0845 458 2711
www.rabdf.co.uk   office@rabdf.org.uk

Royal Forestry Society of England, Wales and N.I.
102 High Street, Tring, Herts. HP23 4AF   0144 282 2028
www.rfs.org.uk   rfshq@rfs.org.uk

Royal Highland and Agricultural Society of Scotland
Royal Highland Centre, Ingliston, Edinburgh EH28 8NF   0131 335 6200
www.rhass.org.uk   info@rhass.org.uk

Royal Institution of Chartered Surveyors (RICS)
12 Great George Street, Parliament Square, London SW1P 3AD   0207 222 7000
www.rics.org   contactrics@rics.org

Royal Society for the Protection of Birds
The Lodge, Sandy, Bedfordshire SG19 2DL   0176 768 0551
www.rspb.org.uk

Royal Welsh Agricultural Society
Llanelwedd, Builth Wells, Powys LD2 3SY   0198 255 3683
www.rwas.co.uk

Rural Payments Agency
Kings House, 33 Kings Road, Reading RG1 3BU   0118 958 3626
www.rpa.gov.uk

Scottish Executive Environment and Rural Affairs Department (SEERAD)
Pentland House, 47 Robb's Loan, Edinburgh EH14 1TY   0131 556 8400
www.scotland.gov.uk   ceu@scotland.gsi.gov.uk

Tenant Farmers' Association
5 Brewery Court, Theale, Reading, Berks. RG7 5AJ   0118 930 6130
www.tfa.org.uk   tfa@tfa.org.uk

The Stationery Office
The Publications Centre, PO Box 276, London SW8 5DT   0870 600 5522
www.tso.co.uk

Ulster Farmers Union
475 Antrim Road, Belfast BT15 3DA   0289 037 0222
www.ufuni.org

Welsh Assembly Government, Agriculture and Rural Affairs Department
Crown Offices, Cathays Park, Cardiff, CF10 3NQ   0300 060 3300
www.countryside.wales.gov.uk   webmaster@wales.gsi.gov.uk

Women's Food and Farming Union
National Agricultural Centre, Stoneleigh Park, Warks. CV8 2LZ   0247 669 3171
www.wfu.org.uk

RESEARCH ORGANISATIONS

Biotechnology and Biological Sciences Research Council (BBSRC)
Polaris House, North Star Avenue, Swindon, Wilts. SN2 IUH   0179 341 3200
www.bbsrc.ac.uk

Broom's Barn Research Station
Higham, Bury St. Edmunds, Suffolk IP28 6NP   0128 481 2200

www.rothamsted.bbsrc.ac.uk   Brooms.barn@bbsrc.ac.uk

CEDAR (Centre for Dairy Research)
Arborfield Hall Farm, Reading Road, Arborfield, Reading,
RG2 9HX   0118 976 0964

East Malling Research
New Road,East Malling, Kent ME19 6BJ   0173 284 3833
www.emr.ac.uk   enquiries@emr.ac.uk

Elm Farm Organic Research Centre
Hamstead Marshall, Newbury, Berkshire RG20 0HR   0148 865 8298
www.efrc.com

Hannah Research Institute
Ayr, Scotland KA6 5HL   0129 247 7006
www.hannahresearch.org.uk

Institute for Animal Health
Compton, Newbury, Berks. RG20 7NN   0163 557 8411
www.iah.ac.uk   iah@bbsrc.ac.uk

Institute of Food Research
Norwich Research Park, Colney, Norwich NR4 7UA   01603 255 0000
www.ifr.ac.uk

Institute of Grassland and Environmental Research (IGER)
Aberystwyth Research Centre, Plas Gogerddan, Aberystwyth,
Ceredigion SY23 3EB   0197 082 3000
North Wyke Research Station, Okehampton, Devon EX20 2SB   0183 788 3500

Kingshay Farming Trust
Bridge Farm, West Bradley, Glastonbury, Somerset BA6 8LU   0145 885 1555
www.kingshay.com   contact.us@kingshay.co.uk

Macauley Land Use Research Institute
Craigiebuckler, Aberdeen AB15 8QH   0122 431 8611
www.macaulay.ac.uk   enquiries@macaulay.co.uk

Morley Research Centre
Morley St. Botolph, Wymondham, Norfolk NR18 9DB   0195 371 3200

NIAB
Huntingdon Road, Cambridge CB3 0LE   0122 334 2200
www.niab.com   info@niab.com

Processors and Growers Research Organisation (PGRO)
The Research Station, Great North Road, Thornhaugh,
Peterborough PE8 6HJ   0178 078 2585
www.pgro.org   info@prgo.com

Roslin Institute
Roslin, Midlothian EH25 9RG   0131 651 9100
www.roslin.ac.uk

Rothamsted Research
Harpenden, Hertfordshire AL5 2JQ   0158 276 3133
www.rothamsted.ac.uk

Rowett Research Institute
Greenburn Road, Bucksburn, Aberdeen AB21 9SB   0122 471 6226
www.rowett.co.uk

Scottish Crop Research Institute (SCRI)
Mylnefield, Invergowrie, Dundee DD2 5DA   0844 928 5428
www.scri.ac.uk   info@scri.ac.uk

UNIVERSITY AGRICULTURAL ECONOMICS

(Farm Business Survey work)

Northern: School of Agriculture, Food and Rural Development, University
of Newcastle, Newcastle-upon-Tyne NE1 7RU   0191 222 6902

North Eastern: Rural Business Research Unit, Askham Bryan College, Askham
Bryan, York YO23 3FR   01904 772 219

East Midlands: Rural Business Research Unit, University of Nottingham,
Sutton Bonington Campus, Loughborough,
Leics. LE12 5RD   0115 951 6070

Eastern: Rural Business Unit, Centre for Rural Economics Research,
19 Silver Street, Cambridge CB3 9EP   0122 333 7169

Southern: Department of Agriculture and Food Economics
The University of Reading, 4 Earley Gate,
Whiteknights, PO Box 237, Reading RG6 6AR   0118 987 5123

South Western: Centre for Rural Research, The University of Exeter,
Lafrowda House, St. German's Road, Exeter
EX4 6TL   0139 226 3836

Wales: Institute of Rural Studies, University of Wales,

Aberystwyth, Llanbadarn Campus,	
Aberystwyth, Ceredigion SY23 3AL	0197 062 1986

Scottish Agricultural College
Regional Offices:
North: SAC Aberdeen, Ferguson Building, Craibstone Estate,
Bucksburn, Aberdeen AB21 9YA   0122 471 1000
East: SAC Edinburgh, Bush Estate, Penecuik, Midlothian,
EH26 0PH   0131 535 3430
West: SAC Auchincruive, Ayr KA6 5HW   0129 252 5343

Northern Ireland (Advisory Services also)
Economics & Statistics Division, DARDNI, Dundonald House,
Upper Newtownards Road, Belfast BT4 3SB   0289 052 4999

NATIONAL AGRICULTURAL COLLEGES

Cranfield University, Silsoe Campus
Silsoe, Bedford MK45 4DT   0152 586 3000
www.cranfield.ac.uk

Harper Adams University College
Edgmond, Newport, Shropshire TF10 8NB   0195 282 0280
www.harper-adams.ac.uk

Institute of Rural Sciences
Llanbadarn Campus, Aberystwyth, Ceredigion SY23 3AL   0197 062 4471
www.irs.aber.ac.uk   irs-enquiries@aber.ac.uk

Royal Agricultural College
Stroud Road, Cirencester, Glos. GL7 6JS   0128 565 2531
www.royagcol.ac.uk

Scottish Agricultural College (student recruitment)
Auchincruive Campus, Ayr KA6 5HW   0800 269 453
www.sac.ac.uk

Shuttleworth College
Old Warden Park, Biggleswade, Beds. SG18 9DX   0176 7626 222
www.shuttleworth.ac.uk   enquiries@shuttleworth.ac.uk

Writtle College
Lordship Road, Writtle, Chelmsford, Essex CM1 3RR   0124 542 4200
www.writtle.ac.uk   info@writtle.ac.uk

INDEX